INSIDE STORIES

for Senior Students

edited by

Glen Kirkland / Richard Davies

Harcourt Canada

Toronto Orlando San Diego London Sydney

Canadian Cataloguing in Publication Data

Main entry under title:

Inside stories for senior students
ISBN 0-7747-1408-5

1. Short stories, Canadian (English).* 2. Short stories, American. 3. Short stories - Translations into English. 4. Short stories, English.
I. Kirkland, Glen. II. Davis, Richard

PN6120.I57 1992 808.83'1 C92-093774-8

Thanks to all the teachers and students who have contributed to our work with stories. Thanks, too, to Murray Lamb, Lydia Fletcher, and Laura Edlund for their assisstance and support.

G.K. R.D.

Acknowledgements
The authors and publisher gratefully acknowledge the reviewers listed below for their contribution to the development of this program.

Anne Payne—Coordinator of English, Modern Languages and Gifted Education, Father Lacombe High School, Calgary, Alberta
Elizabeth Fraser—English Department Head, Grande Prairie Composite High School, Grande Prairie, Alberta
Myron Moxley—English Department Head, Kitsilano Secondary School, Vancouver, British Columbia
Sylvia Unkovich—English Department Head, Gladstone Secondary School, Vancouver, British Columbia
Barbara Terpstra—English Department Head, Jarvis Collegiate, Toronto, Ontario
Norah Allingham—English Teacher, City Adult Learning Centre, Toronto, Ontario

Printed in Canada

6 7 8 9 10 03 02 01 00 99

Table of Contents

UNIT SIX
The Texture of Story 236

UNIT SEVEN
Perspectives on Story 270

UNIT EIGHT
Stories for Further Reading 308

To the Student

Welcome to *Inside Stories for Senior Students*. The thirty-four stories in this collection will give you glimpses into the lives of a variety of characters and will invite you to become involved in their conflicts and concerns. The range of stories and authors is wide, including those old and new, and from around the world—including Canada, the United States, Russia, France, New Zealand, India, Zimbabwe, and Britain. Of the fourteen Canadian authors represented, some are well-known (e.g., Valgardson, Munro, Laurence, Findley, Shields, Buckler), while others are recently recognized (e.g., Choy, Fawcett, Potrebenko, King).

As you read the stories, you will meet characters who differ greatly in their goals and problems, in their responses to conflict, and in their outlooks on life. Some characters—such as those in "Small Potatoes" and "On the Right Track"—will be familiar to you, with common struggles. However, others—such as those in "The Lottery" and "The Guest"—are caught in stranger predicaments. Because the stories address significant conflicts, themes, and concerns, they will encourage you to reflect and will provoke thoughtful discussions.

Inside Stories for Senior Students offers a rich collection of stories, plus a variety of ways to consider, examine, and respond to them. In the first six units, follow-up journal topics, questions, activities, and projects invite you to give, reflect upon, and refine your thoughts and feelings about each story. "Perspectives on Story" adds an extra dimension to your experiences with stories in the text and is followed by ten additional stories. Finally, a glossary will help you with the terms and concepts frequently used when responding to and discussing stories.

May you enjoy the many opportunities the text provides for journeys into fictional realms that are entertaining, moving, thought-provoking, and, occasionally, startling. As well, may the experience provided by the stories and other features in *Inside Stories for Senior Students* leave each of you with a deeper understanding of yourself, human nature, and the world.

Glen Kirkland / Richard Davies

1

Purpose and the Short Story

If we think back on all the stories we have known, we realize quickly that stories have been and still are an important part of our lives. As children, we heard stories, watched stories played out on television or in movies, and told stories of our own. As we've grown, we've become more independent in our experiences with stories.

Often over the years, we've sat back, enjoyed a particular story, and let that story slip from our memories as we moved on to other things in our lives. However fleeting, our enjoyment of such stories is important. Stories can entertain us by stimulating our imagination and by making us laugh, cry, or hold our breath in suspense; such stories take us away from our immediate worlds and leave us refreshed. Stories that simply distract us are not insignificant; rather, they are a valid form of entertainment and worthwhile if, at that time, our aim is to be entertained.

In addition to entertaining us, some stories *change* us, though we might not be aware of how. Through them, we might, for example, be strengthened when a character's concerns reflect our own, better understand someone in our life because of a character's similarity, or become more aware of a pattern in life—such as the relationship between a character's motivation and his or her actions. Because some stories are written chiefly to illuminate or comment on some aspect of life that the writer has decided is significant and worth examining in depth, stories can take us deeper into life.

This unit offers us four very different, vivid, and thought-provoking stories. "Identities" follows a character into a tough, threatening world and to a startling conclusion. In Nancy Lord's "Small Potatoes," a woman reflects on a changing friendship. The third selection, "The Shining Houses," presents conflicting perspectives within a community. Finally, "War" takes us into a train compartment where several passengers explore their grief and worry over their soldier sons.

When reading a story from this unit or any story—whether it's one written chiefly to entertain or one written chiefly to illuminate an aspect of life—we can enrich our experience by taking time to develop our personal and critical responses. Among readers' first, personal responses to a story, we can expect differences simply because each reader is a unique individual and brings to the story different expectations, associations, experiences, and feelings. For example, you might enjoy a story and find it profound, while a friend might find the same story dull and unappealing. By exploring and sharing personal responses, we learn more about how we read and what makes the story meaningful.

To develop critical responses to a story, we consider, share, and refine our responses, all the while returning to the story to ensure our views or the views of others are indeed confirmed by the story's details. Often critical responses are developed with emphasis on a specific feature and how that feature contributes to the story's meaning and impact. For example, we might examine one of the following:

- content (e.g., the central character's motivation or response to the conflict);
- structure (e.g., development of the conflict or theme in the story's beginning, middle, and end);
- technique (e.g., how the point of view contributes to the story's impact);
- language (e.g., how the imagery contributes to the story's meaning);
- significance (e.g., the story's value as a comment on life).

As we read, then respond personally and critically to the stories in this unit, we can deepen our enjoyment and understanding of stories, and ultimately grow as readers.

W.D. Valgardson

Identities

... it has been a reckless, haphazard path.
Retracing it is impossible.

Normally, he goes clean-shaven into the world, but the promise of a Saturday liquid with sunshine draws him first from his study to the back yard, from there to his front lawn. The smell of burning leaves stirs the memories of childhood car rides, narrow lanes adrift with yellow leaves, girls on plodding horses, unattended stands piled high with pumpkins, onions, beets, so that each one was, in its own way, a still life. Always, there were salmon tins glinting with silver, set above hand-painted signs instructing purchasers to deposit twenty-five or fifty cents. This act of faith, containing all the stories he has read in childhood about the North—cabins left unlocked, filled with supplies for hapless wayfarers—wakes in him a desire to temporarily abandon the twice-cut yards and hundred-year-old oaks.

He does not hurry, for he has no destination. He meanders, instead, through the suburban labyrinth of cul-de-sacs, bays and circles, losing and finding himself endlessly. Becoming lost is made all the easier because the houses repeat themselves with superficial variations. There grows within him, however, a vague unease with symmetry, with nothing left to chance, no ragged edges, no unkempt vacant lots, no houses rendered unique by necessity and indifference.

The houses all face the sun. They have no artificial divisions. There is room enough for everyone. Now, as he passes grey stone gates, the yards are all proscribed by stiff picket fences, and quickly, a certain untidiness creeps in: a fragment of glass, a chocolate bar wrapper, a plastic horse, cracked sidewalks with ridges of stiff grass.

Although he has on blue jeans—matching pants and jacket made in Paris—he is driving a grey Mercedes Benz. Gangs of young men follow the car with their unblinking eyes. The young men stand and lean in tired, watchful knots close to phone booths and seedy-looking grocery stores.

Their hair glistens as though shellacked. Their jackets gleam with studs. Eagles, tigers, wolves and serpents ride their backs.

He passes a ten-foot wire fence enclosing a playground bare of equipment and pounded flat. The gate is double locked, the fence cut and rolled into a cone. Three boys throw stones at pigeons. Paper clogs the fence like drifted snow. The school is sheathed in heavy screens. Its yellow brick is pockmarked, chipped.

The houses are squat, as though they were once taller and have, slowly, sunk into the ground. Each has a band of dirt around the bottom. The blue glow of television sets lights the windows. On the front steps of a red-roofed house, a man sits. He wears black pants, a tartan vest, a brown snap-brimmed hat. Beside him is a suitcase.

Fences here are little more than fragments. Cars jam the narrow streets, and he worries that he might strike the unkempt children who dart back and forth like startled fish. Street lights come on. He takes them as a signal to return the way he came, but it has been a reckless, haphazard path. Retracing it is impossible. He is overtaken by sudden guilt. He has left no message for his wife.

There have been no trees or drifting leaves, no stands covered in produce, no salmon tins, but time has run away with him. His wife, he realizes, will have returned from bridge, his children gathered for supper. He also knows that, at first, they have blamed his absence on a neighbour's hospitality and gin. However, by the time he can return, annoyance will have blossomed into alarm. His safe return will, he knows from childhood and years of being locked in domestic grief, degenerate to recriminations and apology.

Faced with this, he decides to call the next time he sees a store or phone booth. So intent is he upon the future that he dangerously ignores the present and does not notice the police car, concealed in the shadows of a side street, nose out and follow him.

Ahead, there is a small store with windows covered in hand-painted signs and vertical metal bars. On the edge of the light, three young men and a girl slouch. One of the men has a beard and, in spite of the advancing darkness, wears sunglasses. He has on a fringed leather vest. His companions wear leather jackets. Their peaked caps make their heads seem flat, their foreheads nonexistent. The girl is better looking than she should be for such companions. She is long-legged and wears a white turtleneck sweater that accentuates her breasts.

In spite of his car, he hopes his day-old beard, which he strokes upward with the heel of his hand, will, when combined with his clothes, provide immunity. He slips his wallet into his shirt pocket, does up the metal buttons on his jacket and slips a ten-dollar bill into his back pocket. Recalling a television show, he decides that if he is accosted, he will say that the ten is all he's got, that he stole the car and ask them if they know a buyer.

He eases out of the car, edges nervously along the fender and past the grille. The store window illuminates the sidewalk like a stage. Beyond the light, everything is obscured by darkness. He is so intent upon the three men and the girl that he does not notice the police car drift against the curb, nor the officer who advances with a pistol in his hand.

When the officer, who is inexperienced, who is nervous because of the neighbourhood, who is suspicious because of the car and because he has been trained to see an unshaven man in blue jeans as a potential thief and not as a probable owner, orders him to halt, he is surprised. When he turns part way around and recognizes the uniform, he does not feel fear but relief. Instinctively relaxing, certain of his safety, in the last voluntary movement of his life, he reaches his hand toward his wallet for his identity.

1. In your journal, record your thoughts, associations, or feelings about the story. You might choose to focus on one of the following:
   - thoughts the story raised about identity;
   - how you might have reacted in the same situation;
   - events or situations the story brought to mind.

   Share your journal entry with two or three classmates.
2. Consider the protagonist's motivation. How is his motivation related to his fate?
3. Comment on the title, "Identities," and examine the various identities in the story. What comments does the story make? Support your ideas with details from the text, and, if you choose, with your own experience.
4. Valgardson's chosen point of view allowed him to include certain details, but not others, and to construct the story in a specific way. In a small group, discuss what Valgardson did focus on and what he left out.
5. Choose one of the following activities:
   a) Write a news story reporting the final events in "Identities." You might include quotations from "interviews" with the police officer, witnesses, and so on.
   b) Improvise a conversation between the policeman and his superior officer as they review the events.
   c) Write an editorial about the events and the aftermath.

Nancy Lord

Small Potatoes

Every trip you take away more, emptying the house of those things that make it most yours. Load by load, you're moving away.

I make my own trail, not because it's quicker but because there's more to see. I don't do it enough anymore, traipsing through with an eye for rose hips or for the spider's snare with its lump of fluttering, tormented moth. As I bend branches, I'm comforted that there is still so much unfenced and untrammeled space. It hasn't come to that yet, that people here feel the need to mark it off and use it up.

Even as a little girl in Boston, I was looking for this. The day I learned about the Westward Movement—settlers trundling along in covered wagons, as it was presented—I raced around after school, drunk with the concept of first steps into unknown territory, stamping my feet into any unblemished patch of snow, shouting "Pioneer! Pioneer! Pioneer!"

When I came to Alaska, it was with the sure knowledge that here were places that, truly, no one had stepped. And it mattered, the sense of putting a foot down and knowing I was the first to look upon the world from exactly that vantage point. Every sight—of mountain or mouse hole—was a discovery.

You said it was the same for you, growing up in the Midwest. When we met, it was as though we'd once been members of the same backyard club, sisters who shared a coded language. When you spoke, it was as though you were saying my own thoughts. I felt we were resuming a friendship instead of beginning one.

That first summer, working together in the cannery, I lived in my tent and you lived in your van. Days off, we mucked about in the bay after clams, caking ourselves with mud that dried to a ghost-gray skin. Other times we hiked into the hills to fields of chamomile we picked for tea. I wonder if you still think about the day we walked the bluff's edge, weaving back around the ravines and then on out to the points of land where fireweed rippled in the sea breeze. Eagles rode the thermals above us, and we watched two at play, diving at each other and once locking talons as they tumbled above us. We agreed we both wanted to be birds in our next lives.

Now that the cold has come, causing the country to lie down and curl up around itself, it's easier to get through here. Only a couple of weeks ago, the trees and bushes were still lunging around, frothing with fevered leaves and seed, stretching, the grasses dizzy over my head. Now the exuberance is gone, leaving jaundiced alders, berries fallen or pinched to skin, grasses pale and brittle as though the frost has sucked the green resilience out of them. Yesterday's wind has turned the remaining leaves to bare their undersides like submissive bellies; it's flattened the grasses so they all lie in one direction. I bully my way through, kicking loose the snarls that catch my feet. The morning's frost flakes off and sprinkles down.

It's only when I reach the highway that the sun clears the trees. It's warmer, instantly, and I pause to unzip my jacket at the throat. It's early and a Saturday; there's no traffic this far out the road. Most people are still waking up, drinking coffee beside stoked stoves and staring out windows at reminders of chores to be done before freezeup: gardens to be turned, skirting to be nailed, wood to be split and stacked. The first hard frost, no matter how late, always comes before any of us is ready. In homes up and down the road, lists—the must-dos of fall—are being assembled.

You, too, will have your list, that you've brought from Anchorage: weatherstripping to stick to the bottom of the door, mousetraps to set, a load of firewood to arrange for delivery. Your list is different from the rest of ours, now that you come only on an occasional weekend. It's not the list of buttoning-up, of drawing shelter close like a wrap of sweater. Instead, it's a list of absentee fixes, of purchases. The mousetraps will bang shut in the silence after you, catless, have closed the door behind you; the wood will arrive one day, heaved from the back of a pickup to lie in a pile at your doorstep like a yardful of stumps.

Walking along the empty road, I think again of the eagles that tumbled with locked talons, the day we discovered the old log cabin. It stood just at the edge of the bluff, ramshackle, the roof partly fallen in and the windows broken out. I poked my head through an opening and smelled the damp rot that was somehow satisfying in its earthiness. "Move," you said in your eager way and slung a leg over the splintered sill. We pawed through the debris, and you dug out an old spoon, tarnished green. Later, we sat outside, chewing on chives we found clumped against a wall, trailing them from our mouths like strings of licorice. We wondered who had lived there and where they had gone, and what it must have been like to have settled this land before the roads came through. Just as we wanted to be birds the next time around, we decided we'd been Indians, or explorers, or calicoed prairie wives before; we felt that much affinity for the open country.

This trip, besides your list of to-dos, you'll bring other things—groceries, cleaning supplies, new candles. You'll also have a second list—items you've decided you need in Anchorage and want to remember to take back. I've watched this ebb and flow between your two households. In comes the sack of groceries, out goes the smaller bag of garbage you'll drop in the dumpster as you pass through town. In comes the new broom. Out go the favorite chamois shirt, the binoculars, the game of Scrabble, the bread knife, and the vegetarian cookbook.

When you made the decision to work in Anchorage, that's just how you put it—you would work there, but it was temporary, a job away from home. Home would remain here, and you'd get back to it on weekends, as often as you could. You'd only be "camping out" in your furnished apartment, drinking out of jelly jars and browning toast in the oven. Your real, complete, household would be here, waiting.

I've watched it happen, though, the ebb of possessions. It's not like tides anymore, a wash in and out; it's like the flood of a river now. Every trip you take away more, emptying the house of those things that make it most yours. Load by load, you're moving away.

When I turn off to your place, I study the ruts, wondering if you're really here. You said you would be, when we talked. "This weekend for sure," you said, sounding guilty, regretful.

"I want to spend some time with you. We'll pick cranberries. Plan on it."

It's funny in a way, how we've stayed so close through everything. Always, our friendship endured. We both looked for men to share our lives with, and expected that someday we would. I suppose I was jealous when you began spending so much time with Ron. And for me there was Patrick, and Mike, and Galen. They were all good men—yours and mine—but then you and I would always find ourselves together again, across one of our kitchen tables, drinking tea and talking. Every time it was as though we were finally able to communicate in the same language again, after having tried to get by with foreigners. I remember telling you about Galen and football and fishing. I had told him, while he was watching football on television, that I was going to hike down to the river to fish. He told me to wait—he would drive me down when the game was over. I didn't need to tell you that what I really wanted was the walk, that fishing was an excuse to carry a rod down and back through the woods, that I had to feel guilty because he offered a ride I didn't want, and then that he accused me of trying to rush him away from his game. You were already nodding; you knew exactly what I'd meant to begin with and what he would say, and even that the last three minutes of the game would go on and on.

The men came and went, for each of us, but neither of us ever found one that was a friend in the way we were to each other, someone with whom we could talk, saying everything without insult or doubt or misunderstanding and knowing what the other meant.

And now, each of us is by herself.

The ruts don't tell me much. The mud's frozen hard, tire tracks printed in it. Where it was wettest, it's crystallized like quartz, pointed spears of brown ice radiating from each pit. They crunch under my feet, shattering. It's clear that no one has driven in or out this morning.

The low light has that luminescent quality, as though it were slipping under the sides of things, filling them from within. The bent grasses along the road glow yellow; frost melting to dew magnifies in beads along the edges. You always used to remark on it, summer evenings when the light slanted in from the north, washing the trees and fields with an underwater greenness.

When I reach the top of the rise, I can see the roof of your house. The shakes catch the sunlight the same as the grass, the cedar burnished like gold. But it's the chimney I watch. Straining my sight against the wall of spruce that rises behind, I look for the wavy distortion the heat from a dampered, smokeless fire causes. The trees stand still as a painted backdrop, and I know that you're not here after all.

You're busy, I know. Things come up. It's hard to get away. You would be here if you could, pulling muffins from the oven and pouring springwater into your kettle.

I keep walking toward your house. As it materializes, top to bottom, I think how systematically it went the other way, the summer you built it. I'm still amazed at the assurance with which you did it. When you started you didn't even know the names of what you needed—joists or studs, rafters or siding. They were all just boards to you. The times I came to help, it was "Cut all those boards to look like this" and "Use those big nails over there." You knew exactly what you wanted, as if by instinct. And when it was done, one board nailed to the next, it was one solid piece—no holes, nothing extra sticking out.

Seven years later, there it is—still standing, still surprising me. With time, the rough-cut spruce, once so banana blond, has grayed to distinction. It reminds me of a Wyeth painting, with its patina of fog and seclusion.

In the beginning, when we moved to the hill, the places we found were simple and rough. Yours was a homestead cabin, with an uneven floor that sloped downhill. A pencil dropped in the kitchen rolled to the door, and in wet weather water seeped up through the floorboards. My place was less historically pleasing—plywood, its walls lined with cardboard from cases of beer. I tightened it up with some ceiling insulation, installed a barrel stove, and spent winter nights reading by a kerosene lamp. Later, when you built your own place, I settled into my rental in the trees. We joked about my electricity and your sheetrock. "It's real uptown," we said. "We better watch out that we don't get citified."

Your top story stares at me first, the two south windows like eyes flashing, the smaller one caught in a wink. Beneath it more windows, none matching, line either side of the L. The short leg thrusts forward, throwing a small shadow like a wedge of night against the longer. You did right with the angles, capturing the best of the winter sun and avoiding the flat, spiritless faces common to new construction. The porch, along the side, adds an air of leisure and comfort, as though it might be hung with an old-fashioned wicker swing.

As I get closer, the look of desertion looms larger. The road cuts away, with the spur into your yard crowded from both sides by grass. The center strip of weeds stands firm; months have passed since it's been pushed over by the belly of a car. The yard, too, grows wild: nettles collapsed over the splitting block, a dry pushki stalk parting the legs of a sawhorse.

I climb the steps, the sound of my boots a thudding of arrival. The door is padlocked. I tug on the lock, testing. When it holds, I move down the porch, nudging with my foot at a coffee can along the way. It's empty except for a stiff paintbrush.

Framing my gloved hands around my eyes, I press against the window to see inside. Plates and cups are stacked on a dish towel beside the sink, ready to be put away. There's a fancy cookie tin and a stick of margarine on the counter. Beyond the wood stove I can see the edge of a chair and some magazines—*New Yorkers*—scattered on the floor; their covers are like fall leaves—one mostly orange, another green and yellow. Ragg socks lie where they were pulled heel over toe.

My breath—I've tried to hold it in—finally steams up my space in the window. The interior pulls away as though masked by a cloud.

It's part of your plan, I know, to leave it every time like this—odds and ends of food and clothing lying around—so that when you return it feels like coming home, as though you've never really left.

"I can't eat the scenery." It's what you said when you took the job in Anchorage. You were joking, sort of—parodying what the business people said when they argued for more, faster growth. We both knew what the choice was—money and some professional achievement instead of the space and self-sufficiency and, yes, scenery that was ours here. Now you dress in suits and nylons and sit at a desk, reviewing plans and writing up reports. You told me that you don't even have a window in your office, and that the traffic after work is hell.

There's sacrifice either way, of course. Living here, I'll never be rich or influential. I'll never be quoted in the newspaper twice in a week; in fact, I may not even manage to read the paper twice in a week. Waking to knead bread and collect eggs from the henhouse, my days fill with mundane essentials. Instead of waiting in a traffic jam, I may spend an entire winter day chaining up my car and winching it through snowdrifts to the road. My words fall into cliché, howdy-do, and the sluggish thought that goes with chatter in the post office line or reporting to the cats at home. Work is what I can find, always strictly for money as I support a lifestyle the way others support too many children.

Sitting on the edge of your porch, I let my legs dangle. I look back the way I came, across to the mountains. Snowfields divide the pale sky from the water below as though bleeding off the color, draining it down the cracked and broken glaciers to the concentrate, undiluted blue of bay. There's never a time watching the mountains that I don't marvel at where I live, and I cannot imagine living where I couldn't watch the snowline rise and fall with the seasons.

And when I look around me again, I see the fenceposts of your garden. There it is, the old plot, looking small and indistinguishable from the rest of the field except for the gray posts that tilt like lightning-struck trees above the grass. Its chicken wire sags from one post to the next; moose, walking through, have pulled it free. In one corner, where it's still strung high, weeds—some climbing vines—have laced it together.

That's all that's left of the garden you turned by hand, layering in truckloads of horse manure and seaweed. You were so proud of what you grew—the early radishes, the chard, the heads of cabbage soft and leathery as medicine balls. I helped you dig potatoes when the plants lay limp over the hills and the soil was cold in our hands; they were small that year, the season short. Perfect for boiling, you said, content with what you had.

When was that, that all that happened—that the fireweed sneaked back across the fenceline as though it had never been spaded under, that the chicken wire loosened and the posts were heaved out by frost? All that's left looks so *old*, I can't believe it has anything to do with us. Somehow, we've become the ones who came before, as much a part of the past as the early homesteaders at the edge of the bluff or the later ones with sunken floors and cardboard walls.

Although you've left and I'm still here, the time when our lives were new and as brilliant as bright nails and fresh-sawn lumber is behind us both. Our first steps through—finding our ways along trails we parted, past rows we planted, up steps we hammered together—are history. I go on, holding to the vision, but I know now that you'll never be so satisfied again with small potatoes.

I drop down off the edge of the porch, landing harder than I expect. I've sat too long, stiffening. I walk over to the garden and around one side. The vine, I think, may be some surviving peas, but it's not; it's nothing I recognize, the leaves scalloped and tinted red, as though they've rusted over. I step across the fence and kick through the grass, searching for some sign. It's all weeds, as far as I can tell, the same as beyond the fence. I step out again and start back toward your house, wondering where I can find something to write a note with—charcoal, wax, anything—but there's nothing here, in this yard grayed out, gone to seed.

Instead, halfway back, I stop and pick some weeds: stalks of fireweed still stuck with wisps of fluff; brittle mare's tail; a handful of grasses fringed with seed cases; the paperlike shell of some cup-shaped flower; a spiky pushki head, each pod spread like a parasol. I place them, inelegant and unarranged, in the paintbrush's can and set the whole bouquet against your door. When you come—whenever you come—they'll be waiting, frozen in time. Although snow may have buried the country, smoothing this morning's rugged beauty into flat, forgetful obliteration, these will stay as now, a reminder to you of what came before.

1. In your journal, record your thoughts, associations, or feelings about the story. You might choose to focus on one of the following:
   - thoughts the story brought to mind about the nature of friendship;
   - details in the story that were vivid or memorable for you;
   - thoughts on the title, "Small Potatoes."

   Share your journal entry with two or three classmates.
2. a) Why did the narrator and her friend both choose to live in the Alaskan countryside? Why does the friend leave? Why does the narrator stay? What does the narrator enjoy most about her life?

   b) If *you* could choose to live anywhere, where would you choose? Why?
3. If this story were a letter from the narrator to her friend, what would be the narrator's purpose in writing the letter?
4. What does the narrator think of her friend? Why does the narrator leave the bouquet by her friend's door? How do you think the friend would interpret the gesture?
5. What relationships are there between the setting and the mood, and the season and the friendship?
6. Either write a letter the narrator receives from her friend shortly before winter sets in *or*, with a partner, improvise the next meeting between the two friends.

Alice Munro

The Shining Houses

... set side by side in long rows in the wound of the earth.

Mary sat on the back steps of Mrs. Fullerton's house, talking—or really listening—to Mrs. Fullerton, who sold her eggs. She had come in to pay the egg money, on her way to Edith's Debbie's birthday party. Mrs. Fullerton did not pay calls herself and she did not invite them, but, once a business pretext was established, she liked to talk. And Mary found herself exploring her neighbour's life as she had once explored the lives of grandmothers and aunts—by pretending to know less than she did, asking for some story she had heard before; this way, remembered episodes emerged each time with slight differences of content, meaning, colour, yet with a pure reality that usually attaches to things which are at least part legend. She had almost forgotten that there are people whose lives can be seen like this. She did not talk to many old people any more. Most of the people she knew had lives like her own, in which things were not sorted out yet, and it is not certain if this thing, or that, should be taken seriously. Mrs. Fullerton had no doubts or questions of this kind. How was it possible, for instance, not to take seriously the broad blithe back of Mr. Fullerton, disappearing down the road on a summer day, not to return?

"I didn't know that," said Mary. "I always thought Mr. Fullerton was dead."

"He's no more dead than I am," said Mrs. Fullerton, sitting up straight. A bold Plymouth Rock walked across the bottom step and Mary's little boy, Danny, got up to give rather cautious chase. "He's just gone off on his travels, that's what he is. May of gone up north, may of gone to the States, I don't know. But he's not dead. I would of felt it. He's not old neither, you know, not old like I am.

He was my second husband, he was younger. I never made any secret of it. I had this place and raised my children and buried my first husband, before ever Mr. Fullerton came upon the scene. Why, one time down in the post office we was standing together by the wicket and I went over to put a letter in the box and left my bag behind me, and Mr. Fullerton turns to go after me and the girl calls to him, she says, here, your mother's left her purse!"

Mary smiled, answering Mrs. Fullerton's high-pitched and not trustful laughter. Mrs. Fullerton was old, as she had said—older than you might think, seeing her hair still fuzzy and black, her clothes slatternly-gay, dime-store brooches pinned to her ravelling sweater. Her eyes showed it, black as plums, with a soft inanimate sheen; things sank into them and they never changed. The life in her face was all in the nose and mouth, which were always twitching, fluttering, drawing tight grimace-lines down her cheeks. When she came around every Friday on her egg deliveries her hair was curled, her blouse held together by a bunch of cotton flowers, her mouth painted, a spidery and ferocious line of red; she would not show herself to her new neighbours in any sad old-womanish disarray.

"Thought I was his mother," she said. "I didn't care. I had a good laugh. But what I was telling you," she said, "a day in summer, he was off work. He had the ladder up and he was picking me the cherries off of my black-cherry tree. I came out to hang my clothes and there was this man I never seen before in my life, taking the pail of cherries my husband hands down to him. Helping himself, too, not backward, he sat down and ate cherries out of my pail. Who's that, I said to my husband, and he says, just a fellow passing. If he's a friend of yours, I said, he's welcome to stay for supper. What are you talking about, he says, I never seen him before. So I never said another thing. Mr. Fullerton went and talked to him, eating my cherries I intended for a pie, but that man would talk to anybody, tramp, Jehovah's Witness, anybody—that didn't need to mean anything."

"And half an hour after that fellow went off," she said, "Mr. Fullerton comes out in his brown jacket and his hat on. I have to meet a man downtown. How long will you be, I said. Oh, not long. So off he goes down the road, walking down to where the old tram went—we was all in the bush then—and something made me look after him. He must be hot in that coat, I said. And that's when I knew he wasn't coming back. Yet I couldn't've expected it, he liked it here. He was talking about putting chinchillas in the back yard. What's in a man's mind even when you're living with him you will never know."

"Was it long ago?" said Mary.

"Twelve years. My boys wanted me to sell then and go and live in rooms. But I said no. I had my hens and a nanny goat too at that time. More or less a pet. I had a pet coon too for a while, used to feed him chewing gum. Well, I said, husbands maybe come and go, but a place you've lived fifty years is something else. Making a joke of it with my family. Besides, I thought, if Mr. Fullerton was to come back, he'd come back here, not knowing where else to go. Of course he'd hardly know where to find me, the way it's changed now. But I always had the idea he might of suffered a loss of memory and it might come back. That has happened.

"I'm not complaining. Sometimes it seems to me about as reasonable a man should go as stay. I don't mind changes, either, that helps out my egg business. But this baby-sitting. All the time one or the other is asking me about baby-sitting. I tell them I got my own house to sit in and I raised my share of children."

Mary, remembering the birthday party, got up and called to her little boy. "I thought I might offer my black cherries for sale next summer," Mrs. Fullerton said. "Come and pick your own and they're fifty cents a box. I can't risk my old bones up a ladder no more."

"That's too much," Mary said, smiling. "They're cheaper than that at the supermarket." Mrs. Fullerton already hated the supermarket for lowering the price of eggs. Mary shook out her last cigarette and left it with her, saying she had another package in her purse. Mrs. Fullerton was fond of a cigarette but would not accept one unless you took her by surprise. Baby-sitting would pay for them, Mary thought. At the same time she was rather pleased with Mrs. Fullerton for being so unaccommodating. When Mary came out of this place, she always felt as if she were passing through barricades. The house and its surroundings were so self-sufficient, with their complicated and seemingly unalterable layout of vegetables and flower beds, apple and cherry trees, wired chicken-run, berry patch and wooden walks, woodpile, a great many roughly built dark little sheds, for hens or rabbits or a goat. Here was no open or straightforward plan, no order that an outsider could understand; yet what was haphazard time had made final. The place had become fixed, impregnable, all its accumulations necessary, until it seemed that even the washtubs, mops, couch springs and stacks of old police magazines on the back porch were there to stay.

Mary and Danny walked down the road that had been called, in Mrs. Fullerton's time, Wicks Road, but was now marked on the maps of the subdivision as Heather Drive. The name of the subdivision was Garden Place, and its streets were named for flowers. On either side of the road the earth was raw; the ditches were running full. Planks were laid across the open ditches, planks approached the doors of the newest houses. The new, white and shining houses, set side by side in long rows in the wound of the earth. She always thought of them as white houses, though of course they were not entirely white. They were stucco and siding, and only the stucco was white; the siding was painted in shades of blue, pink, green and yellow, all fresh and vivid colours. Last year, just at this time, in March, the bulldozers had come in to clear away the brush and second-growth and great trees of the mountain forest; in a little while the houses were going up among the boulders, the huge torn stumps, the unimaginable upheavals of that earth. The houses were frail at first, skeletons of new wood standing up in the dusk of the cold spring days. But the roofs went on, black and green, blue and red, and the stucco, the siding; the windows were put in, and plastered with signs that said, Murry's Glass, French's Hardwood Floors; it could be seen that the houses were real. People who would live in them came out and tramped around in the mud on Sundays. They were for people like Mary and her husband and their child, with not much money but expectations of more; Garden Place was already put down, in the minds of people who understood addresses, as less luxurious than Pine Hills but more desirable than Wellington Park. The bathrooms were beautiful, with three-part mirrors, ceramic tile, and coloured plumbing. The cupboards in the kitchen were light birch or mahogany, and there were copper lighting fixtures there and in the dining ells. Brick planters, matching the fireplaces, separated the living rooms and halls. The rooms were all large and light and the basements dry, and all this soundness and excellence seemed to be clearly, proudly indicated on the face of each house—those ingenuously similar houses that looked calmly out at each other, all the way down the street.

Today, since it was Saturday, all the men were out working around their houses. They were digging drainage ditches and making rockeries and clearing off and burning torn branches and brush. They worked with competitive violence and energy, all this being new to them; they were not men who made their livings by physical work. All day Saturday and Sunday they worked like this, so that in a year or two there should be green terraces, rock walls, shapely flower beds and ornamental shrubs. The earth must be heavy to dig now; it had been raining last night and this morning. But the day was brightening; the clouds had broken, revealing a long thin triangle of sky, its blue still cold and delicate, a winter colour. Behind the houses on one side of the road were pine trees, their ponderous symmetry not much stirred by any wind. These were to be cut down any day now, to make room for a shopping centre, which had been promised when the houses were sold.

And under the structure of this new subdivision, there was still something else to be seen; that was the old city, the old wilderness city that had lain on the side of the mountain. It had to be called a city because there were tramlines running into the woods, the houses had numbers and there were all the public buildings of a city, down by the water. But houses like Mrs. Fullerton's had been separated from each other by uncut forest and a jungle of wild blackberry and salmonberry bushes; these surviving houses, with thick smoke coming out of their chimneys, walls unpainted and patched and showing different degrees of age and darkening, rough sheds and stacked wood and compost heaps and grey board fences around them—these appeared every so often among the large new houses of Mimosa and Marigold and Heather Drive—dark, enclosed, expressing something like savagery in their disorder and the steep, unmatched angles of roofs and lean-tos; not possible on these streets, but there.

"What are they saying," said Edith, putting on more coffee. She was surrounded in her kitchen by the ruins of the birthday party—cake and molded jellies and cookies with animal faces. A balloon rolled underfoot. The children had been fed, had posed for flash cameras and endured the birthday games; now they were playing in the back bedrooms and the basement, while their parents had coffee. "What are they saying in there?" said Edith.

"I wasn't listening," Mary said, holding the empty cream pitcher in her hand. She went to the sink window. The rent in the clouds had been torn wide open and the sun was shining. The house seemed too hot.

"Mrs. Fullerton's house," said Edith, hurrying back to the living-room. Mary knew what they were talking about. Her neighbours' conversation, otherwise not troubling, might at any moment snag itself on this subject and eddy menacingly in familiar circles of complaint, causing her to look despairingly out of windows, or down into her lap, trying to find some wonderful explanatory word to bring it to a stop; she did not succeed. She had to go back; they were waiting for cream.

A dozen neighbourhood women sat around the living room, absently holding the balloons they had been given by their children. Because the children on the street were so young, and also because any gathering-together of the people who lived there was considered a healthy thing in itself, most birthday parties were attended by mothers as well as children. Women who saw each other every day met now in earrings, nylons and skirts, with their hair fixed and faces applied. Some of the men were there too—Steve, who was Edith's husband, and others he had invited in for beer; they were all in their work clothes. The subject just introduced was one of the few on which male and female interest came together.

"I tell you what I'd do if I was next door to it," Steve said, beaming good-naturedly in expectation of laughter. "I'd send my kids over there to play with matches."

"Oh, funny," Edith said. "It's past joking. You joke, I try to do something. I even phoned the Municipal Hall."

"What did they say?" said Mary Lou Ross.

"Well *I* said couldn't they get her to paint it, at least, or pull down some of the shacks, and they said no they couldn't. I said I thought there must be some kind of ordinance applied to people like that and they said they knew how I *felt* and they were very *sorry*—"

"But no?"

"But no."

"But what about the chickens, I thought—"

"Oh, they wouldn't let you or me keep chickens, but she has some special dispensation about that too, I forgot how it goes."

"I'm going to stop buying them," Janie Inger said. "The supermarket's cheaper and who cares that much about fresh? And my God, the smell. I said to Carl I knew we were coming to the sticks but I somehow didn't picture us next door to a barnyard."

"Across the street is worse than next door. It makes me wonder why we ever bothered with a picture window, whenever anybody comes to see us I want to draw the drapes so they won't see what's across from us."

"Okay, okay," Steve said, cutting heavily through these female voices. "What Carl and I started out to tell you was that, if we can work this lane deal, she has got to go. It's simple and it's legal. That's the beauty of it."

"What lane deal?"

"We are getting to that. Carl and I been cooking this for a couple of weeks, but we didn't like to say anything in case it didn't work out. Take it, Carl."

"Well she's on the lane allowance, that's all," Carl said. He was a real estate salesman, stocky, earnest, successful. "I had an idea it might be that way, so I went down to the Municipal Hall and looked it up."

"What does that mean, dear?" said Janie, casual, wifely.

"This is it," Carl said. "There's an allowance for a lane, there always has been, the idea being if the area ever got built up they would put a lane through. But they never thought that would happen, people just built where they liked. She's got part of her house and half a dozen shacks sitting right where the lane has to go through. So what we do now, we get the municipality to put through a lane. We need a lane anyway. Then she has to get out. It's the law."

"It's the law," said Steve, radiating admiration. "What a smart boy. These real estate operators are smart boys."

"Does she get anything?" said Mary Lou. "I'm sick of looking at it and all but I don't want to see anybody in the poorhouse."

"Oh, she'll get paid. More than it's worth. Look, it's to her advantage. She'll get paid for it, and she couldn't sell it, she couldn't give it away."

Mary set her coffee cup down before she spoke and hoped her voice would sound all right, not emotional or scared. "But remember she's been here a long time," she said. "She was here before most of us were born." She was trying desperately to think of other words, words more sound and reasonable than these; she could not expose to this positive tide any notion that they might think flimsy and romantic, or she would destroy her argument. But she had no argument. She could try all night and never find any words to stand up to their words, which came at her now invincibly from all sides; *shack, eyesore, filthy, property, value.*

"Do you honestly think that people who let their property get so rundown have that much claim to our consideration?" Janie said, feeling her husband's plan was being attacked.

"She's been here forty years, now we're here," Carl said. "So it goes. And whether you realize it or not, just standing there that house is bringing down the resale value of every house on this street. I'm in the business, I know."

And these were joined by other voices; it did not matter much what they said as long as they were full of self-assertion and anger. That was their strength, proof of their adulthood, of themselves and their seriousness. The spirit of anger rose among them, bearing up their young voices, sweeping them together as on a flood of intoxication, and they admired each other in this new behaviour as property-owners as people admire each other for being drunk.

"We might as well get everybody now," Steve said. "Save going around to so many places."

It was supper time, getting dark out. Everybody was preparing to go home, mothers buttoning their children's coats, children clutching, without much delight, their balloons and whistles and paper baskets full of jelly beans. They had stopped fighting, almost stopped noticing each other; the party had disintegrated. The adults too had grown calmer and felt tired.

"Edith! Edith, have you got a pen?"

Edith brought a pen and they spread the petition for the lane, which Carl had drawn up, on the dining-room table, clearing away the paper plates with smears of dried ice cream. People began to sign mechanically as they said goodbye. Steve was still scowling slightly; Carl stood with one hand on the paper, businesslike, but proud. Mary knelt on the floor and struggled with Danny's zipper. She got up and put on her own coat, smoothed her hair, put on her gloves and took them off again. When she could not think of anything else to do she walked past the dining-room table on her way to the door. Carl held out the pen.

"I can't sign that," she said. Her face flushed up, at once, her voice was trembling. Steve touched her shoulder.

"What's the matter, honey?"

"I don't think we have the right. We haven't the right."

"Mary, don't you care how things look? You live here too."

"No, I—I don't care." Oh, wasn't it strange, how in your imagination, when you stood up for something your voice rang, people started, abashed; but in real life they all smiled in rather a special way and you saw that what you had really done was serve yourself up as a conversational delight for the next coffee party.

"Don't worry, Mary, she's got money in the bank," Janie said. "She must have. I asked her to baby-sit for me once and she practically spit in my face. She isn't exactly a charming old lady, you know."

"I know she isn't a charming old lady," Mary said.

Steve's hand still rested on her shoulder. "Hey what do you think we are, a bunch of ogres?"

"Nobody wants to turn her out just for the fun of it," Carl said. "It's unfortunate. We all know that. But we have to think of the community."

"Yes," said Mary. But she put her hands in the pockets of her coat and turned to say thank you to Edith, thank you for the birthday party. It occurred to her that they were right, for themselves, for whatever it was they had to be. And Mrs. Fullerton was old, she had dead eyes, nothing could touch her. Mary went out and walked with Danny up the street. She saw the curtains being drawn across living-room windows; cascades of flowers, of leaves, of geometrical designs, shut off these rooms from the night. Outside it was quite dark, the white houses were growing dim, the clouds breaking and breaking, and smoke blowing from Mrs. Fullerton's chimney. The pattern of Garden Place, so assertive in the daytime, seemed to shrink at night into the raw black mountainside.

The voices in the living room have blown away, Mary thought. If they would blow away and their plans be forgotten, if one thing could be left alone. But these are people who win, and they are good people; they want homes for their children, they help each other when there is trouble, they plan a community—saying that word as if they found a modern and well-proportioned magic in it, and no possibility anywhere of a mistake.

There is nothing you can do at present but put your hands in your pockets and keep a disaffected heart.

1. In your journal, record your thoughts, associations, or feelings about the story. You might choose to focus on one of the following:
   - your response to Mrs. Fullerton;
   - how you might have acted if you lived in the neighborhood;
   - questions you have about the story.

   Share your journal entry with two or three classmates.
2. Create a chart contrasting Mary's view of Mrs. Fullerton with her neighbors' views. What else could Mary have said to change her neighbors' feelings about Mrs. Fullerton?
3. Examine the various beliefs and values implicit in the story. Which of these beliefs does the author seem to hold? What comment does the story make? Do you agree? Support your response with details from the story and, if you choose, from your own experience.
4. Examine the language of the story. Note phrases and images that are particularly strong. How do they contribute to the story's meaning or conflicts?
5. Improvise the conversation that takes place later that evening between Mary and her husband as they discuss Mrs. Fullerton and the petition.
6. Imagine that Mrs. Fullerton learns about the petition and appears at a community meeting to give a speech. What does she say? Write the speech Mrs. Fullerton gives.

Luigi Pirandello

War

"Nasty world," muttered the husband with a sad smile.

The passengers who had left Rome by the night express had had to stop until dawn at the small station of Fabriano in order to continue their journey by the small old-fashioned "local" joining the main line with Sulmona.

At dawn, in a stuffy and smoky second-class carriage in which five people had already spent the night, a bulky woman, in deep mourning, was hoisted in—almost like a shapeless bundle. Behind her, puffing and moaning, followed her husband—a tiny man, thin and weakly, his face death-white, his eyes small and bright and looking shy and uneasy.

Having at last taken a seat he politely thanked the passengers who had helped his wife and who had made room for her; then he turned round to the woman trying to pull down the collar of her coat and politely enquired:

"Are you all right, dear?"

The wife, instead of answering, pulled up her collar again to her eyes, so as to hide her face.

"Nasty world," muttered the husband with a sad smile.

And he felt it his duty to explain to his travelling companions that the poor woman was to be pitied for the war was taking away from her her only son, a boy of twenty to whom both had devoted their entire life, even breaking up their home at Sulmona to follow him to Rome where he had to go as a student, then allowing him to volunteer for war with an assurance, however, that at least for six months he would not be sent to the front and now, all of a sudden, receiving a wire saying that he was due to leave in three days' time and asking them to go and see him off.

The woman under the big coat was twisting and wriggling, at times growling like a wild animal, feeling certain that all those explanations would not have aroused even a shadow of sympathy from those people who—most likely—were in the same plight as herself. One of them, who had been listening with particular attention, said:

"You should thank God that your son is only leaving now for the front. Mine has been sent there the first day of the war. He has already come back twice wounded and been sent back again to the front."

"What about me? I have two sons and three nephews at the front," said another passenger.

"Maybe, but in our case it is our *only* son," ventured the husband.

"What difference can it make? You may spoil your only son with excessive attentions, but you cannot love him more than you would all your other children if you had any. Paternal love is not like bread that can be broken into pieces and split amongst the children in equal shares. A father gives *all* his love to each one of his children without discrimination, whether it be one or ten, and, if I am suffering now for my two sons, I am not suffering half for each of them but double...."

"True ... true ..." sighed the embarrassed husband, "but suppose (of course we all hope it will never be your case) a father has two sons at the front and he loses one of them, there is still one left to console him ... while ..."

"Yes," answered the other, getting cross, "a son left to console him but also a son left for whom he must survive, while in the case of the father of an only son if the son dies the father can die too and put an end to his distress. Which of the two positions is the worse? Don't you see how my case would be worse than yours?"

"Nonsense," interrupted another traveller, a fat, red-faced man with bloodshot eyes of the palest grey.

He was panting. From his bulging eyes seemed to spurt inner violence of an uncontrolled vitality which his weakened body could hardly contain.

"Nonsense," he repeated, trying to cover his mouth with his hand so as to hide the two missing front teeth. "Nonsense. Do we give life to our children for our own benefit?"

The other travellers stared at him in distress. The one who had had his son at the front since the first day of the war sighed: "You are right. Our children do not belong to us, they belong to the Country...."

"Bosh," retorted the fat traveller. "Do we think of the Country when we give life to our children? Our sons are born because ... well, because they must be born and when they come to life they take our own life with them. This is the truth. We belong to them but they never belong to us. And when they reach twenty they are exactly what we were at their age. We too had a father and mother, but there were so many other things as well ... girls, cigarettes, illusions, new ties ... and the Country, of course, whose call we would have answered—when we were twenty—even if father and mother had said no. Now, at our age, the love of our Country is still great, of course, but stronger than it is the love for our children. Is there any one of us here who wouldn't gladly take his son's place at the front if he could?"

There was a silence all round, everybody nodding as to approve.

"Why then," continued the fat man, "shouldn't we consider the feelings of our children when they are twenty? Isn't it natural that at their age they should consider the love for their Country (I am speaking of decent boys, of course) even greater than the love for us? Isn't it natural that it should be so, as after all they must look upon us as upon old boys who cannot move any more and must stay at home? If Country exists, if Country is a natural necessity like bread, of which each of us must eat in order not to die of hunger, somebody must go to defend it. And our sons go, when they are twenty, and they don't want tears, because if they die, they die inflamed and happy (I am speaking, of course, of decent boys). Now, if one dies young and happy, without having the ugly sides of life, the boredom of it, the pettiness, the bitterness of disillusion ... what more can we ask for him? Everyone should stop crying: everyone should laugh, as I do ... or at least thank God—as I do—because my son, before dying, sent me a message saying that he was dying satisfied at having ended his life in the best way he could have wished. That is why, as you see, I do not even wear mourning...."

He shook his light fawn coat as to show it; his livid lip over his missing teeth was trembling, his eyes were watery and motionless and soon after he ended with a shrill laugh which might well have been a sob.

"Quite so ... quite so ..." agreed the others.

The woman who, bundled in a corner under her coat, had been sitting and listening had—for the last three months—tried to find in the words of her husband and her friends something to console her in her deep sorrow, something that might show her how a mother should resign herself to send her son not even to death but to a probable danger of life. Yet not a word had she found amongst the many which had been said ... and her grief had been greater in seeing that nobody—as she thought—could share her feelings.

But now the words of the traveller amazed and almost stunned her. She suddenly realized that it wasn't the others who were wrong and could not understand her but herself who could not rise up to the same height of those fathers and mothers willing to resign themselves, without crying, not only to the departure of their sons but even to their death.

She lifted her head, she bent over from her corner trying to listen with great attention to the details which the fat man was giving to his companions about the way his son had fallen as a hero, for his King and his Country, happy and without regrets. It seemed to her that she had stumbled into a world she had never dreamt of, a world so far unknown to her and she was so pleased to hear everyone joining in congratulating that brave father who could so stoically speak of his child's death.

Then suddenly, just as if she had heard nothing of what had been said and almost as if waking up from a dream, she turned to the old man, asking him:

"Then ... is your son really dead?"

Everybody stared at her. The old man, too, turned to look at her, fixing his great, bulging, horribly watery light grey eyes, deep in her face. For some little time he tried to answer, but words failed him. He looked and looked at her, almost as if only then—at that silly, incongruous question—he had suddenly realized at last that his son was really dead ... gone for ever ... for ever. His face contracted, became horribly distorted, then he snatched in haste a handkerchief from his pocket and, to the amazement of everyone, broke into harrowing, heart-rending, uncontrollable sobs.

1. In your journal, record your thoughts, associations, or feelings about the story. You might choose to focus on one of the following:
   - thoughts this story brought to mind for you;
   - questions or comments you have for any of the characters;
   - the character(s) you sympathized with most.

   Share your journal entry with two or three classmates.
2. Working in a small group, develop a chart indicating each parent's outlook. Is there one which you feel is ideal? Compare your views with those of other groups.
3. This story deals with war, but it contains no soldiers or battles. What comment do you think it makes about war? What other comments does the story make? Explain.
4. How does the grieving mother respond to the fat man's comments? How do you suppose she will react to the man's "harrowing, heart-rending, uncontrollable sobs"?
5. Pirandello describes in detail the physical appearance of the characters. Examine the details and suggest why Pirandello included them. What contribution do the details make?
6. Compose a letter that the grieving woman might write to her son who is at the war front.

2

Characters in Conflict

Almost everyday we tell and hear stories. Typically, these stories focus on people—ourselves or others—and involve conflict. The person focused on in each story has certain goals or needs and faces obstacles in meeting them—hence the "conflict." How the person responds to the conflict and whether the obstacle is overcome or not dominate the story. Because we care about people and want to understand more deeply ourselves and life, we listen to and tell these stories.

It's also often for these reasons that we read stories and watch movies. Whether a story focuses more on the conflict and the character's actions *or* on the character's thoughts and feelings while responding to the conflict, the "human interest" that readers want is there. When reading conflict- and action-oriented stories, we may only become *acquainted* with characters and curious about their fate; but, when reading stories that focus on a character's thoughts and feelings, we get to *know* and *understand* the characters as they move through the events of their stories.

As we read a thought-provoking story that focuses on a character in conflict, we're often first interested in the character as a human being, curious about the way he or she will respond to the conflict, and concerned about that character's well-being. We might think of our similar experiences and compare ourselves with the character. As we become more involved with the story, we might predict the character's actions, hope for certain twists in the plot, or feel strongly for the character. As we explore, reflect on, and share our thoughts and feelings from the first reading, we lay a foundation for critical perspectives on the story.

When responding critically we work to deepen our understanding of how the character's nature, predicament, and/or reactions work to give the story meaning and significance. So, for example, we might ask ourselves:

- How has the protagonist responded to the conflict? What do those responses reveal about the character's nature and motivation?
- What do the central character's responses to the conflict reveal about his or her outlook on life?
- What does the protagonist's response to the conflict suggest about human nature?
- Are the protagonist's thoughts and actions believable? Why, or why not?
- Is the protagonist someone with whom you can sympathize? Why, or why not?
- What function(s) do the story's minor characters have?

The selections in this unit present characters confronted by significant conflicts in their lives. Against the backdrop of a family's efforts in a new culture, a boy helps his grandmother fulfill her last wish in Wayson Choy's "The Jade Peony." In "Imagine a Day at the End of Your Life," reflections on his life and relationships bring a father to a new way of seeing and being. Margaret Laurence's "Horses of the Night" introduces us to Chris, a young man struggling against enormous odds to realize his dreams. We see him and his trials through the eyes of his cousin Vanessa and, in turn, see her own outlook on life and her changes. Set in French colonial Africa, the final story, "The Guest," presents a schoolteacher whose beliefs contradict his obligations. As he wrestles with a dilemma, we are invited to reflect on the relationship between our own actions and beliefs.

Each story draws us into a character's world and invites us to respond and reflect as we consider the character's thoughts, feelings, and actions in moments of crisis and challenge.

Wayson Choy

The Jade Peony

Death, *I thought,* He is in this room, *and I would work harder alongside her.*

When Grandmama died at 83 our whole household held its breath. She had promised us a sign of her leaving, final proof that her present life had ended well. My parents knew that without any clear sign, our own family fortunes could be altered, threatened. My stepmother looked endlessly into the small cluttered room the ancient lady had occupied. Nothing was touched; nothing changed. My father, thinking that a sign should appear in Grandmama's garden, looked at the frost-killed shoots and cringed: *no, that could not be it.*

My two older teenage brothers and my sister, Liang, age 14, were embarrassed by my parents' behaviour. What would all the white people in Vancouver think of us? We were Canadians now, *Chinese-Canadians,* a hyphenated reality that my parents could never accept. So it seemed, for different reasons, we all held our breath waiting for *something.*

I was eight when she died. For days she had resisted going into the hospital ... *a cold, just a cold* ... and instead gave constant instruction to my stepmother and sister on the boiling of ginseng roots mixed with bitter extract. At night, between wracking coughs and deadly silences, Grandmama had her back and chest rubbed with heated camphor oil and sipped a bluish decoction of an herb called Peacock's Tail. When all these failed to abate her fever, she began to arrange the details of her will. This she did with my father, confessing finally: "I am too stubborn. The only cure for old age is to die."

My father wept to hear this. I stood beside her bed; she turned to me. Her round face looked darker, and the gentleness of her eyes, the thin, arching eyebrows, seemed weary. I brushed the few strands of gray, brittle hair from her face; she managed to smile at me. Being the youngest, I had spent nearly all my time with her and could not imagine that we would ever be parted. Yet when she spoke, and her voice hesitated, cracked, the sombre shadows of her room chilled me. Her wrinkled brow grew wet with fever, and her small body seemed even more diminutive.

"I—I am going to the hospital, Grandson." Her hand reached out for mine. "You know, Little Son, whatever happens I will never leave you." Her palm felt plush and warm, the slender, old fingers boney and firm, so magically strong was her grip that I could not imagine how she could ever part from me. Ever.

Her hands *were* magical. My most vivid memories are of her hands: long, elegant fingers, with impeccable nails, a skein of fine, barely-seen veins, and wrinkled skin like light pine. Those hands were quick when she taught me, at six, simple tricks of juggling, learnt when she was a village girl in Southern Canton; a troupe of actors had stayed on her father's farm. One of them, "tall and pale as the whiteness of petals," fell in love with her, promising to return. In her last years his image came back like a third being in our two lives. He had been magician, acrobat, juggler, and some of the things he taught her she had absorbed and passed on to me through her stories and games. But above all, without realizing it then, her hands conveyed to me the quality of their love.

Most marvellous for me was the quick-witted skill her hands revealed in making windchimes for our birthdays: windchimes in the likeness of her lost friend's only present to her, made of bits of string and scraps, in the centre of which once hung a precious jade peony. This wondrous gift to her broke apart years ago, in China, but Grandmama kept the jade pendant in a tiny red silk envelope, and kept it always in her pocket, until her death.

These were not ordinary, carelessly made chimes, such as those you now find in our Chinatown stores, whose rattling noises drive you mad. But making her special ones caused dissension in our family, and some shame. Each one that she made was created from a treasure trove of glass fragments and castaway costume jewellery, in the same way that her first windchime had been made. The problem for the rest of the family was in the fact that Grandmama looked for these treasures wandering the back alleys of Keefer and Pender Streets, peering into our neighbours' garbage cans, chasing away hungry, nervous cats and shouting curses at them.

"All our friends are laughing at us!" Older Brother Jung said at last to my father, when Grandmama was away having tea at Mrs. Lim's.

"We are not poor," Oldest Brother Kiam declared, "yet she and Sek-Lung poke through those awful things as if—" he shoved me in frustration and I stumbled against my sister, "—they were beggars!"

"She will make Little Brother crazy!" Sister Liang said. Without warning, she punched me sharply in the back; I jumped. "You see, look how *nervous* he is!"

I lifted my foot slightly, enough to swing it back and kick Liang in the shin. She yelled and pulled back her fist to punch me again. Jung made a menacing move towards me.

"Stop this, all of you!" My father shook his head in exasperation. How could he dare tell the Grand Old One, his aging mother, that what was somehow appropriate in a poor village in China, was an abomination here. How could he prevent me, his youngest, from accompanying her? If she went walking into those alley-ways alone she could well be attacked by hoodlums. "She is not a beggar looking for food. She is searching for—for...."

My stepmother attempted to speak, then fell silent. She, too, seemed perplexed and somewhat ashamed. They all loved Grandmama, but she was *inconvenient*, unsettling.

As for our neighbours, most understood Grandmama to be harmlessly crazy, others that she did indeed make lovely toys but for what purpose? Why? they asked, and the stories she told me, of the juggler who smiled at her, flashed in my head.

Finally, by their cutting remarks, the family did exert enough pressure so that Grandmama and I no longer openly announced our expeditions. Instead, she took me with her on "shopping trips," ostensibly for clothes or groceries, while in fact we spent most of our time exploring stranger and more distant neighbourhoods, searching for splendid junk: jangling pieces of a vase, cranberry glass fragments embossed with leaves, discarded glass beads from Woolworth necklaces.... We would sneak them all home in brown rice sacks, folded into small parcels, and put them under her bed. During the day when the family was away at school or work, we brought them out and washed every item in a large black pot of boiling lye and water, dried them quickly, carefully, and returned them, sparkling, under her bed.

Our greatest excitement occurred when a fire gutted the large Chinese Presbyterian Church, three blocks from our house. Over the still-smoking ruins the next day, Grandmama and I rushed precariously over the blackened beams to pick out the stained glass that glittered in the sunlight. Small figure bent over, wrapped against the autumn cold in a dark blue quilted coat, happily gathering each piece like gold, she became my spiritual playmate: "There's a good one! *There*!"

Hours later, soot-covered and smelling of smoke, we came home with a Safeway carton full of delicate fragments, still early enough to steal them all into the house and put the small box under her bed. "These are special pieces," she said, giving the box a last push, "because they come from a sacred place." She slowly got up and I saw, for the first time, her hand begin to shake. But then, in her joy, she embraced me. Both of our hearts were racing, as if we were two dreamers. I buried my face in her blue quilt, and for a moment, the whole world seemed silent.

"My juggler," she said, "he never came back to me from Honan … perhaps the famine…." Her voice began to quake. "But I shall have my sacred windchime … I shall have it again."

One evening, when the family was gathered in their usual places in the parlour, Grandmama gave me her secret nod: a slight wink of her eye and a flaring of her nostrils. There was *trouble* in the air. Supper had gone badly, school examinations were due, father had failed to meet an editorial deadline at the *Vancouver Chinese Times.* A huge sigh came from Sister Liang.

"But it is useless this Chinese they teach you!" she lamented, turning to Stepmother for support. Silence. Liang frowned, dejected, and went back to her Chinese book, bending the covers back.

"Father," Oldest Brother Kiam began, waving his bamboo brush in the air, "you must realize that this Mandarin only confuses us. We are Cantonese speakers…."

"And you do not complain about Latin, French or German in your English school?" Father rattled his newspaper, signal that his patience was ending.

"But, Father, those languages are *scientific*," Kiam jabbed his brush in the air. "We are in a scientific, logical world."

Father was silent. We could all hear Grandmama's rocker.

"What about Sek-Lung?" Older Brother Jung pointed angrily at me. "He was sick last year, but this year he should have at least started Chinese school, instead of picking over garbage cans!"

"He starts next year," Father said, in a hard tone that immediately warned everyone to be silent. Liang slammed her book.

Grandmama went on rocking quietly in her chair. She complimented my mother on her knitting, made a remark about the "strong beauty" of Kiam's brushstrokes which, in spite of himself, immensely pleased him. All this babbling noise was her family torn and confused in a strange land: everything here was so very foreign and scientific.

The truth was, I was sorry not to have started school the year before. In my innocence I had imagined going to school meant certain privileges worthy of all my brothers' and sister's complaints. The fact that my lung infection in my fifth and sixth years, mistakenly diagnosed as TB, earned me some reprieve, only made me long for school the more. Each member of the family took turns on Sunday, teaching me or annoying me. But it was the countless hours I spent with Grandmama that were my real education. Tapping me on my head she would say, "Come, Sek-Lung, we have *our* work," and we would walk up the stairs to her small crowded room. There, in the midst of her antique shawls, the old ancestral calligraphy and multi-coloured embroidered hangings, beneath the mysterious shelves of sweet herbs and bitter potions, we would continue doing what we had started that morning: the elaborate windchime for her death.

"I can't last forever," she declared, when she let me in on the secret of this one. "It will sing and dance and glitter," her long fingers stretched into the air, pantomiming the waving motion of her ghost chimes; "My spirit will hear its sounds and see its light and return to this house and say goodbye to you."

Deftly she reached into the Safeway carton she had placed on the chair beside me. She picked out a fish-shape amber piece, and with a long needle-like tool and a steel ruler, she scored it. Pressing the blade of a cleaver against the line, with the fingers of her other hand, she lifted up the glass until it cleanly snapped into the exact shape she required. Her hand began to tremble, the tips of her fingers to shiver, like rippling water.

"You see that, Little One?" She held her hand up. "That is my body fighting with Death. He is in this room now."

My eyes darted in panic, but Grandmama remained calm, undisturbed, and went on with her work. Then I remembered the glue and uncorked the jar for her. Soon the graceful ritual movements of her hand returned to her, and I became lost in the magic of her task: she dabbed a cabalistic mixture of glue on one end and skillfully dropped the braided end of a silk thread into it. This part always amazed me: the braiding would slowly, *very* slowly, *unknot*, fanning out like a prized fishtail. In a few seconds the clear, homemade glue began to harden as I blew lightly over it, welding to itself each separate silk strand.

Each jam-sized pot of glue was precious; each large cork had been wrapped with a fragment of pink silk. I remember this part vividly, because each cork was treated to a special rite. First we went shopping in the best silk stores in Chinatown for the perfect square of silk she required. It had to be a deep pink, a shade of colour blushing toward red. And the tone had to match—as closely as possible—her precious jade carving, the small peony of white and light-red jade, her most lucky possession. In the centre of this semi-translucent carving, no more than an inch wide, was a pool of pink light, its veins swirling out into the petals of the flower.

"This colour is the colour of my spirit," she said, holding it up to the window so I could see the delicate pastel against the broad strokes of sunlight. She dropped her voice, and I held my breath at the wonder of the colour. "This was given to me by the young actor who taught me how to juggle. He had four of them, and each one had a centre of this rare colour, the colour of Good Fortune." The pendant seemed to pulse as she turned it: "Oh, Sek-Lung! He had white hair and white skin to *his toes*! *It's true*, I saw him bathing." She laughed and blushed, her eyes softened at the memory. The silk had to match the pink heart of her pendant: the colour was magical for her, to hold the unravelling strands of her memory....

It was just six months before she died that we really began to work on her windchime. Three thin bamboo sticks were steamed and bent into circlets; 30 exact lengths of silk thread, the strongest kind, were cut and braided at both ends and glued to stained glass. Her hands worked on their own command, each hand racing with a life of its own: cutting, snapping, braiding, knotting.... Sometimes she breathed heavily and her small body, growing thinner, sagged against me. *Death,* I thought, *He is in this room,* and I would work harder alongside her. For months Grandmama and I did this every other evening, a half dozen pieces each time. The shaking in her hand grew worse, but we said nothing. Finally, after discarding hundreds, she told me she had the necessary 30 pieces. But this time, because it was a sacred chime, I would not be permitted to help her tie it up or have the joy of raising it. "Once tied," she said, holding me against my disappointment, "not even I can raise it. Not a sound must it make until I have died."

"What will happen?"

"Your father will then take the centre braided strand and raise it. He will hang it against my bedroom window so that my ghost may see it, and hear it, and return. I must say goodbye to this world properly or wander in this foreign devil's land forever."

"You can take the streetcar!" I blurted, suddenly shocked that she actually meant to leave me. I thought I could hear the clear-chromatic chimes, see the shimmering colours on the wall: I fell against her and cried, and there in my crying I knew that she would die. I can still remember the touch of her hand on my head, and the smell of her thick woolen sweater pressed against my face. "I will always be with you, Little Sek-Lung, but in a different way ... you'll see."

Months went by, and nothing happened. Then one late September evening, when I had just come home from Chinese School, Grandmama was preparing supper when she looked out our kitchen window and saw a cat—a long, lean white cat—jump into our garbage pail and knock it over. She ran out to chase it away, shouting curses at it. She did not have her thick sweater on and when she came back into the house, a chill gripped her. She leaned against the door: "That was not a cat," she said, and the odd tone of her voice caused my father to look with alarm at her. "I cannot take back my curses. It is too late." She took hold of my father's arm: "It was all white and had pink eyes like sacred fire."

My father started at this, and they both looked pale. My brothers and sister, clearing the table, froze in their gestures.

"The fog has confused you," Stepmother said. "It was just a cat."

But Grandmama shook her head, for she knew it was a sign. "I will not live forever," she said. "I am prepared."

The next morning she was confined to her bed with a severe cold. Sitting by her, playing with some of my toys, I asked her about the cat.

"Why did father jump at the cat with the pink eyes? He didn't see it, you did."

"But he and your mother know what it means."

"What?"

"My friend, the juggler, the magician, was as pale as white jade, and he had pink eyes." I thought she would begin to tell me one of her stories, a tale of enchantment or of a wondrous adventure, but she only paused to swallow; her eyes glittered, lost in memory. She took my hand, gently opening and closing her fingers over it. "Sek-Lung," she sighed, "*he* has come back to me."

Then Grandmama sank back into her pillow and the embroidered flowers lifted to frame her wrinkled face. I saw her hand over my own and my own began to tremble. I fell fitfully asleep by her side. When I woke up it was dark and her bed was empty. She had been taken to the hospital and I was not permitted to visit.

A few days after that she died of the complications of pneumonia. Immediately after her death my father came home and said nothing to us, but walked up the stairs to her room, pulled aside the drawn lace curtains of her window and lifted the windchimes to the sky.

I began to cry and quickly put my hand in my pocket for a handkerchief. Instead, caught between my fingers, was the small, round firmness of the jade peony. In my mind's eye I saw Grandmama smile and heard, softly, the pink centre beat like a beautiful, cramped heart.

1. In your journal, record your thoughts and feelings about the story. You might explore one of the following:
   - your feelings about the grandmother;
   - thoughts the story left you with about relationships between generations;
   - reflections on specific details in the story.

   Share your writing with two or three classmates.
2. What is the central conflict of the story? How is the family affected by the conflict? How is the conflict resolved?
3. According to the narrator, the family's experience of being new in Canada involves a "hyphenated reality." Compare the ways in which the various members see and respond to this experience. You might also consider your own and/or others' experiences.
4. Of what Sek-Lung gained and learned from the time he spent with his grandmother, what do you think will be most significant in his life? Explain.
5. a) What does the jade peony represent to Sek-Lung? How did it acquire that meaning for him?
   b) Consider the various references to color in the story. What observations can you make about the author's use of color symbolism?
6. Write a poem that Sek-Lung might have written about his grandmother.

Ann Beattie

Imagine a Day at the End of Your Life

I got to feeling like a dinosaur,
passing the time until the great disaster.

Sometimes I do feel subsumed by them. My wife, Harriet, only wanted two children in the first place. With the third and fourth, I was naturally pressing for a son. The fifth, Michael, was an accident. Allison was third and Denise was number four. Number one, Carolyn, was always the most intelligent and the most troublesome; Joan was always the one whose talent I thought would pan out, but there's no arguing with what she says: dancers are obsessive, vain people, and many of them have problems with drugs and drink, and it's no fun to watch people disfigure their bodies in the name of art. Allison was rather plain. She developed a good sense of humor, probably as compensation for not being as attractive or as talented as the older ones. The fourth, Denise, was almost as talented at painting as Joan was at dance, but she married young and gave it up, except for creating her family's Christmas card. Michael is a ski instructor in Aspen—sends those tourists down the slopes with a smile. I think he likes the notion of keeping people at a distance. He has felt overwhelmed all his life.

My wife's idea of real happiness is to have all the family lined up on the porch in their finery, with their spouses and all the children, being photographed like the Royal Family. She's always bustled with energy. She gave the rocking chair to Goodwill last spring because, she said, it encouraged lethargy.

Harriet is a very domestic woman, but come late afternoon she's at the Remington, conjuring up bodies buried in haystacks and mass murderers at masked balls—some of the weirdest stuff you can imagine. She's done quite well financially writing these mysteries, and every couple of years we hire a driver and set off across the United States, stopping to see friends and family. At night, in the motel room, she puts the typewriter on the bureau, piles pillows on one of the chairs, and starts typing. Nothing interferes with her concentration. At home, she might run off after lunch to examine an animal in the zoo, or even march onto a construction site with her tape recorder to ask questions about ditch digging. She has a lot of anecdotes, and that keeps things lively. We get more than our share of invitations to parties. People would have us to breakfast if we'd go.

Harriet says that I'm spoiled by how much fun we have and that it's going to be hard to settle for the way life will be when we're old. At the end of every year we've got a dozen new friends. Policemen who've taken a liking to her, or whoever's new at the local library. Last year a man who imported jumping beans lived with us for a month, when he was down on his luck. Those boxes, out in the hallway, sounded like the popcorn machine at the movies.

Some people undervalue what Harriet does, or don't have sympathy with my having resigned my position on the route, but how many more years are dairies going to deliver, anyway? I got to feeling like a dinosaur, passing the time until the great disaster. I felt like a vanishing breed, is what I mean. And how many people would go on doing what they've been doing if they had the means to do otherwise?

The girls are good-natured about their mother, and I think that Allison and Denise, in particular, quite admire her. Things didn't ever really come together and take shape for those two, but that's understandable, because no matter how much you try, every parent does have favorites. I was quite taken aback by Carolyn because she was so attractive and intelligent. Maybe instead of saying that she was a real favorite, I should say that she was a real shock. She walked at eight months! Never took time to crawl. One day, outside the playpen, she pulled herself up and took off across the rug. There she went. She married a fool, but she seems happy with his foolishness. Joan is remarried to a very nice man who owns a bank—flat out owns it!—in Michigan. She's recovered well from her bad first marriage, which isn't surprising, considering that she's in her first year of law school and has inherited two daughters. There are three dalmations, too. Dogs that eat her out of house and home. Allison works as a buyer for a big department store, and she's pretty close to her younger sister, Denise. All year, Allison thinks about sweaters, contracts with people to knit sweaters, goes to look at the plants where sweaters are manufactured. That's what we get as gifts: sweaters. She and Denise go on sweater-shopping expeditions in the spring. Harriet and I get postcards telling us what the towns look like, what they ate for dinner, and sometimes anecdotes about how the two of them located some interesting sweater.

Michael, lately, is the problem. That's the way it is: you hope and hope for a particular child and that's the one who's always eluding you. He'll plan a trip home and cancel it at the last minute, send pictures that are too blurry to see his face. Occasionally I get mad and tell him that he neglects his mother and me, but those comments just roll off his back. He says that he doesn't cause us any trouble and that he doesn't ask for anything, which isn't the issue at all. He keeps bringing up that he offered to teach me to ski and that I turned him down. I'm not athletically inclined. He takes that personally. It's so often the way that the position you're in as a parent gets reversed, so that one day you're the one who lags behind. You're the one who won't try anything new. Michael's always been a rather argumentative boy, but I've never believed in fighting fire with fire. Harriet says he's the apple of my eye, but as I said to her: "What does that mean? That when Michael's here, I see red?" With the last three, I think, both she and I slacked off.

Live in the present, Harriet's always telling me. As a joke, she's named the man who runs the morgue in her mysteries, who's a worrywart, after me. But I never did hold with the notion that you should have children and then cast them to the wind. They're interesting people. Between them, they know seven foreign languages. If I want advice about what stock to buy, I can call one son-in-law, and if I want to criticize the president, I can call another. Naturally, my children don't see eye-to-eye about how to live, and sometimes they don't even speak to one another, or they write letters I'm sure they later regret. Still, I sense great loyalty between them.

The last time the whole family was here was for our fortieth wedding anniversary. The TV ran night and day, and no one could keep on top of the chaos in the kitchen. Allison and Joan had even given friends the phone number, as if they were going into exile instead of visiting their parents for the weekend. The phone rang off the hook. Allison brought her dog and Joan brought her favorite dalmation, and the two got into such an awful fight that Allison's had to spend the night in the backseat of her car. All night long, inside the house, the other dog paced, wanting to get at it. At the end of the visit, when the last car pulled away, Harriet admitted to me that it had been too much for her. She'd gone into the kitchen and stood a broom upside down in the corner and opened the scissors facing the bristles. She'd interviewed a woman who practiced voodoo, and the woman had told her that that was a surefire way to get rid of guests. Harriet felt a little guilty that it had worked: initially, Denise had said that she was going to leave early Monday morning, but by Sunday noon she was gone—and the last to leave.

I have in my possession cassettes of music the children thought their mother and I should be aware of, photocopies of grandchildren's report cards, California wine with a label saying that it was bottled especially for Joan, and an ingenious keychain you can always find because when you whistle, it beeps. My anniversary present from Allison was a photo album, in a very nice, compact size, called a "brag book." She has filled it with pictures of the grandchildren and the husbands and cats and dogs, and with some cartoons that she thought were amusing. And then there was another brag book that was empty, with a note inside saying that I could brag about whatever I wanted.

For a long while the albums just stayed on the coffee table, buried under magazines or Harriet's fan mail. Then one day when I was coming up the front walk, I looked down and saw a ginkgo leaf. It was as bright as a jewel. I was amazed, even though the neighbor had had that tree, and the leaves had blown over our property, for years. I put the leaf on the coffee table, and then it occurred to me that I could put it in the brag book—press it between the plastic pages—maybe even add some other leaves.

The next day, I put the leaf underneath the plastic, and then I went out and started to look for other leaves. By the end of the week, the book was filled up. I have no memory of doing anything like that as a child. I did collect stamps for a while, but the leaves were a different thing entirely.

To be truthful, there are a few pages in the book right in the middle that aren't filled, but it's getting cold and the leaves are losing their color fast. It may be next year before it's filled. I worked on the front of the book because I had some sense of how I wanted it to begin, and then I filled the back of the book, because I found the perfect leaf to end with, but I wasn't sure about the rest. I thought there might be some particularly unusual leaves, if I went far enough afield.

So yesterday I drove out to the woods in Batesville, to look. If I'd been looking for birds, there were certainly enough of them. It was the sort of day—with all that blue sky and with the tree bark almost jumping out at you in the strong light—that makes you think: Why don't I do this every day? Why isn't everybody out walking? That's the mystery to me—not that there are so many duplicitous people and so many schemes and crimes, but that out there, in the real world, people are so rarely where they should be. I don't usually think about mortality, but the albums were a present commemorating forty years of marriage, which would put anyone in mind of what had happened, as well as what was inevitable. That day in the woods, I thought: Don't run away from the thought of death. Imagine a day at the end of your life. I wasn't thinking of people who were hospitalized or who saw disaster coming at them on the highway. I was thinking of a day that was calm, that seemed much like other days, when suddenly things speeded up—or maybe slowed down—and everything seemed to be happening with immediacy. The world is going on, and you know it. You're not decrepit, you're not in pain, nothing dramatic is happening. A sparrow flies overhead, breeze rustles leaves. You're going along and suddenly your feet *feel* the ground. I don't mean that your shoes are comfortable. Or even that the ground is solid and that you have a moment when you realize that you are a temporary person, passing. I mean that it seems possible to feel the ground, solid below you, while at the same time the air reminds you that there's a lightness, and then you soak that in, let it sink down, so that suddenly you know that the next wind might blow you over, and that wouldn't be a bad thing. You might squint in the sunlight, look at a leaf spiraling down, genuinely surprised that you were there to see it. A breeze comes again, rippling the surface of a pond. A bird! A leaf! Clouds elongate and stretch thinly across a silvery sky. Flowers, in the distance. Or, in early evening, a sliver of moon. Then imagine that you aren't there any longer, but at a place where you can touch those things that were always too dazzlingly high or too far in the distance—light-years would have been required to get to them—and suddenly you can pluck the stars from the sky, gather all fallen leaves at once.

1. In your journal, record your thoughts and feelings about the story. You might explore one of the following:
   - your response to the narrator;
   - any questions you have about the narrator and his family;
   - reflections on your own family.

   Share your writing with two or three classmates.
2. In a small group, consider the question: Is the father in the story happy with his life? Support your answers with details from the story. Compare your views with those of other groups.
3. Describe each character and his or her relationship to the narrator. Then, define the conflict.
4. Every detail of a story should be included for an express purpose. Why has the detail of placing autumn leaves in an album been included?
5. At what point does the narrator have an epiphany? What are the results of the epiphany? Support your answer.
6. Describe an epiphany in your life. What became clear? What events preceded the epiphany? What was the outcome? Represent that moment in one of the following ways:
   - writing (e.g., poem, descriptive passage);
   - a visual presentation (e.g., collage, drawing);
   - selected mass media product (e.g., song lyric excerpt, description of a movie clip).

Margaret Laurence

Horses of the Night

He simply appeared to be absent, elsewhere.

I never knew I had distant cousins who lived up north, until Chris came down to Manawaka to go to high school. My mother said he belonged to a large family, relatives of ours, who lived at Shallow Creek, up north. I was six, and Shallow Creek seemed immeasurably far, part of a legendary winter country where no leaves grew and where the breath of seals and polar bears snuffled out steamily and turned to ice.

"Could plain people live there?" I asked my mother, meaning people who were not Eskimos. "Could there be a farm?"

"How do you mean?" she said, puzzled. "I told you. That's where they live. On the farm. Uncle Wilf—that was Chris's father, who died a few years back—he got the place as a homestead, donkey's years ago."

"But how could they grow anything? I thought you said it was up north."

"Mercy," my mother said, laughing, "it's not *that* far north, Vanessa. It's about a hundred miles beyond Galloping Mountain. You be nice to Chris, now, won't you? And don't go asking him a whole lot of questions the minute he steps inside the door."

How little my mother knew of me, I thought. Chris had been fifteen. He could be expected to feel only scorn towards me. I detested the fact that I was so young. I did not think I would be able to say anything at all to him.

"What if I don't like him?"

"What if you don't?" my mother responded sharply. "You're to watch your manners, and no acting up, understand? It's going to be quite difficult enough without that."

"Why does he have to come here, anyway?" I demanded crossly. "Why can't he go to school where he lives?"

"Because there isn't any high school up there," my mother said. "I hope he gets on well here, and isn't too homesick. Three years is a long time. It's very good of your grandfather to let him stay at the Brick House."

She said this last accusingly, as though she suspected I might be thinking differently. But I had not thought of it one way or another. We were all having dinner at the Brick House because of Chris's arrival. It was the end of August, and sweltering. My grandfather's house looked huge and cool from the outside, the high low-sweeping spruce trees shutting out the sun with their dusky out-fanned branches. But inside it wasn't cool at all. The woodstove in the kitchen was going full blast, and the whole place smelled of roasting meat.

Grandmother Connor was wearing a large mauve apron. I thought it was a nicer colour than the dark bottle-green of her dress, but she believed in wearing sombre shades lest the spirit give way to vanity, which in her case was certainly not much of a risk. The apron came up over her shapeless bosom and obscured part of her cameo brooch, the only jewellery she ever wore, with its portrait of a fiercely bearded man whom I imagined to be either Moses or God.

"Isn't it nearly time for them to be getting here, Beth?" Grandmother Connor asked.

"Train's not due until six," my mother said. "It's barely five-thirty, now. Has Father gone to the station already?"

"He went an hour ago," my grandmother said.

"He would," my mother commented.

"Now, now, Beth," my grandmother cautioned and soothed.

At last the front screen door was hurled open and Grandfather Connor strode into the house, followed by a tall lanky boy. Chris was wearing a white shirt, a tie, grey trousers. I thought, unwillingly, that he looked handsome. His face was angular, the bones showing through the brown skin. His grey eyes were slightly slanted, and his hair was the colour of couchgrass at the end of summer when it has been bleached to a light yellow by the sun. I had not planned to like him, not even a little, but somehow I wanted to defend him when I heard what my mother whispered to my grandmother before they went into the front hall.

"Heavens, look at the shirt and trousers—must've been his father's, the poor kid."

I shot out into the hall ahead of my mother, and then stopped and stood there.

"Hi, Vanessa," Chris said.

"How come you knew who I was?" I asked.

"Well. I knew your mother and dad only had one of a family, so I figured you must be her," he replied grinning.

The way he spoke did not make me feel I had blundered. My mother greeted him warmly but shyly. Not knowing if she were expected to kiss him or to shake hands, she finally did neither. Grandmother Connor, however, had no doubts. She kissed him on both cheeks and then held him at arm's length to have a proper look at him.

"Bless the child," she said.

Coming from anyone else, this remark would have sounded ridiculous, especially as Chris was at least a head taller. My grandmother was the only person I have ever known who could say such things without appearing false.

"I'll show you your room, Chris," my mother offered.

Grandfather Connor, who had been standing in the living room doorway in absolute silence, looking as granite as a statue in the cemetery, now followed Grandmother out to the kitchen.

"Train was forty minutes late," he said weightily.

"What a shame," my grandmother said. "But I thought it wasn't due until six, Timothy."

"Six!" my grandfather cried. "That's the mainline train. The local's due at five-twenty."

This was not correct, as both my grandmother and I knew. But neither of us contradicted him.

"What on earth are you cooking a roast for, on a night like this?" my grandfather went on. "A person could fry an egg on the sidewalk, it's that hot. Potato salad would've gone down well."

Privately I agreed with this opinion, but I could never permit myself to acknowledge agreement with him on anything. I automatically and emotionally sided with Grandmother in all issues, not because she was inevitably right but because I loved her.

"It's not a roast," my grandmother said mildly. "It's mock-duck. The stove's only been going for an hour. I thought the boy would be hungry after the trip."

My mother and Chris had come downstairs and were now in the living room. I could hear them there, talking awkwardly, with pauses.

"Potato salad," my grandfather declaimed, "would've been plenty good enough. He'd have been lucky to get it, if you ask me anything. Wilf's family hasn't got two cents to rub together. It's me that's paying for the boy's keep."

The thought of Chris in the living room, and my mother unable to explain, was too much for me. I sidled over to the kitchen door, intending to close it. But my grandmother stopped me.

"No," she said, with unexpected firmness. "Leave it open, Vanessa."

I could hardly believe it. Surely she couldn't want Chris to hear? She herself was always able to move with equanimity through a huricane because she believed that a mighty fortress was her God. But the rest of us were not like that, and usually she did her best to protect us. At the time I felt only bewilderment. I think now that she must have realised Chris would have to learn the Brick House sooner or later, and he might as well start right away.

I had to go into the living room. I had to know how Chris would take my grandfather. Would he, as I hoped, be angry and perhaps even speak out? Or would he, meekly, only be embarrassed?

"Wilf wasn't much good, even as a young man," Grandfather Connor was trumpeting. "Nobody but a simpleton would've taken up a homestead in a place like that. Anybody could've told him that land's no use for a thing except hay."

Was he going to remind us again how well he had done in the hardware business? Nobody had ever given him a hand, he used to tell me. I am sure he believed that this was true. Perhaps it even was true.

"If the boy takes after his father, it's a poor lookout for him," my grandfather continued.

I felt the old rage of helplessness. But as for Chris—he gave no sign of feeling anything. He was sitting on the big wing-backed sofa that curled into the bay window like a black and giant seashell. He began to talk to me, quite easily, just as though he had not heard a word my grandfather was saying.

This method proved to be the one Chris always used in any dealings with my grandfather. When the bludgeoning words came, which was often, Chris never seemed, like myself, to be holding back with a terrible strained force for fear of letting go and speaking out and having the known world unimaginably fall to pieces. He would not argue or defend himself, but he did not apologise, either. He simply appeared to be absent, elsewhere. Fortunately there was very little need for response, for when Grandfather Connor pointed out your shortcomings, you were not expected to reply.

But this aspect of Chris was one which I noticed only vaguely at the time. What won me was that he would talk to me and wisecrack as though I were his same age. He was—although I didn't know the phrase then—a respecter of persons.

On the rare evenings when my parents went out, Chris would come over to mind me. These were the best times, for often when he was supposed to be doing his homework, he would make fantastic objects for my amusement, or his own—pipecleaners twisted into the shape of wildly prancing midget men, or an old set of Christmas-tree lights fixed onto a puppet theatre with a red velvet curtain that really pulled. He had skill in making miniature things of all kinds. Once for my birthday he gave me a leather saddle no bigger than a matchbox, which he had sewn himself, complete in every detail, stirrups and horn, with the criss-cross lines that were the brand name of his ranch, he said, explaining it was a reference to his own name.

"Can I go to Shallow Creek sometime?" I asked one evening.

"Sure. Some summer holidays, maybe. I've got a sister about your age. The others are all grownup."

I did not want to hear. His sisters—for Chris was the only boy—did not exist for me, not even as photographs, because I did not want them to exist. I wanted him to belong only here. Shallow Creek existed, though, no longer filled with ice mountains in my mind but as some beckoning country beyond all ordinary considerations.

"Tell me what it's like there, Chris."

"My gosh, Vanessa, I've told you before, about a thousand times."

"You never told me what your house is like."

"Didn't I? Oh well—it's made out of trees grown right there beside the lake."

"Made out of trees? Gee. Really?"

I could see it. The trees were still growing, and the leaves were firmly and greenly on them. The branches had been coaxed into formations of towers and high-up nests where you could look out and see for a hundred miles or more.

"That lake, you know," Chris said. "It's more like an inland sea. It goes on for ever and ever amen, that's how it looks. And you know what? Millions of years ago, before there were any human beings at all, that lake was full of water monsters. All different kinds of dinosaurs. Then they all died off. Nobody knows for sure why. Imagine them—all those huge creatures, with necks like snakes and some of them had hackles on their heads, like a rooster's comb only very tough, like hard leather. Some guys from Winnipeg came up a few years back, there, and dug up dinosaur bones, and they found footprints in the rocks."

"Footprints in the *rocks*?"

"The rocks were mud, see, when the dinosaurs went trampling through, but after trillions of years the mud turned into stone and there were these mighty footprints with the claws still showing. Amazing, eh?"

I could only nod, fascinated and horrified. Imagine going swimming in those waters. What if one of the creatures had lived on?

"Tell me about the horses," I said.

"Oh, them. Well, we've got these two riding horses. Duchess and Firefly. I raised them, and you should see them. Really sleek, know what I mean? I bet I could make racers out of them."

He missed the horses, I thought with selfish satisfaction, more than he missed his family. I could visualise the pair, one sorrel and one black, swifting through all the meadows of summer.

"When can I go, Chris?"

"Well, we'll have to see. After I get through high school, I won't be at Shallow Creek much."

"Why not?"

"Because," Chris said, "what I am going to be is an engineer, civil engineer. You ever seen a really big bridge, Vanessa? Well, I haven't either, but I've seen pictures. You take the Golden Gate Bridge in San Francisco, now. Terrifically high—all those thin ribs of steel, joined together to go across this very wide stretch of water. It doesn't seem possible, but it's there. That's what engineers do. Imagine doing something like that, eh?"

I could not imagine it. It was beyond me.

"Where will you go?" I asked. I did not want to think of his going anywhere.

"Winnipeg, to college," he said with assurance.

The Depression did not get better, as everyone had been saying it would. It got worse, and so did the drought. That part of the prairies where we lived was never dustbowl country. The farms around Manawaka never had a total crop failure, and afterwards, when the drought was over, people used to remark on the fact proudly, as though it had been due to some virtue or special status, like the Children of Israel being afflicted by Jehovah but never in real danger of annihilation. But although Manawaka never knew the worst, what it knew was bad enough. Or so I learned later. At the time I saw none of it. For me, the Depression and drought were external and abstract, malevolent gods whose names I secretly learned although they were concealed from me, and whose evil I sensed only superstitiously, knowing they threatened us but not how or why. What I really saw was only what went on in our family.

"He's done quite well all through, despite everything," my mother said. She sighed, and I knew she was talking about Chris.

"I know," my father said. "We've been over all this before, Beth. But quite good just isn't good enough. Even supposing he managed to get a scholarship, which isn't likely, it's only tuition and books. What about room and board? Who's going to pay for that? Your father?"

"I see I shouldn't have brought up the subject at all," my mother said in an aloof voice.

"I'm sorry," my father said impatiently. "But you know, yourself, he's the only one who might possibly—"

"I can't bring myself to ask Father about it, Ewen. I simply cannot do it."

"There wouldn't be much point in asking," my father said, "when the answer is a foregone conclusion. He feels he's done his share, and actually, you know, Beth, he has, too. Three years, after all. He may not have done it gracefully, but he's done it."

We were sitting in the living room, and it was evening. My father was slouched in the grey armchair that was always his. My mother was slenderly straight-backed in the blue chair in which nobody else ever sat. I was sitting on the footstool, beige needlepoint with mathematical roses, to which I had staked my own claim. This seating arrangement was obscurely satisfactory to me, perhaps because predictable, like the three bears. I was pretending to be colouring into a scribbler on my knee, and from time to time my lethargic purple crayon added a feather to an outlandish swan. To speak would be to invite dismissal. But their words forced questions in my head.

"Chris isn't going away, is he?"

My mother swooped, shocked at her own neglect.

"My heavens—are you still up, Vanessa? What am I thinking of?"

"Where is Chris going?"

"We're not sure yet," my mother evaded, chivvying me up the stairs. "We'll see."

He would not go, I thought. Something would happen, miraculously, to prevent him. He would remain, with his long loping walk and half-slanted grey eyes and his talk that never excluded me. He would stay right here. And soon, because I desperately wanted to, and because every day mercifully made me older, quite soon I would be able to reply with such a lightning burst of knowingness that it would astound him, when he spoke of the space or was it some black sky that never ended anywhere beyond this earth. Then I would not be innerly belittled for being unable to figure out what he would best like to hear. At that good and imagined time, I would not any longer be limited. I would not any longer be young.

I was nine when Chris left Manawaka. The day before he was due to go, I knocked on the door of his room in the Brick House.

"Come in," Chris said. "I'm packing. Do you know how to fold socks, Vanessa?"

"Sure. Of course."

"Well, get folding on that bunch there, then."

I had come to say goodbye, but I did not want to say it yet. I got to work on the socks. I did not intend to speak about the matter of college, but the knowledge that I must not speak about it made me uneasy. I was afraid I would blurt out a reference to it in my anxiety not to. My mother had said, "He's taken it amazingly well—he doesn't even mention it, so we mustn't either."

"Tomorrow night you'll be in Shallow Creek," I ventured.

"Yeh." He did not look up. He went on stuffing clothes and books into his suitcase.

"I bet you'll be glad to see the horses, eh?" I wanted him to say he didn't care about the horses any more and that he would rather stay here.

"It'll be good to see them again," Chris said. "Mind handing over those socks now, Vanessa? I think I can just squash them in at the side here. Thanks. Hey, look at that, will you? Everything's in. Am I an expert packer or am I an expert packer?"

I sat on his suitcase for him so it would close, and then he tied a piece of rope around it because the lock wouldn't lock.

"Ever thought what it would be like to be a traveller, Vanessa?" he asked.

I thought of Richard Halliburton, taking an elephant over the Alps and swimming illicitly in the Taj Mahal lily pool by moonlight.

"It would be keen," I said, because this was the word Chris used to describe the best possible. "That's what I'm going to do someday."

He did not say, as for a moment I feared he might, that girls could not be travellers.

"Why not?" he said. "Sure you will, if you really want to. I got this theory, see, that anybody can do anything at all, anything, if they really set their minds to it. But you have to have this total concentration. You have to focus on it with your whole mental powers, and not let it slip away by forgetting to hold it in your mind. If you hold it in your mind, like, then it's real, see? You take most people, now. They can't concentrate worth a darn."

"Do you think I can?" I enquired eagerly, believing that this was what he was talking about.

"What?" he said. "Oh—sure. Sure I think you can. Naturally."

Chris did not write after he left Manawaka. About a month later we had a letter from his mother. He was not at Shallow Creek. He had not gone back. He had got off the northbound train at the first stop after Manawaka, cashed in his ticket, and thumbed a lift with a truck to Winnipeg. He had written to his mother from there, but had given no address. She had not heard from him since. My mother read Aunt Tess's letter aloud to my father. She was too upset to care whether I was listening or not.

"I can't think what possessed him, Ewen. He never seemed irresponsible. What if something should happen to him? What if he's broke? What do you think we should do?"

"What can we do? He's nearly eighteen. What he does is his business. Simmer down, Beth, and let's decide what we're going to tell your father."

"Oh Lord," my mother said. "There's that to consider, of course."

I went out without either of them noticing. I walked to the hill at the edge of the town, and down into the valley where the scrub oak and poplar grew almost to the banks of the Wachakwa River. I found the oak where we had gone last autumn, in a gang, to smoke cigarettes made of dried leaves and pieces of newspaper. I climbed to the lowest branch and stayed there for a while.

I was not consciously thinking about Chris. I was not thinking of anything. But when at last I cried, I felt relieved afterwards and could go home again.

Chris departed from my mind, after that, with quickness that was due to the other things that happened. My Aunt Edna, who was a secretary in Winnipeg, returned to Manawaka to live because the insurance company cut down on staff and she could not find another job. I was intensely excited and jubilant about her return, and could not see why my mother seemed the opposite, even though she was as fond of Aunt Edna as I was. Then my brother Roderick was born, and that same year Grandmother Connor died. The strangeness, the unbelievability, of both these events took up all of me.

When I was eleven, almost two years after Chris had left, he came back without warning. I came home from school and found him sitting in our living room. I could not accept that I had nearly forgotten him until this instant. Now that he was present, and real again, I felt I had betrayed him by not thinking of him more.

He was wearing a navy-blue serge suit. I was old enough now to notice that it was a cheap one and had been worn a considerable time. Otherwise, he looked the same, the same smile, the same knife-boned face with no flesh to speak of, the same unresting eyes.

"How come you're here?" I cried. "Where have you been, Chris?"

"I'm a traveller," he said. "Remember?"

He was a traveller all right. One meaning of the word *traveller* in our part of the world, was a travelling salesman. Chris was selling vacuum cleaners. That evening he brought out his line and showed us. He went through his spiel for our benefit, so we could hear how it sounded.

"Now look, Beth," he said, turning the appliance on and speaking loudly above its moaning roar, "see how it brightens up this old rug of yours? Keen, eh?"

"Wonderful," my mother laughed. "Only we can't afford one."

"Oh well—" Chris said quickly, "I'm not trying to sell one to you. I'm only showing you. Listen, I've only been in this job a month, but I figure this is really a going thing. I mean, it's obvious, isn't it? You take all those old wire carpet-beaters of yours, Beth. You could kill yourself over them and your carpet isn't going to look one-tenth as good as it does with this."

"Look, I don't want to seem—" my father put in, "but, hell, they're not exactly a new invention, and we're not the only ones who can't afford—"

"This is a pretty big outfit, you know?" Chris insisted. "Listen, I don't plan to stay, Ewen. But a guy could work at it for a year or so, and save—right? Lots of guys work their way through university like that."

I needed to say something really penetrating, something that would show him I knew the passionate truth of his conviction.

"I bet—" I said, "I bet you'll sell a thousand, Chris."

Two years ago, this statement would have seemed self-evident, unquestionable. Yet now, when I had spoken, I knew that I did not believe it.

The next time Chris visited Manawaka, he was selling magazines. He had the statistics worked out. If every sixth person in town would get a subscription to *Country Guide*, he could make a hundred dollars in a month. We didn't learn how he got on. He didn't stay in Manawaka a full month. When he turned up again, it was winter. Aunt Edna phoned.

"Nessa? Listen, kiddo, tell your mother she's to come down if it's humanly possible. Chris is here, and Father's having fits."

So in five minutes we were scurrying through the snow, my mother and I, with our overshoes not even properly done up and our feet getting wet. We need not have worried. By the time we reached the Brick House, Grandfather Connor had retired to the basement, where he sat in the rocking chair beside the furnace, making occasional black pronouncements like a subterranean oracle. These loud utterances made my mother and aunt wince, but Chris didn't seem to notice any more than he ever had. He was engrossed in telling us about the mechanism he was holding. It had a cranker handle like an old-fashioned sewing machine.

"You attach the ball of wool here, see? Then you set this little switch here, and adjust this lever, and you're away to the races. Neat, eh?"

It was a knitting machine. Chris showed us the finished products. The men's socks he had made were coarse wool, one pair in grey heather and another in maroon. I was impressed.

"Gee—can I do it, Chris?"

"Sure. Look, you just grab hold of the handle right here."

"Where did you get it?" my mother asked.

"I've rented it. The way I figure it, Beth, I can sell these things at about half the price you'd pay in a store, and they're better quality."

"Who are you going to sell them to?" Aunt Edna enquired.

"You take all these guys who do outside work—they need heavy socks all year round, not just in winter. I think this thing could be quite a gold mine."

"Before I forget," my mother said, "how's your mother and the family keeping?"

"They're okay," Chris said in a restrained voice. "They're not short of hands, if that's what you mean, Beth. My sisters have their husbands there."

Then he grinned, casting away the previous moment, and dug into his suitcase.

"Hey, I haven't shown you—these are for you, Vanessa, and this pair is for Roddie."

My socks were cherry-coloured. The very small ones for my brother were turquoise.

Chris only stayed until after dinner, and then he went away again.

After my father died, the whole order of life was torn. Nothing was known or predictable any longer. For months I lived almost entirely within myself, so when my mother told me one day that Chris couldn't find any work at all because there were no jobs and so he had gone back to Shallow Creek to stay, it made scarcely any impression on me. But that summer, my mother decided I ought to go away for a holiday. She hoped it might take my mind off my father's death. What, if anything, was going to take her mind off his death, she did not say.

"Would you like to go to Shallow Creek for a week or so?" she asked me. "I could write to Chris's mother."

Then I remembered, all in a torrent, the way I had imagined it once, when he used to tell me about it—the house fashioned of living trees, the lake like a sea where monsters had dwelt, the grass that shone like green wavering light while the horses flew in the splendour of their pride.

"Yes," I said. "Write to her."

The railway did not go through Shallow Creek, but Chris met me at Challoner's Crossing. He looked different, not only thinner, but—what was it? Then I saw that it was the fact that his face and neck were tanned red-brown, and he was wearing denims, farm pants, and a blue plaid shirt open at the neck. I liked him like this. Perhaps the change was not so much in him as in myself, now that I was thirteen. He looked masculine in a way I had not been aware of, before.

"C'mon, kid," he said. "The limousine's over here."

It was a wagon and two horses, which was what I had expected, but the nature of each was not what I had expected. The wagon was a long and clumsy one, made of heavy planking, and the horses were both plough horses, thick in the legs, and badly matched as a team. The mare was short and stout, matronly. The gelding was very tall and gaunt, and he limped.

"Allow me to introduce you," Chris said. "Floss—Trooper—this is Vanessa."

He did not mention the other horses, Duchess and Firefly, and neither did I, not all the fortnight I was there. I guess I had known for some years now, without realising it, that the pair had only ever existed in some other dimension.

Shallow Creek wasn't a town. It was merely a name on a map. There was a grade school a few miles away, but that was all. They had to go to Challoner's Crossing for their groceries. We reached the farm, and Chris steered me through the crowd of aimless cows and wolfish dogs in the yard, while I flinched with panic.

It was perfectly true that the house was made out of trees. It was a fair-sized but elderly shack, made out of poplar poles and chinked with mud. There was an upstairs, which was not so usual around here, with three bedrooms, one of which I was to share with Chris's sister, Jeannie, who was slightly younger than I, a pallid-eyed girl who was either too shy to talk or who had nothing to say. I never discovered which, because I was so reticent with her myself, wanting to push her away, not to recognise her, and at the same time experiencing a shocked remorse at my own unacceptable feelings.

Aunt Tess, Chris's mother, was severe in manner and yet wanting to be kind, worrying over it, making tentative overtures which were either ignored or repelled by her older daughters and their monosyllabic husbands. Youngsters swam in and out of the house like shoals of nameless fishes. I could not see how so many people could live here, under one roof, but then I learned they didn't. The married daughters had their own dwelling places, nearby, but some kind of communal life was maintained. They wrangled endlessly but they never left one another alone, not even for a day.

Chris took no part at all, none. When he spoke, it was usually to the children, and they would often follow him around the yard or

to the barn, not pestering but just trailing along in clusters of three or four. He never told them to go away. I liked him for this, but it bothered me, too. I wished he would return his sisters' bickering for once, or tell them to clear out, or even yell at one of the kids. But he never did. He closed himself off from squabbling voices just as he used to do with Grandfather Connor's spearing words.

The house had no screens on the doors or windows, and at meal times the flies were so numerous you could hardly see the food for the iridescent-winged blue-black bodies squirming all over it. Nobody noticed my squeamishness except Chris, and he was the only one from whom I really wanted to conceal it.

"Fan with your hand," he murmured.

"It's okay," I said quickly.

For the first time in all the years we had known each other, we could not look the other in the eye. Around the table, the children stabbed and snivelled, until Chris's oldest sister, driven frantic, shrieked, *Shut up shut up shut up.* Chris began asking me about Manawaka then, as though nothing were going on around him.

They were due to begin haying, and Chris announced that he was going to camp out in the bluff near the hayfields. To save himself the long drive in the wagon each morning, he explained, but I felt this wasn't the real reason.

"Can I go, too?" I begged. I could not bear the thought of living in the house with all the others who were not known to me, and Chris not here.

"Well, I don't know—"

"Please. Please, Chris. I won't be any trouble, I promise."

Finally he agreed. We drove out in the big hayrack, its slatted sides rattling, its old wheels jolting metallically. The road was narrow and dirt, and around it the low bushes grew, wild rose and blueberry and wolf willow with silver leaves. Sometimes we would come to a bluff of pale-leaved poplar trees, and once a red-winged blackbird flew up out of the branches and into the hot dusty blue of the sky.

Then we were there. The hayfields lay beside the lake. It was my first view of the water which had spawned saurian giants so long ago. Chris drove the hayrack through the fields of high coarse grass and on down almost to the lake's edge, where there was no shore but only the green rushes like floating meadows in which the water birds nested. Beyond the undulating reeds the open lake stretched, deep, green-grey, out and out, beyond sight.

No human word could be applied. The lake was not lonely or untamed. These words relate to people, and there was nothing of people here. There was no feeling about the place. It existed in some world in which man was not yet born. I looked at the grey reaches of it and felt threatened. It was like the view of God which I had held since my father's death. Distant, indestructible, totally indifferent.

Chris had jumped down off the hayrack.

"We're not going to camp *here*, are we?" I asked and pleaded.

"No. I just want to let the horses drink. We'll camp up there in the bluff."

I looked. "It's still pretty close to the lake, isn't it?"

"Don't worry," Chris said, laughing. "You won't get your feet wet."

"I didn't mean that."

Chris looked at me.

"I know you didn't," he said. "But let's learn to be a little tougher, and not let on, eh? It's necessary."

Chris worked through the hours of sun, while I lay on the half-formed stack of hay and looked up at the sky. The blue air trembled and spun with the heat haze, and the hay on which I was lying held the scents of grass and dust and wild mint.

In the evening, Chris took the horses to the lake again, and then he drove the hayrack to the edge of the bluff and we spread out our blankets underneath it. He made a fire and we had coffee and a tin of stew, and then we went to bed. We did not wash, and we slept in our clothes. It was only when I was curled up uncomfortably with the itching blanket around me that I felt a sense of unfamiliarity at being here, with Chris only three feet away, a self-consciousness I would not have felt even the year before. I do not think he felt this sexual strangeness. If he wanted me not to be a child—and he did—it was not with the wish that I would be a woman. It was something else.

"Are you asleep, Vanessa?" he asked.

"No. I think I'm lying on a tree root."

"Well, shift yourself, then," he said. "Listen, kid, I never said anything before, because I didn't really know what to say, but—you know how I felt about your dad dying, and that, don't you?"

"Yes," I said chokingly. "It's okay. I know."

"I used to talk with Ewen sometimes. He didn't see what I was driving at, mostly, but he'd always listen, you know? You don't find many guys like that."

We were both silent for a while.

"Look," Chris said finally. "Ever noticed how much brighter the stars are when you're completely away from any houses? Even the lamps up at the farm, there, make enough of a glow to keep you from seeing properly like you can out here. What do they make you think about, Vanessa?"

"Well—"

"I guess most people don't give them much thought at all, except maybe to say—*very pretty*—or like that. But the point is, they aren't like that. The stars and planets, in themselves, are just not like that, not *pretty*, for heaven's sake. They're gigantic—some of them burning—imagine those worlds tearing through space and made of pure fire. Or the ones that are absolutely dead—just rock or ice and no warmth in them. There must be some, though, that have living creatures. You wonder what *they* could look like, and what they feel. We won't ever get to know. But somebody will know, someday. I really believe that. Do you ever think about this kind of thing at all?"

He was twenty-one. The distance between us was still too great. For years I had wanted to be older so I might talk with him, but now I felt unready.

"Sometimes," I said, hesitantly, making it sound like *Never.*

"People usually say there must be a God," Chris went on, "because otherwise how did the universe get here? But that's ridiculous. If the stars and planets go on to infinity, they could have existed forever, for no reason at all. Maybe they weren't ever created. Look—what's the alternative? To believe in a God who is brutal. What else could He be? You've only got to look anywhere around you. It would be an insult to Him to believe in a God like that. Most people don't like talking about this kind of thing—it embarrasses them, you know? Or else they're not interested. I don't mind. I can always think about things myself. You don't actually need anyone to talk to. But about God, though—if there's a war, like it looks there will be, would people claim that was planned? What kind of a God would pull a trick like that? And yet, you know, plenty of guys would think it was a godsend, and who's to say they're wrong? It would be a job, and you'd get around and see places."

He paused, as though waiting for me to say something. When I did not, he resumed.

"Ewen told me about the last war, once. He hardly ever talked about it, but this once he told me about seeing the horses in the mud, actually going under, you know? And the way their eyes looked when they realised they weren't going to get out. Ever seen horses' eyes when they're afraid, I mean really berserk with fear, like in a bush-fire? Ewen said a guy tended to concentrate on the horses because he didn't dare think what was happening to the men. Including himself. Do you ever listen to the news at all, Vanessa?"

"I—"

I could only feel how foolish I must sound, still unable to reply as I would have wanted, comprehendingly. I felt I had failed myself utterly. I could not speak even the things I knew. As for the other things, the things I did not know, I resented Chris's facing me with them. I took refuge in pretending to be asleep, and after a while Chris stopped talking.

Chris left Shallow Creek some months after the war began, and joined the Army. After his basic training he was sent to England. We did not hear from him until about a year later, when a letter arrived for me.

"Vanessa—what's wrong?" my mother asked.

"Nothing."

"Don't fib," she said firmly. "What did Chris say in his letter, honey?"

"Oh—not much."

She gave me a curious look and then she went away. She would never have demanded to see the letter. I did not show it to her and she did not ask about it again.

Six months later my mother heard from Aunt Tess. Chris had been sent home from England and discharged from the Army because of a mental breakdown. He was now in the provincial mental hospital and they did not know how long he would have to remain there. He had been violent, before, but now he was not violent. He was, the doctors had told his mother, passive.

Violent. I could not associate the word with Chris, who had been so much the reverse. I could not bear to consider what anguish must have catapulted him into that even greater anguish. But the way he was now seemed almost worse. How might he be? Sitting quite still, wearing the hospital's grey dressing-gown, the animation gone from his face?

My mother cared about him a great deal, but her immediate thought was not for him.

"When I think of you, going up to Shallow Creek that time," she said, "and going out camping with him, and what might have happened—"

I, also, was thinking of what might have happened. But we were not thinking of the same thing. For the first time I recognised, at least a little, the dimensions of his need to talk that night. He must have understood perfectly well how impossible it would be, with a thirteen-year-old. But there was no one else. All his life's choices had grown narrower and narrower. He had been forced to return to the alien lake of home, and when finally he saw a means of getting away, it could only be into a turmoil which appalled him and which he dreaded even more than he knew. I had listened to his words, but I had not really heard them, not until now. It would not have made much difference to what happened, but I wished it were not too late to let him know.

Once when I was on holiday from college, my mother got me to help her clean out the attic. We sifted through boxes full of junk, old clothes, schoolbooks, bric-a-brac that once had been treasures. In one of the boxes I found the miniature saddle that Chris had made for me a long time ago.

"Have you heard anything recently?" I asked, ashamed that I had not asked sooner.

She glanced up at me. "Just the same. It's always the same. They don't think there will be much improvement."

Then she turned away.

"He always used to seem so—hopeful. Even when there was

really nothing to be hopeful about. That's what I find so strange. He *seemed* hopeful, didn't you think?"

"Maybe it wasn't hope," I said.

"How do you mean?"

I wasn't certain myself, I was thinking of all the schemes he'd had, the ones that couldn't possibly have worked, the unreal solutions to which he'd clung because there were no others, the brave and useless strokes of fantasy against a depression that was both the world's and his own.

"I don't know," I said. "I just think things were always more difficult for him than he let on, that's all. Remember that letter?"

"Yes."

"Well—what it said was that they could force his body to march and even to kill, but what they didn't know was that he'd fooled them. He didn't live inside it any more."

"Oh Vanessa—" my mother said. "You must have suspected right then."

"Yes, but—"

I could not go on, could not say that the letter seemed only the final heartbreaking extension of that way he'd always had of distancing himself from the absolute unbearability of battle.

I picked up the tiny saddle and turned it over in my hand.

"Look. His brand, the name of his ranch. The Criss-Cross."

"What ranch?" my mother said, bewildered.

"The one where he kept his racing horses. Duchess and Firefly."

Some words came into my head, a single line from a poem I had once heard. I knew it referred to a lover who did not want the morning to come, but to me it had another meaning, a different relevance.

Slowly, slowly, horses of the night—

The night must move like this for him, slowly, all through the days and nights. I could not know whether the land he journeyed through was inhabited by terrors, the old monster-kings of the lake, or whether he had discovered at last a way for himself to make the necessary dream perpetual.

I put the saddle away once more, gently and ruthlessly, back into the cardboard box.

1. In your journal, record your thoughts and feelings about the story. You might explore one of the following:
   - your feelings about Chris;
   - questions you have about Chris' motivation and/or his eventual fate;
   - how you might have reacted in Chris' circumstances.

   Share your writing with two or three classmates.
2. Examine the references to horses in the story. At the time each reference is made, how does it relate to Chris' state?
3. In a small group, consider the questions: What function does Vanessa have in the story? What functions do the other characters have? Present your views to the class.
4. At the story's conclusion, Vanessa seems to have resolved her inner conflict. What was the conflict? What decisions or beliefs has she come to?
5. What does Chris' struggle suggest about human nature? What comment on life does the story make? Give support from the story and from personal experience.
6. Reflect on a relative or friend you've know well over some years. In a memoir, present this person and the ways in which he or she has changed significantly or remained the same.

Albert Camus

The Guest

"You're from around these parts and you are a man. But you must sign; that's the rule."

The schoolmaster was watching the two men climb toward him. One was on horseback, the other on foot. They had not yet tackled the abrupt rise leading to the schoolhouse built on the hillside. They were toiling onward, making slow progress in the snow, among the stones, on the vast expanse of the high, deserted plateau. From time to time the horse stumbled. He could not be heard yet but the breath issuing from his nostrils could be seen. The schoolmaster calculated that it would take them a half hour to get onto the hill. It was cold; he went back into the school to get a sweater.

He crossed the empty, frigid classroom. On the blackboard the four rivers of France, drawn with four different colored chalks, had been flowing toward their estuaries for the past three days. Snow had suddenly fallen in mid-October after eight months of drought without the transition of rain, and the twenty pupils, more or less, who lived in the villages scattered over the plateau had stopped coming. With fair weather they would return. Daru now heated only the single room that was his lodging, adjoining the classroom. One of the windows faced, like the classroom windows, the south. On that side the school was a few kilometers from the point where the plateau began to slope toward the south. In clear weather the purple mass of the mountain range where the gap opened onto the desert could be seen.

Somewhat warmed, Daru returned to the window from which he had first noticed the two men. They were no longer visible. Hence they must have tackled the rise. The sky was not so dark, for the snow had stopped falling during the night. The morning had dawned with a dirty light which had scarcely become brighter as the ceiling of clouds lifted. At two in the afternoon it seemed as if the day were merely beginning. But still this was better than those three days when the thick snow was falling amidst unbroken darkness with little gusts of wind that rattled the double door of the classroom. Then Daru had spent long hours in his room, leaving it only to go to the shed and feed the chickens or get some coal. Fortunately the delivery truck from Tadjid, the nearest village to the north, had brought his supplies two days before the blizzard. It would return in forty-eight hours.

Besides, he had enough to resist a siege, for the little room was cluttered with bags of wheat that the administration had left as a supply to distribute to those of his pupils whose families had suffered from the drought. Actually they had all been victims because they were all poor. Every day Daru would distribute a ration to the children. They had missed it, he knew, during these bad days. Possibly one of the fathers or big brothers would come this afternoon and he could supply them with grain. It was just a matter of carrying them over to the next harvest. Now shiploads of wheat were arriving from France and the worst was over. But it would be hard to forget that poverty, that army of ragged ghosts wandering in the sunlight, the plateaus burned to a cinder month after month, the earth shriveled up little by little, literally scorched, every stone bursting into dust under one's foot. The sheep had died then by thousands, and even a few men, here and there, sometimes without anyone's knowing.

In contrast with such poverty, he who lived almost like a monk, in his remote schoolhouse, had felt like a lord with his white-washed walls, his narrow couch, his unpainted shelves, his well, and his weekly provisioning with water and food. And suddenly this snow, without warning, without the foretaste of rain. This is the way the region was, cruel to live in, even without men, who didn't help matters either. But Daru had been born here. Everywhere else, he felt exiled.

He went out and stepped forward on the terrace in front of the schoolhouse. The two men were now halfway up the slope. He recognized the horseman to be Balducci, the old gendarme he had known for a long time. Balducci was holding at the end of a rope an Arab walking behind him with hands bound and head lowered. The gendarme waved a greeting to which Daru did not reply, lost as he was in contemplation of the Arab dressed in a faded blue *jellaba*, his feet in sandals but covered with socks of heavy raw wool, his head crowned with a narrow, short *chèche*. Balducci was holding back his horse in order not to hurt the Arab, and the group was advancing slowly.

Within earshot, Balducci shouted, "One hour to do the three kilometers from El Ameur!" Daru did not answer. Short and square in his thick sweater, he watched them climb. Not once had the Arab raised his head. "Hello," said Daru when they got up onto the terrace. "Come in and warm up." Balducci painfully got down from his horse without letting go of the rope. He smiled at the schoolmaster from under his bristling mustache. His little dark eyes, deepset under a tanned forehead, and his mouth surrounded with wrinkles made him look attentive and studious. Daru took the bridle, led the horse to the shed, and came back to the two men who were now waiting for him in the school. He led them into his room. "I am going to heat up the classroom," he said. "We'll be more comfortable there."

When he entered the room again, Balducci was on the couch. He had undone the rope tying him to the Arab, who had squatted near the stove. His hands still bound, the *chèche* pushed back on his head, the Arab was looking toward the window. At first Daru noticed only his huge lips, fat, smooth, almost Negroid; yet his nose was straight, his eyes dark and full of fever. The *chèche* uncovered an obstinate forehead and, under the weathered skin now rather discolored by the cold, the whole face had a restless and rebellious look. "Go into the other room," said the schoolmaster, "and I'll make you some mint tea." "Thanks," Balducci said. "What a chore! How I long for retirement." And addressing his prisoner in Arabic, he said, "Come on, you." The Arab got up and, slowly, holding his bound wrists in front of him, went into the classroom.

With the tea, Daru brought a chair. But Balducci was already sitting in state at the nearest pupil's desk, and the Arab had squatted against the teacher's platform facing the stove, which stood between the desk and the window. When he held out the glass of tea to the prisoner, Daru hesitated at the sight of his bound hands. "He might perhaps be untied." "Sure," said Balducci. "That was for the trip." He started to get to this feet. But Daru, setting the glass on the floor, had knelt beside the Arab. Without saying anything, the Arab watched him with his feverish eyes. Once his hands were free, he rubbed his swollen wrists against each other, took the glass of tea and sucked up the burning liquid in swift little sips.

"Good," said Daru. "And where are you headed?"

Balducci withdrew his mustache from the tea. "Here, son."

"Odd pupils! And you're spending the night?"

"No. I'm going back to El Ameur. And you will deliver this fellow to Tinguit. He is expected at police headquarters."

Balducci was looking at Daru with a friendly little smile.

"What's this story?" asked the schoolmaster. "Are you pulling my leg?"

"No, son. Those are the orders."

"The orders? I'm not . . ." Daru hesitated, not wanting to hurt the old Corsican. "I mean, that's not my job."

"What! What's the meaning of that? In wartime people do all kinds of jobs."

"Then I'll wait for the declaration of war!"

Balducci nodded. "O.K. But the orders exist and they concern you too. Things are bubbling, it appears. There is talk of a forthcoming revolt. We are mobilized, in a way."

Daru still had his obstinate look.

"Listen, son," Balducci said. "I like you and you've got to understand. There's only a dozen of us at El Ameur to patrol the whole territory of a small department and I must be back in a hurry. He couldn't be kept there. His village was beginning to stir; they wanted to take him back. You must take him to Tinguit tomorrow before the day is over. Twenty kilometers shouldn't faze a husky fellow like you. After that, all will be over. You'll come back to your pupils and your comfortable life."

Behind the wall the horse could be heard snorting and pawing the earth. Daru was looking out the window. Decidedly the weather was clearing and the light was increasing over the snowy plateau. When all the snow was melted, the sun would take over again and once more would burn the fields of stone. For days still, the unchanging sky would shed its dry light on the solitary expanse where nothing had any connection with man.

"After all," he said, turning around toward Balducci, "what did he do?" And, before the gendarme had opened his mouth, he asked, "Does he speak French?"

"No, not a word. We had been looking for him for a month, but they were hiding him. He killed his cousin."

"Is he against us?"

"I don't think so. But you can never be sure."

"Why did he kill?"

"A family squabble, I think. One owed grain to the other, it seems. It's not at all clear. In short, he killed his cousin with a billhook. You know, like a sheep, *kreezk*!"

Balducci made the gesture of drawing a blade across his throat, and the Arab, his attention attracted, watched him with a sort of anxiety. Daru felt a sudden wrath against the man, against all men with their rotten spite, their tireless hates, their blood lust.

But the kettle was singing on the stove. He served Balducci more tea, hesitated, then served the Arab again, who drank avidly a second time. His raised arms made the *jellaba* fall open, and the schoolmaster saw his thin, muscular chest.

"Thanks, son," Balducci said. "And now I'm off."

He got up and went toward the Arab, taking a small rope from his pocket.

"What are you doing?" Daru asked dryly.

Balducci, disconcerted, showed him the rope.

"Don't bother."

The old gendarme hesitated. "It's up to you. Of course, you are armed?"

"I have my shotgun."

"Where?"

"In the trunk."

"You ought to have it near your bed."

"Why? I have nothing to fear."

"You're crazy, son. If there's an uprising, no one is safe; we're all in the same boat."

"I'll defend myself. I'll have time to see them coming."

Balducci began to laugh, then suddenly the mustache covered the white teeth. "You'll have time? O.K. That's just what I was saying. You always have been a little cracked. That's why I like you; my son was like that."

At the same time he took out his revolver and put it on the desk. "Keep it; I don't need two weapons from here to El Ameur."

The revolver shone against the black paint of the table. When the gendarme turned toward him, the schoolmaster caught his smell of leather and horseflesh.

"Listen, Balducci," Daru said suddenly, "all this disgusts me, beginning with your fellow here. But I won't hand him over. Fight, yes, if I have to. But not that."

The old gendarme stood in front of him and looked at him severely.

"You're being a fool," he said slowly. "I don't like it either. You don't get used to putting a rope on a man even after years of it, and you're even ashamed—yes, ashamed. But you can't let them have their way."

"I won't hand him over," Daru said again.

"It's an order, son, and I repeat it."

"That's right. Repeat to them what I've said to you: I won't hand him over."

Balducci made a visible effort to reflect. He looked at the Arab and at Daru. At last he decided.

"No, I won't tell them anything. If you want to drop us, go ahead; I'll not denounce you. I have an order to deliver the prisoner and I'm doing so. And now you'll just sign this paper for me."

"There's no need. I'll not deny that you left him with me."

"Don't be mean with me. I know you'll tell the truth. You're from around these parts and you are a man. But you must sign; that's the rule."

Daru opened his drawer, took out a little square bottle of purple ink, the red wooden penholder with the "sergeant-major" pen he used for models of handwriting, and signed. The gendarme carefully folded the paper and put it into his wallet. Then he moved toward the door.

"I'll see you off," Daru said.

"No," said Balducci. "There's no use being polite. You insulted me."

He looked at the Arab, motionless in the same spot, sniffed peevishly, and turned away toward the door "Good-by, son," he said. The door slammed behind him. His footsteps were muffled by the snow. The horse stirred on the other side of the wall and several chickens fluttered in fright. A moment later Balducci reappeared outside the window leading the horse by the bridle. He walked toward the little rise without turning around and disappeared from sight with the horse following him.

Daru walked back toward the prisoner, who, without stirring, never took his eyes off him. "Wait," the schoolmaster said in Arabic and went toward the bedroom. As he was going through the door, he had a second thought, went to the desk, took the revolver, and stuck it in his pocket. Then, without looking back, he went into his room.

For some time he lay on his couch watching the sky gradually close over, listening to the silence. It was this silence that had seemed painful to him during the first days here, after the war. He had requested a post in the little town at the base of the foothills separating the upper plateaus from the desert. There rocky walls, green and black to the north, pink and lavender to the south, marked the frontier of eternal summer. He had been named to a post farther north, on the plateau itself. In the beginning, the solitude and the silence had been hard for him on these wastelands peopled only by stones. Occasionally, furrows suggested cultivation, but they had been dug to uncover a certain kind of stone good for building. The only plowing here was to harvest rocks. Elsewhere a thin layer of soil accumulated in the hollows would be scraped out to enrich paltry village gardens. This is the way it was: bare rock covered three quarters of the region. Towns sprang up, flourished, then disappeared; men came by, loved one another or fought bitterly, then died. No one in this desert, neither he nor his guest, mattered. And yet, outside this desert neither of them, Daru knew, could have really lived.

When he got up, no noise came from the classroom. He was amazed at the unmixed joy he derived from the mere thought that the Arab might have fled and that he would be alone with no decision to make. But the prisoner was there. He had merely stretched out between the stove and the desk and he was staring at the ceiling. In that position, his thick lips were particularly noticeable, giving him a pouting look. "Come," said Daru. The Arab got up and followed him. In the bedroom the schoolmaster pointed to a chair near the table under the window. The Arab sat down without ceasing to watch Daru.

"Are you hungry?"

"Yes," the prisoner said.

Daru set the table for two. He took flour and oil, shaped a cake in a frying pan, and lighted the little stove that functioned on bottled gas. While the cake was cooking, he went out to the shed to get cheese, eggs, dates, and condensed milk. When the cake was done he set it on the window sill to cool, heated some condensed milk diluted with water, and beat up the eggs into an omelette. In one of his motions he bumped into the revolver stuck in his right pocket. He set the bowl down, went into the classroom, and put the revolver in his desk drawer. When he came back to the room, night was falling. He put on the light and served the Arab. "Eat," he said. The Arab took a piece of the cake, lifted it eagerly to his mouth, and stopped short.

"And you?" he asked.

"After you. I'll eat too."

The thick lips opened slightly. The Arab hesitated, then bit into the cake determinedly.

The meal over, the Arab looked at the schoolmaster. "Are you the judge?"

"No, I'm simply keeping you until tomorrow."

"Why do you eat with me?"

"I'm hungry."

The Arab fell silent. Daru got up and went out. He brought back a camp cot from the shed and set it up between the table and the stove, at right angles to his own bed. From a large suitcase which, upright in a corner, served as a shelf for papers, he took two blankets and arranged them on the cot. Then he stopped, felt useless, and sat down on his bed. There was nothing more to do or to get ready. He had to look at this man. He looked at him therefore, trying to imagine his face bursting with rage. He couldn't do so. He could see nothing but the dark yet shining eyes and the animal mouth.

"Why did you kill him?" he asked in a voice whose hostile tone surprised him.

The Arab looked away. "He ran away. I ran after him."

He raised his eyes to Daru again and they were full of a sort of woeful interrogation. "Now what will they do to me?"

"Are you afraid?"

The Arab stiffened, turning his eyes away.

"Are you sorry?"

The Arab stared at him openmouthed. Obviously he did not understand. Daru's annoyance was growing. At the same time he felt awkward and self-conscious with his big body wedged between the two beds.

"Lie down there," he said impatiently. "That's your bed."

The Arab didn't move. He cried out, "Tell me!"

The schoolmaster looked at him.

"Is the gendarme coming back tomorrow?"

"I don't know."

"Are you coming with us?"

"I don't know. Why?"

The prisoner got up and stretched out on top of the blankets, his feet toward the window. The light from the electric bulb shone straight into his eyes and he closed them at once.

"Why?" Daru repeated, standing beside the bed.

The Arab opened his eyes under the blinding light and looked at him, trying not to blink. "Come with us," he said.

In the middle of the night, Daru was still not asleep. He had gone to bed after undressing completely; he generally slept naked. But when he suddenly realized that he had nothing on, he wondered. He felt vulnerable and the temptation came to him to put his clothes back on. Then he shrugged his shoulders; after all, he wasn't a child and, if it came to that, he could break his adversary in two. From his bed, he could observe him lying on his back, still motionless, his eyes closed under the harsh light. When Daru turned out the light, the darkness seemed to congeal all of a sudden. Little by little, the night came back to life in the window where the starless sky was stirring gently. The schoolmaster soon made out the body lying at his feet. The Arab was still motionless but his eyes seemed open. A faint wind was prowling about the schoolhouse. Perhaps it would drive away the clouds and the sun would reappear.

During the night the wind increased. The hens fluttered a little and then were silent. The Arab turned over on his side with his back to Daru, who thought he heard him moan. Then he listened for his guest's breathing, which had become heavier and more regular. He listened to that breathing so close to him and mused without being able to go to sleep. In the room where he had been sleeping alone for a year, this presence bothered him. But it bothered him also because it imposed on him a sort of brotherhood he refused to accept in the present circumstances; yet he was familiar with it. Men who share the same rooms, soldiers or prisoners, develop a strange alliance as if, having cast off their armor with their clothing, they fraternized every evening, over and above their differences, in the ancient community of dream and fatigue. But Daru shook himself; he didn't like such musings, and it was essential for him to sleep.

A little later, however, when the Arab stirred slightly, the schoolmaster was still not asleep. When the prisoner made a second move, he stiffened, on the alert. The Arab was lifting himself slowly on his arms with almost the motion of a sleepwalker. Seated upright in bed, he waited motionless without turning his head toward Daru, as if he were listening attentively. Daru did not stir; it had just occurred to him that the revolver was still in the drawer of his desk. It was better to act at once. Yet he continued to observe the prisoner, who, with the same slithery motion, put his feet on the ground, waited again, then stood up slowly. Daru was about to call out to him when the Arab began to walk, in a quite natural but extraordinarily silent way. He was heading toward the door at the end of the room that opened into the shed. He lifted the latch with precaution and went out, pushing the door behind him but without shutting it.

Daru had not stirred. "He is running away," he merely thought. "Good riddance!" Yet he listened attentively. The hens were not fluttering; the guest must be on the plateau. A faint sound of water reached him, and he didn't know what it was until the Arab again stood framed in the doorway, closed the door carefully, and came back to bed without a sound. Then Daru turned his back on him and fell asleep. Still later he seemed, from the depths of his sleep, to hear furtive steps around the schoolhouse. "I'm dreaming! I'm dreaming!" he repeated to himself. And he went on sleeping.

When he awoke, the sky was clear; the loose window let in a cold, pure air. The Arab was asleep, hunched up under the blankets now, his mouth open, utterly relaxed. But when Daru shook him he started dreadfully, staring at Daru with wild eyes as if he had never seen him and with such a frightened expression that the schoolmaster stepped back. "Don't be afraid. It is I. You must eat." The Arab nodded his head and said yes. Calm had returned to his face, but his expression was vacant and listless.

The coffee was ready. They drank it seated together on the cot as they munched their pieces of the cake. Then Daru led the Arab under the shed and showed him the faucet where he washed. He went back into the room, folded the blankets on the cot, made his own bed, and put the room in order. Then he went through the classroom and out onto the terrace. The sun was already rising in the blue sky; a soft, bright light enveloped the deserted plateau. On the ridge the snow was melting in spots. The stones were about to reappear. Crouched on the edge of the plateau, the schoolmaster looked at the deserted expanse. He thought of Balducci. He had hurt him, for he had sent him off as though he didn't want to be associated with him. He could still hear the gendarme's farewell and, without knowing why, he felt strangely empty and vulnerable.

At that moment, from the other side of the schoolhouse, the prisoner coughed. Daru listened to him almost despite himself and then, furious, threw a pebble that whistled through the air before sinking into the snow. That man's stupid crime revolted him, but to hand him over was contrary to honor; just thinking of it made him boil with humiliation. He simultaneously cursed his own people who had sent him this Arab and the Arab who had dared to kill and not managed to get away. Daru got up, walked in a circle on the terrace, waited motionless, and then went back into the schoolhouse.

The Arab, leaning over the cement floor of the shed, was washing his teeth with two fingers. Daru looked at him and said, "Come." He went back into the room ahead of the prisoner. He slipped a hunting jacket on over his sweater and put on walking shoes. Standing, he waited until the Arab had put on his *chèche* and sandals. They went into the classroom, and the schoolmaster pointed to the exit saying, "Go ahead." The fellow didn't budge. "I'm coming," said Daru. The Arab went out. Daru went back into the room and made a package with pieces of rusk, dates, and sugar in it. In the classroom, before going out, he hesitated a second in front of his desk, then crossed the threshold and locked the door. "That's the way," he said. He started toward the east, followed by the prisoner. But a short distance from the schoolhouse he thought he heard a slight sound behind him. He retraced his steps and examined the surroundings of the house; there was no one there. The Arab watched him without seeming to understand. "Come on," said Daru.

They walked for an hour and rested beside a sharp needle of limestone. The snow was melting faster and faster and the sun was drinking up the puddles just as quickly, rapidly cleaning the plateau, which gradually dried and vibrated like the air itself. When they resumed walking, the ground rang under their feet. From time to time a bird rent the space in front of them with a joyful cry. Daru felt a sort of rapture before the vast familiar expanse, now almost entirely yellow under its dome of blue sky. They walked an hour more, descending toward the south. They reached a sort of flattened elevation made up of crumbly rocks. From there on, the plateau sloped down—eastward toward a low plain on which could be made out a few spindly trees, and to the south toward outcroppings of rock that gave the landscape a chaotic look.

Daru surveyed the two directions. Not a man could be seen. He turned toward the Arab, who was looking at him blankly. Daru offered the package to him. "Take it," he said. "There are dates, bread, and sugar. You can hold out for two days. Here are a thousand francs too."

The Arab took the package and the money but kept his full hands at chest level as if he didn't know what to do with what was being given him.

"Now look," the schoolmaster said as he pointed in the direction of the east, "there's the way to Tinguit. You have a two-hour walk. At Tinguit are the administration and the police. They are expecting you."

The Arab looked toward the east, still holding the package and the money against his chest. Daru took his elbow and turned him rather roughly toward the south. At the foot of the elevation on which they stood could be seen a faint path. "That's the trail across the plateau. In a day's walk from here you'll find pasturelands and the first nomads. They'll take you in and shelter you according to their law."

The Arab had now turned toward Daru, and a sort of panic was visible in his expression. "Listen," he said.

Daru shook his head. "No, be quiet. Now I'm leaving you." He turned his back on him, took two long steps in the direction of the school, looked hesitantly at the motionless Arab, and started off again. For a few minutes he heard nothing but his own step resounding on the cold ground, and he did not turn his head. A moment later, however, he turned around. The Arab was still there on the edge of the hill, his arms hanging now, and he was looking at the schoolmaster. Daru felt something rise in his throat. But he swore with impatience, waved vaguely, and started off again. He had already gone a distance when he again stopped and looked. There was no longer anyone on the hill.

Daru hesitated. The sun was now rather high in the sky and beginning to beat down on his head. The schoolmaster retraced his steps, at first somewhat uncertainly, then with decision. When he reached the little hill, he was bathed in sweat. He climbed it as fast as he could and stopped, out of breath, on the top. The rock fields to the south stood out sharply against the blue sky, but on the plain to the east a steamy heat was rising. And in that light haze, Daru, with heavy heart, made out the Arab walking slowly on the road to prison.

A little later, standing before the window of the classroom, the schoolmaster was watching the clear light bathing the whole surface of the plateau. Behind him on the blackboard, among the winding French rivers, sprawled the clumsily chalked up words he had just read: "You handed over our brother. You will pay for this." Daru looked at the sky, the plateau, and, beyond, the invisible lands stretching all the way to the sea. In this vast landscape he had loved so much, he was alone.

translated by Justin O'Brien

1. In your journal, record your thoughts and feelings about the story. You might explore one of the following:
   - anyone you know who is similar in nature to Daru;
   - your feelings about Daru's decision;
   - any stories, movies, or situations "The Guest" brings to mind.

   Share your writing with two or three classmates.
2. a) Create a chart with the headings "Facts" and "Inferences." Record under "Facts" all the facts given about Daru in the story; note under "Inferences" the conclusions you draw. In a small group, share and compare charts. Then try to summarize Daru's conflict and outlook on life—i.e., his beliefs or philosophy.

   b) In your group, discuss the following: Is Daru admirable? Does he do the "right thing"? How do he and Balducci compare or contrast?
3. Camus includes numerous geographical and historical details. In a small group, note the details and research the context for Camus' story. What comments does Camus seem to be making?
4. Explain the significance of the title "The Guest."
5. Why do you think the prisoner took the road to prison? How does his action affect Daru? What comment does this make?
6. Report on Daru's choice in one of the following ways:
   - Taking into account his beliefs and context, write Balducci's report to his superiors.
   - As a news columnist today and from your personal, social, and philosophical standpoint, reflect on Daru's choice.

3
Point of View

When developing a story, some of the earliest questions the writer must answer revolve around who will tell the story, and how the story can best be told. Should the story be told by one of the characters or by the author speaking in the third person? If a character should narrate, *which* of the characters? If the author should narrate, how much, if anything, should he or she reveal about the thoughts and feelings of each character?

The answers to these questions will be determined by the author's purpose. For example, the mystery writer who wants to challenge the reader to solve the crime before the detective does would neither have the detective narrate the story nor reveal all of the detective's thoughts; this mystery writer may even decide to stay entirely outside the characters and, like a camera, relate only the action seen and the dialogue heard. On the other hand, a writer wanting to explore sympathetically a character's situation might tell the story from that character's point of view and not stray to other characters for very long.

As point of view directs the telling of the story, it greatly influences our enjoyment and understanding of the stories we read. While writers may choose from many points of view, three are common: first-person, limited omniscient, and omniscient. A fourth, less-common point of view provides an interesting contrast. Following are descriptions and possible effects of each.

- With the **first-person** point of view, a character in the story, minor or major, narrates. First-person stories give readers a strong sense of immediacy, of being close to the characters and the events. In our initial responses as readers, we usually become most sympathetic to the first-person narrator.

- Some writers prefer to write in the third person, but stay by the side of one character. This point of view is called the **limited omniscient** or **third person narrative**. The focus on one character gives the story unity, but allows the narrator more freedom than the first-person point of view offers. This narrator can move easily between describing action and reporting selected thoughts and feelings. For this reason, limited omniscient stories often move at a faster pace than do first-person stories. As readers, we may get caught up with the main character but we are also intrigued with minor characters.
- Of the three common points of view, the **omniscient** point of view provides the greatest flexibility. The narrator can move in and out of the thoughts and feelings of *any* character in the story. Thus, as readers, we may be privy to much more, allowing us to see the differences among various characters' thoughts and feelings.
- A fourth possibility, the **objective** point of view, is used infrequently. In it the narrator/author tells the story as might an impartial outsider or observer; often this point of view makes for a surprise ending.

As we consider further a story and its point of view, we might ask ourselves questions such as these:

- Who is telling the story?
- How much is the reader allowed to know about each character's thoughts and feelings?
- Why did the author choose to tell the story from this point of view?
- How does the point of view help develop conflicts, characterization, or make the story meaningful?
- How would the meaning or impact of the story be changed by retelling it from another point of view?

The four stories in this unit are told from different points of view—each selection reaching us, the readers, in its own way. The omniscient point of view in Timothy Findley's "Foxes" shifts occasionally from the main character to present him and his conflict from another perspective. The first-person point of view in "The Yellow Wall Paper" offers us a personal, sympathetic portrait of an emotional breakdown. Nadine Gordimer's "The Ultimate Safari," also told in the first person, tells of a family's flight from war and starvation. The final selection, "Pelt," illustrates some of the effects an unusual point of view may have: the limited omniscient narration focuses on the perspective of a dog. From this unusual point of view, the story calls into question human activity. In another unit, "The Lottery" is one example of the objective point of view.

In each of these stories, we encounter a point of view that has been selected for particular reasons, inviting us to reflect and share our views as we work to deepen our understanding and appreciation of each story we study.

Timothy Findley

Foxes

The blooming of this image took its time.
It occurred to him slowly that under the weight of all his personal masks, there was a being he had never seen.

THE FACE IS ONLY THE THING TO WRITE.
Roland Barthes

All the appropriate people had been forewarned: Morris Glendenning would be coming to the Royal Ontario Museum to do some private research in the Far Eastern Department. He was not to be approached; he was not to be disturbed.

Glendenning's reclusiveness was legendary, made doubly curious by the fact he was the world's best-known communications expert —a man whose public stances and pronouncements had put him at centre stage as long ago as 1965. The thing was, Morris Glendenning could not bear to be seen.

But, as with most eccentric beings, part of what was eccentric in him seemed determined to thwart whatever else was eccentric. In Morris Glendenning's case, his passion for privacy was undone by his need for warmth—which led to a passion for things made of wool and, as well, to what some considered to be the most eccentric habit of dress in the whole community of North American intellectuals.

He wore old-fashioned galoshes—the kind made of sailcloth and rubber, sporting metal fasteners shaped like little ladders lying on their sides. He was also given to wearing a multiplicity of woollen garments layered across his chest: scarves, sweaters, undervests—each of a prescribed colour. He wore, as well, a navy blue beret, pulled down over the tops of his prominent ears. He was six feet, six inches tall and was made, it seemed, almost entirely of bone. His skin was pale, translucent and shining—as if he polished it at night with a chamois cloth. Glendenning's overcoat was blue and had a military cut—naval, perhaps. It was pinched at the waist and almost reached his ankles. In magazine photographs—taken always on the run—Morris Glendenning had the look of Greta Garbo, heading for doorways and ducking into elevators:

"*COMMUNICATIONS EXPERT ESCAPES YET AGAIN!*"

Mrs. Elston, in charge of secretarial work for the Far Eastern Department at the Royal Ontario Museum, had been told by her boss that Glendenning would be turning up on the Friday morning, last week in February. She was quite looking forward to meeting the famous man. Dr. Dime, the curator, had instructed her to offer all available assistance without stint and without question. On no account, she was told, was he to be approached by staff. "Whatever help he requires, he will solicit: probably by note...." By mid-afternoon, however, on the day of the visit, Mrs. Elston said: "it doesn't take much to guarantee the privacy of someone who doesn't even bother to show up."

At which point Myrna Stovich, her assistant, said "but he *is* here, Mrs. Elston. Or—*some*one is. His overcoat and galoshes are sitting right there...." And she pointed out a huddled, navy blue shape on a chair and a pair of sailcloth overshoes squatting in a large brown puddle.

"For heaven's sake," said Mrs. Elston. "How can that have happened when I've been sitting here all day?"

"You haven't been sitting here all day," said Myrna Stovich. "You took a coffee break and you went to lunch."

The night before, and all that morning, it had snowed. The clouds were a shade of charcoal flannel peculiar to clouds that lower above Toronto at the dirty end of winter. Merely looking at them made you cough. Morris Glendenning had supplemented his already over-protective array of woollen garments with one more scarf, which he pulled down crossways over his radiator ribs and tied against the small of his back. Even before he departed his Rosedale home, he pulled his beret over his ears and bowed his head beneath the elements.

Walking across the Sherbourne Street bridge, Morris set his mind on his destination and, thereby, shut out the presence of his fellow pedestrians. His destination at large was the Royal Ontario Museum but his absolute destination was its collection of Japanese theatre masks.

Long after midnight, Morris Glendenning had sat up watching the snow eradicate the garden and the trees beyond his windows. Now, he was tired. And reflective. Progress with his current work had stalled, partly due to the residue of sorrow over his wife's midsummer death and partly due to the fact he had published a book two months later, in September. The work itself—the massing of materials, the culling of ideas—had been passing through an arid stage and it was only in the last few days that he'd begun to feel remotely creative again. Not that he hadn't traversed this particular desert before. Far from it. After every piece of exploration—after every publication of his findings—after every attempt at articulating the theories rising from his findings, Morris Glendenning—not unlike every other kind of writer—found himself, as if by some sinister miracle of transportation, not at the edge but at the very centre of a wasteland from which he could extract not a single living thought. For days—sometimes for weeks— his mind had all the symptoms of dehydration and starvation: desiccated and paralyzed almost to the point of catatonia. Five days ago it had been in that state. But, now, it was reviving—feeding again, but gently. And all because of a chance encounter with a photograph.

The photograph had appeared in a magazine called *Rotunda*, published by the Royal Ontario Museum; and it showed a Japanese theatre mask recently purchased and brought from the Orient. "Fox," the caption read. But it wasn't quite a fox. It was a *human fox*, alarming in its subtle implications. Reading about it, Morris Glendenning discovered it was one of three or four others—a series of masks created for a seventeenth-century Japanese drama in which a fox becomes a man. Each of the masks, so the article informed him, displayed a separate stage in the transformation of a quintessential fox into a quintessential human being. Glendenning's curiosity was piqued—and more than piqued; a trigger was pulled in the deeps of his consciousness. Something had been recognized, he realized, and he felt the reverberations rising like bubbles to the surface: signals, perhaps—or warnings.

He very well remembered reading David Garnett's horror story *Lady Into Fox*—that masterful, witty morality tale in which the English "hunting class" is put in its place when one of its wives becomes a fox. But here, in these Japanese masks, the process had been reversed. It was the fox who took on human form. On the other hand, this was more or less standard procedure when it came to balancing the myths and customs of the Orient against the myths and customs of the West. Almost inevitably, the icons and symbols employed by custom and by myth were opposites: white in the Orient, black in the West for mourning; respect for, not the arrogation of nature; death, not birth as access to immortality.

Whose fate, Glendenning had written in the margin next to the provocative photograph, *is being fulfilled within this mask? The fox's? Or the man's?*

Clipping the whole page out of the magazine, he slipped it into a file marked *Personae,* and five minutes later, he retrieved it—held it up in the snow-white light from the windows and stared at it, mesmerized. The question became an obsession. Looking into the lacquered face of the mask he imagined stripping off the layers of the human face. Not to the bone, but to the being.

The blooming of this image took its time. It occurred to him slowly that under the weight of all his personal masks, there was a being he had never seen. Not a creature hidden by design—but something buried alive that wanted to live and that had a right to life.

"Foxes into humans," he said out loud as he watched the photograph. *Their choice, not ours.*

Standing in the bathroom, later that afternoon, something sent a shudder through his shoulders and down his back when, in the very instant of switching on the light, he caught the image of his unmasked self in the mirror. And he noted, in that prodding, ever-observant part of his brain—where even the death of his wife had been observed with the keenest objectivity—that what had been unmasked had not been human. What he had seen—and all he had seen—was a pair of pale gold eyes that stared from a surround of darkness he could not identify.

Half an hour later, Morris picked up the telephone and placed a call to the Curator of the Far Eastern Collection at the Royal Ontario Museum, who happened to be his old acquaintance, Harry Dime. What privileges could Harry Dime afford him? Could he inspect the Japanese masks alone?

Privately, Harry Dime would later conclude he should have said no. For all his own awareness of intellectual curiosity, he had no sense at all of the dangerous threshold at which Glendenning stood. Dime had forgotten that, when he returned with these treasures from another time, he brought them with all their magic intact. Not with ancient spells, of course, since all such things are nonsense—but the magic they released in others: in those who beheld them without the impediment of superstition.

On the snowy Friday morning, Morris Glendenning debated whether to walk or to chance the subway. Chancing the subway might mean recognition, and given the loss of time that recognition inevitably produced, he decided to walk. Walking, he was certain no one would see him—let alone recognize him. *How many eyes*, he once had said to Nora, his wife, *meet yours on a crowded avenue?*

Bloor Street on a Friday is always massed with shoppers, most of whom, Glendenning noted, like to give the appearance of worldly indifference. *I could go in and buy that coat if I wanted to*, they seemed to be telling themselves. *But I won't do that today, I'll do that on Monday. Maybe Tuesday* … Their impassivity was almost eerie and it troubled Morris Glendenning.

The street, for all its people and all its motor traffic, was silent beneath the falling snow. Morris could see his own and everyone else's breath. If he paused, he could count the breaths and he could take the pulse of where he stood—each breath embracing so many heart beats—all the heart beats racing, lagging—all the secret rhythms of all the people visible in the frosted air. Even the motor traffic gave the appearance of being alive; as much an appearance of life as the people gave with their wisps and plumes of vapours.

In behind the windows of these vehicles, the faces peering out of the silence were reflected in the clouds of glass that fronted Harry Rosen's; Cartier's; Bemelmans; Eddie Bauer's. Holt Renfrew ... moon phases; passing on Bloor Street.

Morris Glendenning could feel the subway tumbling beneath him, not like an earthquake—merely an indication that something was there, alive and at work, whose underground voice made no more sound than voices make in dreams. Morris paused at the corner of Bellair Street and watched a man he had intimately known in boyhood wander past him with his eyes averted. Later on, both of them would say: *I saw old so-and-so out on Bloor Street, today. He looked appalling; dead ...*

I saw old so-and-so today. We passed.

Here, Morris thought, was a kind of debilitating apartness—an apartness that once had been entirely foreign to all these people: the ones who were perfect strangers and the ones who were intimate friends.

We needed each other. That was why we looked each other in the eye. We needed each other. Morris clenched his jaw, afraid that perhaps his lips had been moving over the words. *We've always shared this dreadful place—these awful storms—this appalling climate—and we knew we couldn't afford to be alone. But now ...*

Now he was approaching the final stretch of Bloor Street before the stop at Avenue Road, where he would wait for the light to change, the way he had waited there for over forty years.

Beyond the veils of snow he could see the vaguest hint of neon, red in the air above him: *Park Plaza Hotel*—though all he could see was part of the *z* and part of the final *a.*

A small crowd of people formed near the curb and Morris Glendenning was aware, all at once, how many of them wore fur hats. A dozen fur hats and fifteen heads.

Not one person was looking at any other; only Morris Glendenning, counting. Why were they so unconcerned with one another? When had they all become collectively impassive?

Probably last Tuesday.

Morris smiled. Rhetorical questions formed the backbone of his profession, but he delighted in providing stupid, banal and irritating answers. It was a form of private entertainment.

Still, it affected everything they did—this intractable indifference. It affected the way they walked, he observed—the speed with which they walked—their gait, as they made their way along the street. They moved, Morris thought—gazing at them through the falling snow—with the kind of apathy acquired by those whom something—bitterness?—has taught that nothing waits for those who hurry home. It came to him slowly, standing on the curb at Avenue Road and Bloor, that, when he rode on the subway and was recognized, it was not their recognition of him that mattered: but their hope that he—in all his ballyhooed wisdom and fame—might recognize them and tell them who they were. *I know you from somewhere:* that's what they yearned for him to say. *I know—I recognize who you are.*

In the cellars at the ROM, there is a labyrinth of halls and passageways that leads, through various degrees of light and temperature, to various sequestered rooms where various treasures lie in wait for someone to come and give them back their meaning. Bits and pieces, shards and corners of time—numbered, catalogued, guessed at.

Morris Glendenning stood in one of these rooms—perspiring, it so happened—holding in his fingers, his fingers encased in white cotton gloves—the very mask he had encountered first in its photographed image.

The door behind him was closed.

The room—effectively—was sound-proofed by its very depth in the cellars and its distance from the active centre of the building. A dread, white light was all he had to see by: "daylight" shining from computered bulbs.

The mask's companions—three in number—were set out, sterile on a sterile tray: the fox on its way to becoming a man.

He thought of surgery.

He thought of layers.

How small, he thought, *the face is.*

Looking down at the others, beyond the mask he held, he counted over the variations and degrees of change—the fox in his hands at one extreme and the trio of variations, lying on their tray, burgeoning feature by feature into a close proximity of Oriental human beauty. The widely tilted, oval eyes of the fox became the evenly centered, almond eyes of a man. Of *a priest*, so the collection's catalogue had told him.

A priest. So apt a designation, it could only be amusing. Though amusing, of course, in a sinister way.

Morris felt like a marauding and possibly destructive child bent on mischief. A vandal, perhaps. Most certainly, he knew he was trespassing here, the victim of an irresistible impulse: *put it on....*

He had spent over three hours standing there, touching—lifting—contemplating the masks. Around him, resting on shelves and laid out, numbered in other sterile trays was the department's whole collection of Japanese theatre masks. Each mask was hidden: slung in a silk and sometimes quite elaborate bag, the drawstrings tied in neat, fastidious bows.

Heads, he thought. *The victims of some revolution.*

The truth was—he dared not open the bags to look.

Some of the bags were darkly stained. And, even though he fully recognized the stains were merely of time and of mildew, he could not bring himself to touch them.

Put it on. Don't be afraid.

Go on.

He held the mask up gently before his face.

He could smell its ... what? Its mustiness?

Or was it muskiness?

He closed his eyes and fitted the moulded inner surface over the contours of his bones.

He waited fully fifteen seconds before he dared to open his eyes.

The masks below him, sitting on their tray, were smiling.

Had they smiled before?

He waited, knowing he must not give up until the whole sensation of the mask had been experienced—no matter how long it took.

He thought he heard a noise somewhere out in the corridor. The voice of someone calling.

He held his breath, in order to hear.

Nothing.

And then, as he began to breathe again, he felt the vibrations of a sound between his face and the mask.

Another voice. But whose?

He was a long way off inside himself and standing in another light. A pattern of leaves threw shadows over what he saw: perhaps the verge of a clearing somewhere.

Creatures—not human—moved before him.

Foxes.

How elegant they were. How delicate: precise and knowing.

Why was he so unconcerned and unafraid?

He began to receive the scent of earth as he had never smelled the earth before: a safe, green, sun-warmed scent.

He looked at his hands. He held them out as far as he could. Human hands—in white gloves. Whose were they?

He tried to speak, but could not.

What emerged, instead of speech, was an inarticulate and strangled sound he had never heard before.

Down below him, where the earth replaced the floor, one of the foxes came and sat at his feet and stared up into his face. It seemed, almost, to know who he was.

Never in all of Morris's life had he been so close to anything wild. He was mesmerized.

Other foxes came, as if to greet him, and they leaned so close against his legs that he could feel their bones against his shins.

The fox that had been the first to come and sit before him narrowed its gaze. It stared so intently, Morris felt that something must be going to happen.

Say something to us, the fox appeared to be saying. Tell us something. Speak to us....

Yes—but how?

Morris was bereft of words. But the impulse to speak was overwhelming. He could feel the sound of something rising through his bowels—and the force of the sound was so alarming that Morris pulled the mask away from his face and thrust it from him—down into the tray from which he had lifted it. When?

How much time had passed. An hour? A day? How far away had he been? Who was he, now? Or what?

He looked—afraid—at the backs of his hands, but they were covered still with the gloves.

The creatures in the tray appeared to stir.

Morris closed his eyes against the notion he was not alone. He did not want to see the floor—for fear the floor was still the sun-warmed ground it had been a moment before.

And yet …

He wanted them back. Their breath and their eyes already haunted him. He waited for their voices—but no voices came.

Morris removed the white cotton gloves. He took a long, deep breath and let it very slowly out between his teeth.

His fingers dipped towards the tray and even before they reached the mask, he smiled—because he could feel the head rising up as sure and real as the sun itself. And when the mask he had chosen was in place, he paused only for seconds before he dared to breathe again; one deep breath, and he found his voice—which was not his human voice but another voice from another time.

Now—at last—he was not alone.

Just before five that afternoon, Mrs. Elston was putting the cover on her IBM Selectric and preparing to leave, when she became aware all at once of someone standing behind her.

"Oh," she said—recovering as best she could. "We thought you were not here, Professor Glendenning."

She smiled—but he did not reply.

His enormous height was bending to the task of pulling on his galoshes.

"Shall we be seeing you tomorrow?" Mrs. Elston asked.

With his back to her, he shook his head.

"Monday, perhaps?"

But he was buckling his galoshes; silent.

He drew his many scarves about him, buttoned his greatcoat, took up his leather bag and started away.

"Professor Glendenning … It was such a great pleasure …"

But Mrs. Elston could not reach him. He was gone and the door swung to and fro.

Mrs. Elston sniffed the air.

"Myrna?" she said. "Do you smell something?"

Myrna Stovich needed no prompting.

"Sure," she said. "Dog."

"But there *can't* be a dog!" said Mrs. Elston.

"Yeah, well," said Myrna. "We also thought there wasn't no Professor Glendenning, didn't we."

"True," Mrs. Elston laughed. "You're quite right, my dear. But… goodness! What a day!" she said. "And now we have to go out into all that snow."

"Yeah," said Myrna Stovich. "Sure. But I like the snow."

"Yes," said Mrs. Elston, and she sighed. "I like it, too, I guess." And then she gave a smile. "I suppose I have to, don't I—seeing it's what we've got."

1. Take a few minutes to record in your journal your first impressions of the story. You might choose one focus from the following:
   - questions about Morris Glendenning or the events of the story;
   - any descriptive details that struck you as being vivid or memorable;
   - the various views of Morris in the story, and your own view of him.

   Share your impressions in a small group.
2. Develop a character sketch of Morris Glendenning. What conflict is he facing? How might he have described it to Nora, his wife, had she been alive still?
3. Why is Morris Glendenning fascinated by the masks? What does he learn from his experience with them? How is he changed by it?
4. With a partner, examine closely the italicized passage on pages 98 to 99. Discuss your interpretations and share your ideas with two other classmates.
5. What comment does the story offer? What outlook on life does it present? Support your responses with details from the story and your own experiences.
6. Choose one of the following activities:
   a) Write the journal entry Morris Glendenning might have made the evening following his visit to the museum.
   b) Write a poem in the first person, from the perspective of Morris Glendenning, about the masks.
   c) Reflect upon and write about any experiences you have had similar to Morris Glendenning's in the story—for example, being drawn to the something powerfully, feeling alone in a crowd.

Note: For background information about the story and the author's thoughts, see pages 292, 295, and 306 in the unit "Perspectives on Story."

Charlotte Perkins Gilman

The Yellow Wall Paper

(I would not say it to a living soul, of course, but this is dead paper and a great relief to my mind)

It is very seldom that mere ordinary people like John and myself secure ancestral halls for the summer.

A colonial mansion, a hereditary estate, I would say a haunted house, and reach the height of romantic felicity—but that would be asking too much of fate!

Still I will proudly declare that there is something queer about it.

Else, why should it be let so cheaply? And why have stood so long untenanted?

John laughs at me, of course, but one expects that in marriage.

John is practical in the extreme. He has no patience with faith, an intense horror of superstition, and he scoffs openly at any talk of things not to be felt and seen and put down in figures.

John is a physician, and *perhaps*—(I would not say it to a living soul, of course, but this is dead paper and a great relief to my mind)—*perhaps* that is one reason I do not get well faster.

You see, he does not believe I am sick!

And what can one do?

If a physician of high standing, and one's own husband, assures friends and relatives that there is really nothing the matter with one but temporary nervous depression—a slight hysterical tendency—what is one to do?

My brother is also a physician, and also of high standing, and he says the same thing.

So I take phosphates or phosphites—whichever it is—and tonics, and journeys, and air, and exercise, and am absolutely forbidden to "work" until I am well again.

Personally I disagree with their ideas.

Personally I believe that congenial work, with excitement and change, would do me good.

But what is one to do?

I did write for a while in spite of them; but it *does* exhaust me a good deal—having to be so sly about it, or else meet with heavy opposition.

I sometimes fancy that in my condition if I had less opposition and more society and stimulus—but John says the very worst thing I can do is to think about my condition, and I confess it always makes me feel bad.

So I will let it alone and talk about the house.

The most beautiful place! It is quite alone, standing well back from the road, quite three miles from the village. It makes me think of English places that you read about, for there are hedges and walls and gates that lock, and lots of separate little houses for the gardeners and people.

There is a *delicious* garden! I never saw such a garden—large and shady, full of box-bordered paths, and lined with long grape-covered arbors with seats under them.

There were greenhouses, but they are all broken now.

There was some legal trouble, I believe, something about the heirs and co-heirs; anyhow, the place has been empty for years.

That spoils my ghostliness, I am afraid, but I don't care—there is something strange about the house—I can feel it.

I even said so to John one moonlight evening, but he said what I felt was a *draught*, and shut the window.

I get unreasonably angry with John sometimes. I'm sure I never used to be so sensitive. I think it is due to this nervous condition.

But John says if I feel so I shall neglect proper self-control; so I take pains to control myself—before him, at least—and that makes me very tired.

I don't like our room a bit. I wanted one downstairs that opened on the piazza and had roses all over the window, and such pretty, old-fashioned chintz hangings! But John would not hear of it.

He said there was only one window and not room for two beds, and no near room for him if he took another.

He is very careful and loving, and hardly lets me stir without special direction.

I have a schedule prescription for each hour in the day; he takes all care from me, and so I feel basely ungrateful not to value it more.

He said he came here solely on my account, that I was to have perfect rest and all the air I could get. "Your exercise depends on your strength, my dear," said he, "and your food somewhat on your appetite; but air you can absorb all the time." So we took the nursery at the top of the house.

It is a big, airy room, the whole floor nearly, with windows that look all ways, and air and sunshine galore. It was nursery first and then playroom and gymnasium, I should judge; for the windows are barred for little children, and there are rings and things in the walls.

The paint and paper look as if a boys' school had used it. It is stripped off—the paper—in great patches all around the head of my bed, about as far as I can reach, and in a great place on the other side of the room low down. I never saw a worse paper in my life.

One of those sprawling, flamboyant patterns committing every artistic sin.

It is dull enough to confuse the eye in following, pronounced enough to constantly irritate and provoke study, and when you follow the lame, uncertain curves for a little distance they suddenly commit suicide—plunge off at outrageous angles, destroy themselves in unheard-of contradictions.

The color is repellent, almost revolting: a smouldering, unclean yellow, strangely faded by the slow-turning sunlight.

It is a dull yet lurid orange in some places, a sickly sulphur tint in others.

No wonder the children hated it! I should hate it myself if I had to live in this room long.

There comes John, and I must put this away—he hates to have me write a word.

We have been here two weeks, and I haven't felt like writing before, since that first day.

I am sitting by the window now, up in this atrocious nursery, and there is nothing to hinder my writing as much as I please, save lack of strength.

John is away all day, and even some nights when his cases are serious.

I am glad my case is not serious!

But these nervous troubles are dreadfully depressing.

John does not know how much I really suffer. He knows there is no *reason* to suffer, and that satisfies him.

Of course it is only nervousness. It does weigh on me so not to do my duty in any way!

I meant to be such a help to John, such a real rest and comfort, and here I am a comparative burden already!

Nobody would believe what an effort it is to do what little I am able—to dress and entertain, and order things.

It is fortunate Mary is so good with the baby. Such a dear baby!

And yet I *cannot* be with him, it makes me so nervous.

I suppose John never was nervous in his life. He laughs at me so about this wall paper!

At first he meant to repaper the room, but afterwards he said that I was letting it get the better of me, and that nothing was worse for a nervous patient than to give way to such fancies.

He said that after the wall paper was changed it would be the heavy bedstead, and then the barred windows, and then that gate at the head of the stairs, and so on.

"You know the place is doing you good," he said, "and really, dear, I don't care to renovate the house just for a three months' rental."

"Then do let us go downstairs," I said. "There are such pretty rooms there."

Then he took me in his arms and called me a blessed little goose, and said he would go down to the cellar if I wished, and have it whitewashed into the bargain.

But he is right enough about the beds and windows and things.

It is as airy and comfortable a room as anyone need wish, and, of course, I would not be so silly as to make him uncomfortable just for a whim.

I'm really getting quite fond of the big room, all but that horrid paper.

Out of one window I can see the garden, those mysterious deep-shaded arbors, the riotous old-fashioned flowers, and bushes and gnarly trees.

Out of another I get a lovely view of the bay and a little private wharf belonging to the estate. There is a beautiful shaded lane that runs down there from the house. I always fancy I see people walking in these numerous paths and arbors, but John has cautioned me not to give way to fancy in the least. He says that with my imaginative power and habit of story-making, a nervous weakness like mine is sure to lead to all manner of excited fancies, and that I ought to use my will and good sense to check the tendency. So I try.

I think sometimes that if I were only well enough to write a little it would relieve the press of ideas and rest me.

But I find I get pretty tired when I try.

It is so discouraging not to have any advice and companionship about my work. When I get really well John says we will ask Cousin Henry and Julia down for a long visit; but he says he would as soon put fire-works in my pillow-case as to let me have those stimulating people about now.

I wish I could get well faster.

But I must not think about that. This paper looks to me as if it *knew* what a vicious influence it had!

There is a recurrent spot where the pattern lolls like a broken neck and two bulbous eyes stare at you upside-down.

I get positively angry with the impertinence of it and the ever-lastingness. Up and down and sideways they crawl, and those absurd unblinking eyes are everywhere. There is one place where two breadths didn't match, and the eyes go all up and down the line, one a little higher than the other.

I never saw so much expression in an inanimate thing before, and we all know how much expression they have! I used to lie awake as a child and get more entertainment and terror out of blank walls and plain furniture than most children could find in a toy-store.

I remember what a kindly wink the knobs of our big old bureau used to have, and there was one chair that always seemed like a strong friend.

I used to feel that if any of the other things looked too fierce I could always hop into that chair and be safe.

The furniture in this room is no worse than inharmonious, however, for we had to bring it all from downstairs. I suppose when this was used as a playroom they had to take the nursery things out, and no wonder! I never saw such ravages as the children have made here.

The wall paper, as I said before, is torn off in spots, and it sticketh closer than a brother—they must have had perseverance as well as hatred.

Then the floor is scratched and gouged and splintered, the plaster itself is dug out here and there, and this great heavy bed, which is all we found in the room, looks as if it had been through the wars.

But I don't mind it a bit—only the paper.

There comes John's sister. Such a dear girl as she is, and so careful of me! I must not let her find me writing.

She is a perfect and enthusiastic housekeeper, and hopes for no better profession. I verily believe she thinks it is the writing which made me sick!

But I can write when she is out, and see her a long way off from these windows.

There is one that commands the road, a lovely, shaded, winding road, and one that just looks off over the country. A lovely country, too, full of great elms and velvet meadows.

This wall paper has a kind of sub-pattern in a different shade, a particularly irritating one, for you can only see it in certain lights, and not clearly then.

But in the places where it isn't faded, and where the sun is just so, I can see a strange, provoking, formless sort of figure that seems to skulk about behind that silly and conspicuous front design.

There's sister on the stairs!

Well, the Fourth of July is over! The people are all gone, and I am tired out. John thought it might do me good to see a little company, so we just had Mother and Nellie and the children down for a week.

Of course I didn't do a thing. Jennie sees to everything now.

But it tired me all the same.

John says if I don't pick up faster he shall send me to Weir Mitchell in the fall.

But I don't want to go there at all. I had a friend who was in his hands once, and she says he is just like John and my brother, only more so!

Besides, it is such an undertaking to go so far.

I don't feel as if it was worthwhile to turn my hand over for anything, and I'm getting dreadfully fretful and querulous.

I cry at nothing, and cry most of the time.

Of course I don't when John is here, or anybody else, but when I am alone.

And I am alone a good deal just now. John is kept in town very often by serious cases, and Jennie is good and lets me alone when I want her to.

So I walk a little in the garden or down that lovely lane, sit on the porch under the roses, and lie down up here a good deal.

I'm getting really fond of the room in spite of the wall paper. Perhaps *because* of the wall paper.

It dwells in my mind so!

I lie here on this great immovable bed—it is nailed down, I believe—and follow that pattern about by the hour. It is as good as gymnastics, I assure you. I start, we'll say, at the bottom, down in the corner over there where it has not been touched, and I determine for the thousandth time that I *will* follow that pointless pattern to some sort of a conclusion.

I know a little of the principles of design, and I know this thing was not arranged on any laws of radiation, or alternation, or repetition, or symmetry, or anything else that I ever heard of.

It is repeated, of course, by the breadths, but not otherwise.

Looked at in one way, each breadth stands alone; the bloated curves and flourishes—a kind of "debased Romanesque" with *delirium tremens*—go waddling up and down in isolated columns of fatuity.

But, on the other hand, they connect diagonally, and the sprawling outlines run off in great slanting waves of optic horror, like a lot of wallowing seaweeds in full chase.

The whole thing goes horizontally, too, at least it seems so, and I exhaust myself trying to distinguish the order of its going in that direction.

They have used a horizontal breadth for a frieze, and that adds wonderfully to the confusion.

There is one end of the room where it is almost intact, and there, when the cross-lights fade and the low sun shines directly upon it, I can almost fancy radiation after all—the interminable grotesques seem to form around a common centre and rush off in headlong plunges of equal distraction.

It makes me tired to follow it. I will take a nap, I guess.

I don't know why I should write this.

I don't want to.

I don't feel able.

And I know John would think it absurd. But I must say what I feel and think in some way—it is such a relief!

But the effort is getting to be greater than the relief.

Half the time now I am awfully lazy, and lie down ever so much.

John says I mustn't lose my strength, and has me take cod-liver oil and lots of tonics and things, to say nothing of ale and wine and rare meat.

Dear John! He loves me very dearly, and hates to have me sick. I tried to have a real earnest reasonable talk with him the other day, and tell him how I wish he would let me go and make a visit to Cousin Henry and Julia.

But he said I wasn't able to go, nor able to stand it after I got there; and I did not make out a very good case for myself, for I was crying before I had finished.

It is getting to be a great effort for me to think straight. Just this nervous weakness, I suppose.

And dear John gathered me up in his arms, and just carried me upstairs and laid me on the bed, and sat by me and read to me till he tired my head.

He said I was his darling and his comfort and all he had, and that I must take care of myself for his sake, and keep well.

He says no one but myself can help me out of it, that I must use my will and self-control and not let any silly fancies run away with me.

There's one comfort: the baby is well and happy, and does not have to occupy this nursery with the horrid wall paper.

If we had not used it, that blessed child would have! What a fortunate escape! Why, I wouldn't have a child of mine, an impressionable little thing, live in such a room for worlds.

I never thought of it before, but it is lucky that John kept me here, after all. I can stand it so much easier than a baby, you see.

Of course I never mention it to them any more—I am too wise—but I keep watch of it all the same.

There are things in that paper that nobody knows but me, or ever will.

Behind that outside pattern the dim shapes get clearer every day.

It is always the same shape, only very numerous.

And it is like a woman stooping down and creeping about behind that pattern. I don't like it a bit. I wonder—I begin to think—I wish John would take me away from here!

It is so hard to talk with John about my case, because he is so wise, and because he loves me so.

But I tried it last night.

It was moonlight. The moon shines in all around, just as the sun does.

I hate to see it sometimes, it creeps so slowly, and always comes in by one window or another.

John was asleep and I hated to waken him, so I kept still and watched the moonlight on that undulating wall paper till I felt creepy.

The faint figure behind seemed to shake the pattern, just as if she wanted to get out.

I got up softly and went to feel and see if the paper *did* move, and when I came back John was awake.

"What is it, little girl?" he said. "Don't go walking about like that—you'll get cold."

I thought it was a good time to talk, so I told him that I really was not gaining here, and that I wished he would take me away.

"Why, darling!" said he. "Our lease will be up in three weeks and I can't see how to leave before."

"The repairs are not done at home, and I cannot possibly leave town just now. Of course if you were in any danger I could and would, but you really are better, dear, whether you can see it or not. I am a doctor, dear, and I know. You are gaining flesh and color, your appetite is better. I feel really much easier about you."

"I don't weigh a bit more," said I, "nor as much; and my appetite may be better in the evening, when you are here, but it is worse in the morning, when you are away."

"Bless her little heart!" said he with a big hug. "She shall be as sick as she pleases. But now let's improve the shining hours by going to sleep, and talk about it in the morning."

"And you won't go away?" I asked gloomily.

"Why, how can I, dear? It is only three weeks more and then we will take a nice little trip of a few days while Jennie is getting the house ready. Really, dear, you are better!"

"Better in body, perhaps—" I began, and stopped short, for he sat up straight and looked at me with such a stern, reproachful look that I could not say another word.

"My darling," said he, "I beg of you, for my sake and for our child's sake, as well as for your own, that you will never for one instant let that idea enter your mind! There is nothing so dangerous, so fascinating, to a temperament like yours. It is a false and foolish fancy. Can you not trust me as a physician when I tell you so?"

So of course I said no more on that score, and we went to sleep before long. He thought I was asleep first, but I wasn't—I lay there for hours trying to decide whether that front pattern and the back pattern really did move together or separately.

On a pattern like this, by daylight, there is a lack of sequence, a defiance of law, that is a constant irritant to a normal mind.

The color is hideous enough, and unreliable enough, and infuriating enough, but the pattern is torturing.

You think you have mastered it, but just as you get well under way in following, it turns a back somersault, and there you are. It slaps you in the face, knocks you down, and tramples upon you. It is like a bad dream.

The outside pattern is a florid arabesque, reminding one of a fungus. If you can imagine a toadstool in joints, an interminable string of toadstools, budding and sprouting in endless convolutions—why, that is something like it.

That is, sometimes!

There is one marked peculiarity about this paper, a thing nobody seems to notice but myself, and that is that it changes as the light changes.

When the sun shoots in through the east window—I always watch for that first long, straight ray—it changes so quickly that I never can quite believe it.

That is why I watch it always.

By moonlight—the moon shines in all night when there is a moon—I wouldn't know it was the same paper.

At night in any kind of light, in twilight, candlelight, lamplight, and worst of all by moonlight, it becomes bars! The outside pattern, I mean, and the woman behind it is as plain as can be.

I didn't realize for a long time what the thing was that showed behind—that dim sub-pattern—but now I am quite sure it is a woman.

By daylight she is subdued, quiet. I fancy it is the pattern that keeps her so still. It is so puzzling. It keeps me quiet by the hour.

I lie down ever so much now. John says it is good for me, and to sleep all I can.

Indeed he started the habit by making me lie down for an hour after each meal.

It is a very bad habit, I am convinced, for, you see, I don't sleep.

And that cultivates deceit, for I don't tell them I'm awake—oh, no!

The fact is, I am getting a little afraid of John.

He seems very queer sometimes, and even Jennie has an inexplicable look.

It strikes me occasionally, just as a scientific hypothesis, that perhaps it is the paper!

I have watched John when he did not know I was looking, and come into the room suddenly on the most innocent excuses, and I've caught him several times *looking at the paper*! And Jennie too. I caught Jennie with her hand on it once.

She didn't know I was in the room, and when I asked her in a quiet, a very quiet voice, with the most restrained manner possible, what she was doing with the paper, she turned around as if she had been caught stealing, and looked quite angry—asked me why I should frighten her so!

Then she said that the paper stained everything it touched, that she had found yellow smooches on all my clothes and John's, and she wished we would be more careful!

Did not that sound innocent? But I know she was studying that pattern, and I am determined that nobody shall find it out but myself!

Life is very much more exciting now than it used to be. You see, I have something more to expect, to look forward to, to watch. I really do eat better, and am more quiet than I was.

John is so pleased to see me improve! He laughed a little the other day, and said I seemed to be flourishing in spite of my wall paper.

I turned it off with a laugh. I had no intention of telling him it was *because* of the wall paper—he would make fun of me. He might even want to take me away.

I don't want to leave now until I have found it out. There is a week more, and I think that will be enough.

I'm feeling ever so much better! I don't sleep much at night, for it is so interesting to watch developments; but I sleep a good deal during the daytime.

In the daytime it is tiresome and perplexing.

There are always new shoots on the fungus, and new shades of yellow all over it. I cannot keep count of them, though I have tried conscientiously.

It is the strangest yellow, that wall paper! It makes me think of all the yellow things I ever saw—not beautiful ones like buttercups, but old, foul, bad yellow things.

But there is something else about that paper—the smell! I noticed it the moment we came into the room, but with so much air and sun it was not bad. Now we have had a week of fog and rain, and whether the windows are open or not the smell is here.

It creeps all over the house.

I find it hovering in the dining-room, skulking in the parlor, hiding in the hall, lying in wait for me on the stairs.

It gets into my hair.

Even when I go to ride, if I turn my head suddenly and surprise it—there is that smell!

Such a peculiar odor, too! I have spent hours in trying to analyze it, to find what it smelled like.

It is not bad—at first, and very gentle, but quite the subtlest, most enduring odor I ever met.

In this damp weather it is awful. I wake up in the night and find it hanging over me.

It used to disturb me at first. I thought seriously of burning the house—to reach the smell.

But now I am used to it. The only thing I can think of that it is like is the *color* of the paper—a yellow smell!

There is a very funny mark on this wall, low down, near the mopboard. A streak that runs around the room. It goes behind every piece of furniture, except the bed, a long, straight, even *smooch*, as if it had been rubbed over and over.

I wonder how it was done and who did it, and what they did it for. Round and round and round—round and round and round—it makes me dizzy!

I really have discovered something at last.

Through watching so much at night, when it changes so, I have finally found out.

The front pattern *does* move—and no wonder! The woman behind shakes it!

Sometimes I think there are a great many women behind, and sometimes only one, and she crawls around fast, and her crawling shakes it all over.

Then in the very bright spots she keeps still, and in the very shady spots she just takes hold of the bars and shakes them hard.

And she is all the time trying to climb through. But nobody could climb through that pattern—it strangles so; I think that is why it has so many heads.

They get through, and then the pattern strangles them off and turns them upside-down, and makes their eyes white!

If those heads were covered or taken off it would not be half so bad.

I think that woman gets out in the daytime!

And I'll tell you why—privately—I've seen her!

I can see her out of every one of my windows!

It is the same woman, I know, for she is always creeping, and most women do not creep by daylight.

I see her in that long shaded lane, creeping up and down. I see her in those dark grape arbors, creeping all around the garden.

I see her on that long road under the trees, creeping along, and when a carriage comes she hides under the blackberry vines.

I don't blame her a bit. It must be very humiliating to be caught creeping by daylight!

I always lock the door when I creep by daylight. I can't do it at night, for I know John would suspect something at once.

And John is so queer, now, that I don't want to irritate him. I wish he would take another room! Besides, I don't want anybody to get that woman out at night but myself.

I often wonder if I could see her out of all the windows at once.

But, turn as fast as I can, I can only see out of one at one time.

And though I always see her, she *may* be able to creep faster than I can turn!

I have watched her sometimes away off in the open country, creeping as fast as a cloud shadow in a high wind.

If only that top pattern could be gotten off from the under one! I mean to try it, little by little.

I have found out another funny thing, but I shan't tell it this time! It does not do to trust people too much.

There are only two more days to get this paper off, and I believe John is beginning to notice. I don't like the look in his eyes.

And I heard him ask Jennie a lot of professional questions about me. She had a very good report to give.

She said I slept a good deal in the daytime.

John knows I don't sleep very well at night, for all I'm so quiet!

He asked me all sorts of questions, too, and pretended to be very loving and kind.

As if I couldn't see through him!

Still, I don't wonder he acts so, sleeping under this paper for three months.

It only interests me, but I feel sure John and Jennie are secretly affected by it.

Hurrah! This is the last day, but it is enough. John is to stay in town over night, and won't be out until this evening.

Jennie wanted to sleep with me—the sly thing—but I told her I should undoubtedly rest better for a night all alone.

That was clever, for really I wasn't alone a bit! As soon as it was moonlight, and that poor thing began to crawl and shake the pattern, I got up and ran to help her.

I pulled and she shook, I shook and she pulled, and before morning we had peeled off yards of that paper.

A strip about as high as my head and half around the room.

And then when the sun came and that awful pattern began to laugh at me, I declared I would finish it today!

We go away to-morrow, and they are moving all my furniture down again to leave things as they were before.

Jennie looked at the wall in amazement, but I told her merrily that I did it out of pure spite at the vicious thing.

She laughed and said she wouldn't mind doing it herself, but I must not get tired.

How she betrayed herself that time!

But I am here, and no person touches this paper but me—not *alive*!

She tried to get me out of the room—it was too patent! But I said it was so quiet and empty and clean now that I believed I would lie down again and sleep all I could, and not to wake me even for dinner—I would call when I woke.

So now she is gone, and the servants are gone, and the things are gone, and there is nothing left but that great bedstead nailed down, with the canvas mattress we found on it.

We shall sleep downstairs to-night, and take the boat home tomorrow.

I quite enjoy the room, now it is bare again.

How those children did tear about here!

This bedstead is fairly gnawed!

But I must get to work.

I have locked the door and thrown the key down into the front path.

I don't want to go out, and I don't want to have anybody come in, till John comes.

I want to astonish him.

I've got a rope up here that even Jennie did not find. If that woman does get out, and tries to get away, I can tie her!

But I forgot I could not reach far without anything to stand on!

This bed will *not* move!

I tried to lift and push it until I was lame, and then I got so angry I bit off a little piece at one corner—but it hurt my teeth.

Then I peeled off all the paper I could reach standing on the floor. It sticks horribly and the pattern just enjoys it! All those strangled heads and bulbous eyes and waddling fungus growths just shriek with derision!

I am getting angry enough to do something desperate. To jump out of the window would be admirable exercise, but the bars are too strong even to try.

Besides I wouldn't do it. Of course not. I know well enough that a step like that is improper and might be misconstrued.

I don't like to *look* out of the windows even—there are so many of those creeping women, and they creep so fast.

I wonder if they all come out of that wall paper, as I did?

But I am securely fastened now by my well-hidden rope—you don't get *me* out in the road there!

I suppose I shall have to get back behind the pattern when it comes night, and that is hard!

It is so pleasant to be out in this great room and creep around as I please!

I don't want to go outside. I won't, even if Jennie asks me to.

For outside you have to creep on the ground, and everything is green instead of yellow.

But here I can creep smoothly on the floor, and my shoulder just fits in that long smooch around the wall, so I cannot lose my way.

Why, there's John at the door!

It is no use, young man, you can't open it!

How he does call and pound!

Now he's crying for an axe.

It would be a shame to break down that beautiful door!

"John, dear!" said I in the gentlest voice, "the key is down by the front steps, under a plantain leaf!"

That silenced him for a few moments.

Then he said—very quietly indeed, "Open the door, my darling!"

"I can't," said I. "The key is down by the front door, under a plantain leaf!"

And then I said it again, several times, very gently and slowly, and said it so often that he had to go and see, and he got it, of course, and came in. He stopped short by the door.

"What is the matter?" he cried. "For God's sake, what are you doing?"

I kept on creeping just the same, but I looked at him over my shoulder.

"I've got out at last," said I, "in spite of you and Jane! And I've pulled off most of the paper, so you can't put me back!"

Now why should that man have fainted? But he did, and right across my path by the wall, so that I had to creep over him every time!

1. Take a few minutes to record in your journal your first impressions of the story. You might choose one focus from the following:
   - what the story suggests to you about the workings of the human mind;
   - different views of the narrator (hers, her husband's, and yours);
   - a story or movie that "The Yellow Wall Paper" brings to mind.

   Share your impressions in a small group.
2. The story is written as a series of journal entries. With a partner, note on a three-column chart the changes through the entries in the following:
   - the narrator's relationship to her surroundings, particularly the wall paper;
   - the narrator's relationship to other characters;
   - various perceptions of the narrator's health.
3. What comments does the story seem to offer on human nature? on nineteenth century attitudes toward women and toward mental illness?
4. The yellow wall paper is a central image in the story. Explain its significance. What else about the setting is important to the story?
5. Consider the author's decisions regarding point of view. Why do you think she chose this point of view over other possibilities? How does it contribute to the story?
6. Choose one of the following activities:
   a) Compose an additional journal entry or a postscript. Consider first what it will indicate about the central character and who will write it.
   b) Improvise the conversation John and Jennie have, perhaps with the doctor who assumes responsibility for treating the narrator. Share the conversation with the class.

Note: For background information and the author's thoughts, see page 290 in the unit "Perspectives on Story."

Nadine Gordimer

The Ultimate Safari

We wanted to go where there were no bandits and there was food.

"THE AFRICAN ADVENTURE LIVES ON ... YOU CAN DO IT! THE ULTIMATE SAFARI OR EXPEDITION WITH LEADERS WHO KNOW AFRICA."
Travel advertisement, *Observer*, 27 November 1988

That night our mother went to the shop and she didn't come back. Ever. What happened? I don't know. My father also had gone away one day and never come back; but he was fighting in the war. We were in the war, too, but we were children, we were like our grandmother and grandfather, we didn't have guns. The people my father was fighting—the bandits, they are called by our government—ran all over the place and we ran away from them like chickens chased by dogs. We didn't know where to go. Our mother went to the shop because someone said you could get some oil for cooking. We were happy because we hadn't tasted oil for a long time; perhaps she got the oil and someone knocked her down in the dark and took that oil from her. Perhaps she met the bandits. If you meet them, they will kill you. Twice they came to our village and we ran and hid in the bush and when they'd gone we came back and found they had taken everything; but the third time they came back there was nothing to take, no oil, no food, so they burned the thatch and the roofs of our houses fell in. My mother found some pieces of tin and we put those up over part of the house. We were waiting there for her that night she never came back.

We were frightened to go out, even to do our business, because the bandits did come. Not into our house—without a roof it must have looked as if there was no one in it, everything gone—but all through the village. We heard people screaming and running. We were afraid even to run, without our mother to tell us where. I am the middle one, the girl, and my little brother clung against my stomach with his arms round my neck and his legs round my waist like a baby monkey to its mother. All night my first-born brother kept in his hand a broken piece of wood from one of our burnt house-poles. It was to save himself if the bandits found him.

We stayed there all day. Waiting for her. I don't know what day it was; there was no school, no church any more in our village, so you didn't know whether it was a Sunday or a Monday.

When the sun was going down, our grandmother and grandfather came. Someone from our village had told them we children were alone, our mother had not come back. I say "grandmother" before "grandfather" because it's like that: our grandmother is big and strong, not yet old, and our grandfather is small, you don't know where he is, in his loose trousers, he smiles but he hasn't heard what you're saying, and his hair looks as if he's left it full of soap suds. Our grandmother took us—me, the baby, my first-born brother, our grandfather—back to her house and we were all afraid (except the baby, asleep on our grandmother's back) of meeting the bandits on the way. We waited a long time at our grandmother's place. Perhaps it was a month. We were hungry. Our mother never came. While we were waiting for her to fetch us, our grandmother had no food for us, no food for our grandfather and herself. A woman with milk in her breasts gave us some for my little brother, although at our house he used to eat porridge, same as we did. Our grandmother took us to look for wild spinach but everyone else in the village did the same and there wasn't a leaf left.

Our grandfather, walking a little behind some young men, went to look for our mother but didn't find her. Our grandmother cried with other women and I sang the hymns with them. They brought a little food—some beans—but after two days there was nothing again. Our grandfather used to have three sheep and a cow and a vegetable garden but the bandits had long ago taken the sheep and the cow, because they were hungry, too; and when planting time came our grandfather had no seed to plant.

So they decided—our grandmother did; our grandfather made little noises and rocked from side to side, but she took no notice—we would go away. We children were pleased. We wanted to go away from where our mother wasn't and where we were hungry. We wanted to go where there were no bandits and there was food. We were glad to think there must be such a place; away.

Our grandmother gave her church clothes to someone in exchange for some dried mealies and she boiled them and tied them in a rag. We took them with us when we went and she thought we would get water from the rivers but we didn't come to any river and we got so thirsty we had to turn back. Not all the way to our grandparents' place but to a village where there was a pump. She opened the basket where she carried some clothes and the mealies and she sold her shoes to buy a big plastic container for water. I said, *Gogo*, how will you go to church now even without shoes, but she said we had a long journey and too much to carry. At that village we met other people who were also going away. We joined them because they seemed to know where that was better than we did.

To get there we had to go through the Kruger Park. We knew about the Kruger Park. A kind of whole country of animals—elephants, lions, jackals, hyenas, hippos, crocodiles, all kinds of animals. We had some of them in our own country, before the war (our grandfather remembers; we children weren't born yet) but the bandits kill the elephants and sell their tusks, and the bandits and our soldiers have eaten all the buck. There was a man in our village without legs—a crocodile took them off, in our river; but all the same our country is a country of people, not animals. We knew about the Kruger Park because some of our men used to leave home to work there in the places where white people came to stay and look at the animals.

So we started to go away again. There were women and other children like me who had to carry the small ones on their backs when the women got tired. A man led us into the Kruger Park: are we there yet, are we there yet, I kept asking our grandmother. Not yet, the man said, when she asked him for me. He told us we had to take a long way to get round the fence, which he explained would kill you, roast off your skin the moment you touched it, like the wires high up on poles that give electric light in our towns. I've seen that sign of a head without ears or skin or hair on an iron box at the mission hospital we used to have before it was blown up.

When I asked the next time, they said we'd been walking in the Kruger Park for an hour. But it looked just like the bush we'd been walking through all day, and we hadn't seen any animals except the monkeys and birds which live around us at home, and a tortoise that, of course, couldn't get away from us. My first-born brother and the other boys brought it to the man so it could be killed and we could cook and eat it. He let it go because he told us we could not make a fire; all the time we were in the Park we must not make a fire because the smoke would show we were there. Police, wardens, would come and send us back where we came from. He said we must move like animals among the animals, away from the roads, away from the white people's camps. And at that moment I heard—I'm sure I was the first to hear—cracking branches and the sound of something parting grasses and I almost squealed because I thought it was the police, wardens—the people he was telling us to look out for—who had found us already. And it was an elephant, and another elephant, and more elephants, big blots of dark moved wherever you looked between the trees. They were curling their trunks round the red leaves of the mopane trees and stuffing them into their mouths. The babies leaned against their mothers. The almost grown-up ones wrestled like my first-born brother with his friends—only they used trunks instead of arms. I was so interested I forgot to be afraid. The man said we should just stand still and be quiet while the elephants passed. They passed very slowly because elephants are too big to need to run from anyone.

The buck ran from us. They jumped so high they seemed to fly. The wart-hogs stopped dead, when they heard us, and swerved off the way a boy in our village used to zigzag on the bicycle his father had brought back from the mines. We followed the animals to where they drank. When they had gone, we went to their water-holes. We were never thirsty without finding water, but the animals ate, ate all the time. Whenever you saw them they were

eating, grass, trees, roots. And there was nothing for us. The mealies were finished. The only food we could eat was what the baboons ate, dry little figs full of ants, that grow along the branches of the trees at the rivers. It was hard to be like the animals.

When it was very hot during the day we would find lions lying asleep. They were the colour of the grass and we didn't see them at first but the man did, and he led us back and a long way round where they slept. I wanted to lie down like the lions. My little brother was getting thin but he was very heavy. When our grandmother looked for me, to put him on my back, I tried not to see. My first-born brother stopped talking; and when we rested he had to be shaken to get up again, as if he was just like our grandfather, he couldn't hear. I saw flies crawling on our grandmother's face and she didn't brush them off; I was frightened. I picked up a palm leaf and chased them.

We walked at night as well as by day. We could see the fires where the white people were cooking in the camps and we could smell the smoke and the meat. We watched the hyenas with their backs that slope as if they're ashamed, slipping through the bush after the smell. If one turned its head, you saw it had big brown shining eyes like our own, when we looked at each other in the dark. The wind brought voices in our own language from the compounds where the people who work in the camps live. A woman among us wanted to go to them at night and ask them to help us. They can give us the food from the dustbins, she said, she started wailing and our grandmother had to grab her and put a hand over her mouth. The men who led us had told us that we must keep out of the way of our people who worked at the Kruger Park; if they helped us they would lose their work. If they saw us, all they could do was pretend we were not there; they had seen only animals.

Sometimes we stopped to sleep for a little while at night. We slept close together. I don't know which night it was—because we were walking, walking, any time, all the time—we heard the lions very near. Not groaning loudly the way they did far off. Panting, like we do when we run, but it's a different kind of panting: you can hear they're not running, they're waiting, somewhere near. We all rolled closer together, on top of each other, the ones on the edge fighting to get into the middle. I was squashed against a woman who smelled bad because she was afraid but I was glad to hold tight on to her. I prayed to God to make the lions take someone on the edge and go. I shut my eyes not to see the tree from which a lion might jump right into the middle of us, where I was. The man who led us jumped up instead, and beat on the tree with a dead branch. He had taught us never to make a sound but he shouted. He shouted at the lions like a drunk man shouting at nobody in our village. The lions went away. We heard them groaning, shouting back at him from far off.

We were tired, so tired. My first-born brother and the man had to lift our grandfather from stone to stone where we found places to cross the rivers. Our grandmother is strong but her feet were bleeding. We could not carry the basket on our heads any longer, we couldn't carry anything except my little brother. We left our things under a bush. As long as our bodies get there, our grandmother said. Then we ate some wild fruit we didn't know from home and our stomachs ran. We were in the grass called elephant grass because it is nearly as tall as an elephant, that day we had those pains, and our grandfather couldn't just get down in front of people like my little brother, he went off into the grass to be on his own. We had to keep up, the man who led us always kept telling us, we must catch up, but we asked him to wait for our grandfather.

So everyone waited for our grandfather to catch up. But he didn't. It was the middle of the day; insects were singing in our ears and we couldn't hear him moving through the grass. We couldn't see him because the grass was so high and he was so small. But he must have been somewhere there inside his loose trousers and his shirt that was torn and our grandmother couldn't sew because she had no cotton. We knew he couldn't have gone far because he was weak and slow. We all went to look for him, but in groups, so we too wouldn't be hidden from each other in that grass. It got into our eyes and noses; we called him softly but the noise of the insects must have filled the little space left for hearing in his ears. We looked and looked but we couldn't find him. We stayed in that long grass all night. In my sleep I found him curled round in a place he had tramped down for himself, like the places we'd seen where the buck hide their babies.

When I woke up he still wasn't anywhere. So we looked again, and by now there were paths we'd made by going through the grass many times, it would be easy for him to find us if we couldn't find him. All that day we just sat and waited. Everything is very quiet when the sun is on your head, inside your head, even if you lie, like the animals, under the trees. I lay on my back and saw those ugly birds with hooked beaks and plucked necks flying round and round above us. We had passed them often where they were feeding on the bones of dead animals, nothing was ever left there for us to eat. Round and round, high up and then lower down and then high again. I saw their necks poking to this side and that. Flying round and round. I saw our grandmother, who sat up all the time with my little brother on her lap, was seeing them, too.

In the afternoon the man who led us came to our grandmother and told her the other people must move on. He said, If their children don't eat soon they will die.

Our grandmother said nothing.

I'll bring you water before we go, he told her.

Our grandmother looked at us, me, my first-born brother, and my little brother on her lap. We watched the other people getting up to leave. I didn't believe the grass would be empty, all around us, where they had been. That we would be alone in this place, the Kruger Park, the police or the animals would find us. Tears came out of my eyes and nose on to my hands but our grandmother took no notice. She got up, with her feet apart the way she puts them when she is going to lift firewood, at home in our village, she swung my little brother on to her back, tied him in her cloth—the top of her dress was torn and her big breasts were showing but there was nothing in them for him. She said, Come.

So we left the place with the long grass. Left behind. We went with the others and the man who led us. We started to go away, again.

There's a very big tent, bigger than a church or a school, tied down to the ground. I didn't understand that was what it would be, when we got there, away. I saw a thing like that the time our mother took us to the town because she heard our soldiers were there and she wanted to ask them if they knew where our father was. In that tent, people were praying and singing. This one is blue and white like that one but it's not for praying and singing, we live in it with other people who've come from our country. Sister from the clinic says we're 200 without counting the babies, and we have new babies, some were born on the way through the Kruger Park.

Inside, even when the sun is bright it's dark and there's a kind of whole village in there. Instead of houses each family has a little place closed off with sacks or cardboard from boxes—whatever we can find—to show the other families it's yours and they shouldn't come in even though there's no door and no windows and no thatch, so that if you're standing up and you're not a small child you can see into everybody's house. Some people have even made paint from ground rocks and drawn designs on the sacks.

Of course, there really is a roof—the tent is the roof, far, high up. It's like a sky. It's like a mountain and we're inside it; through the cracks paths of dust lead down, so thick you think you could climb them. The tent keeps off the rain overhead but the water comes in at the sides and in the little streets between our places—you can only move along them one person at a time—the small kids like my little brother play in the mud. You have to step over them. My little brother doesn't play. Our grandmother takes him to the clinic when the doctor comes on Mondays. Sister says there's something wrong with his head, she thinks it's because we didn't have enough food at home. Because of the war. Because our father wasn't there. And then because he was so hungry in the Kruger Park. He likes just to lie about on our grandmother all day, on her lap or against her somewhere and he looks at us and looks at us. He wants to ask something but you can see he can't. If I tickle him he may just smile. The clinic gives us special powder to make into porridge for him and perhaps one day he'll be all right.

When we arrived we were like him—my first-born brother and I. I can hardly remember. The people who lived in the village near the tent took us to the clinic, it's where you have to sign that you've come—away, through the Kruger Park. We sat on the grass and everything was muddled. One Sister was pretty with her hair straightened and beautiful high-heeled shoes and she brought us the special powder. She said we must mix it with water and drink it slowly. We tore the packets open with our teeth and licked it all up, it stuck round my mouth and I sucked it from my lips and fingers. Some other children who had walked with us vomited. But I only felt everything in my belly moving, the stuff going down and around like a snake, and hiccups hurt me. Another Sister called us to stand in line on the veranda of the clinic but we couldn't. We sat all over the place there, falling against each other: the Sisters helped each of us up by the arm and then stuck a needle in it. Other needles drew our blood into tiny bottles. This was against sickness, but I didn't understand, every time my eyes dropped closed I thought I was walking, the grass was long. I saw the elephants, I didn't know we were away.

But our grandmother was still strong, she could still stand up, she knows how to write and she signed for us. Our grandmother got us this place in the tent against one of the sides, it's the best kind of place there because although the rain comes in, we can lift the flap when the weather is good and then the sun shines on us, the smells in the tent go out. Our grandmother knows a woman here who showed her where there is good grass for sleeping mats, and our grandmother made some for us. Once every month the food truck comes to the clinic. Our grandmother takes along one of the cards she signed and when it has been punched we get a sack of mealie meal. There are wheelbarrows to take it back to the tent: my first-born brother does this for her and then he and the other boys have races, steering the empty wheelbarrows back to the clinic. Sometimes he's lucky and a man who's bought beer in the village gives him money to deliver it—though that's not allowed, you're supposed to take that wheelbarrow straight back to the Sisters. He buys a cold drink and shares it with me if I catch him. On another day, every month, the church leaves a pile of old clothes in the clinic yard. Our grandmother has another card to get punched, and then we can choose something: I have two dresses, two pants and a jersey, so I can go to school.

The people in the village have let us join their school. I was surprised to find they speak our language; our grandmother told me, That's why they allow us to stay on their land. Long ago, in the time of our fathers, there was no fence that kills you, there was no Kruger Park between them and us, we were the same people under our own king, right from our village we left to this place we've come to.

Now that we've been in the tent so long—I have turned eleven and my little brother is nearly three although he is so small, only his head is big, he's not come right in it yet—some people have dug up the bare ground around the tent and planted beans and mealies and cabbage. The old men weave branches to put up fences round their gardens. No one is allowed to look for work in the towns but some of the women have found work in the village and can buy things. Our grandmother, because she's still strong, finds work where people are building houses—in this village the people build nice houses with bricks and cement, not mud like we used to have at our home. Our grandmother carries bricks for these people and fetches baskets of stones on her head. And so she has money to buy sugar and tea and milk and soap. The store gave her a calendar she has hung up on our flap of the tent. I am clever at school and she collected advertising paper people throw away outside the store and covered my school-books with it. She makes my first-born brother and me do our homework every afternoon before it gets dark because there is no room except to lie down, close together, just as we did in the Kruger Park, in our place in the tent, and candles are expensive. Our grandmother hasn't been able to buy herself a pair of shoes for church yet, but she has bought black school shoes and polish to clean them with for my first-born brother and me. Every morning, when people are getting up in the tent, the babies are crying, people are pushing each other at the taps outside and some children are already pulling the crusts of porridge off the pots we ate from last night, my first-born brother and I clean our shoes. Our grandmother makes us sit on our mats with our legs straight out so she can look carefully at our shoes to make sure we have done it properly. No other children in the tent have real school shoes. When we three look at them it's as if we are in a real house again, with no war, no away.

Some white people came to take photographs of our people living in the tent—they said they were making a film, I've never seen what that is though I know about it. A white woman squeezed into our space and asked our grandmother questions which were told to us in our language by someone who understands the white woman's.

"How long have you been living like this?"

"She means here?" Our grandmother said. "In this tent, two years and one month."

"And what do you hope for the future?"

"Nothing. I'm here."

"But for your children?"

"I want them to learn so that they can get good jobs and money."

"Do you hope to go back to your own country?"

"I will not go back."

"But when the war is over—you won't be allowed to stay here? Don't you want to go home?"

I didn't think our grandmother wanted to speak again. I didn't think she was going to answer the white woman. The white woman put her head on one side and smiled at us.

Our grandmother looked away from her and spoke. "There is nothing. No home."

Why does our grandmother say that? Why? I'll go back. I'll go back through that Kruger Park. After the war, if there are no bandits any more, our mother may be waiting for us. And maybe when we left our grandfather, he was only left behind, he found his way somehow, slowly, through the Kruger Park, and he'll be there. They'll be home, and I'll remember them.

1. Take a few minutes to record in your journal your first impressions of the story. You might choose one focus from the following:
   - your feelings for the narrator and the members of her family;
   - scenes and events in the story that are vivid and memorable for you;
   - thoughts and questions you have about the story's context.

   Share your impressions in a small group.
2. Consider the story's point of view. What does it gain from being told from the perspective of a young girl? Suggest an alternative point of view and consider what impact telling the story from that different perspective would have on the story.
3. Why does the author preface the story with the travel advertisement? Why does she include the interview with the filmmaker?
4. What comment is the author making through her story?
5. Consider the grandmother's response to the interviewer. What reasons for her response are suggested in the text? What others can you suggest?
6. Research the historical and geographical context of the story. Then, choose among the following activities:
   a) Consider the future of the narrator and outline a possible sequel to "The Ultimate Safari."
   b) Write an article for a newspaper's travel section about the adventure advertised in the *Observer*. Use current travel articles as models.
   c) Create an outline of the film for which the grandmother was interviewed. Consider first what else might be included, and examine TV documentaries and current affairs shows to see what they contain.

Carol Emshwiller

Pelt

*"This world is all ours.
All we got to do is pick up the pearls."*

She was a white dog with a wide face and eager eyes, and this was the planet Jaxa, in winter.

She trotted well ahead of the master, sometimes nose to ground, sometimes sniffing the air, and she didn't care if they were being watched or not. She knew that strange things skulked behind iced trees, but strangeness was her job. She had been trained for it, and crisp, glittering Jaxa was, she felt, exactly what she had been trained for, *born* for.

I love it, I love it ... that was in her pointing ears, her waving tail ... I *love* this place.

It was a world of ice, a world with the sound of breaking goblets. Each time the wind blew they came shattering down by the trayful, and each time one branch brushed against another it was, "Skoal," "Down the hatch," "The Queen" ... tink, tink, tink. And the sun was reflected as if from a million cut-glass punch bowls under a million crystal chandeliers.

She wore four little black boots, and each step she took sounded like two or three more goblets gone, but the sound was lost in the other tinkling, snapping, cracklings of the silver, frozen forest about her.

She had figured out at last what that hovering scent was. It had been there from the beginning, the landing two days ago, mingling with Jaxa's bitter air and seeming to be just a part of the smell of the place; she found it in criss-crossing trails about the squatting ship, and hanging, heavy and recent, in hollows behind flat-branched, piney-smelling bushes. She thought of honey, and fat men, and dry fur when she smelled it.

There was something big out there, and more than one of them, more than two. She wasn't sure how many. She had a feeling this was something to tell the master, but what was the signal, the agreed-upon noise for: We are being watched? There was a whisper of sound, short and quick, for: Sighted close, come and shoot. And there was a noise for danger (all these through her throat mike to the receiver at the master's ear), a special, howly bark: Awful, awful—there is something awful going to happen. There was even a noise, a low rumble of sound for: Wonderful, wonderful fur—drop everything and come after *this* one. (And she knew a good fur when she saw one. She had been trained to know.) But there was no sign for: We are being watched.

She'd whined and barked when she was sure about it, but that had got her a pat on the head and a rumpling of the neck fur. "You're doing fine, Baby. This world is all ours. All we got to do is pick up the pearls. This is what we've been waiting for." And Jaxa was, so she did her work and didn't try to tell him any more, for what was one more strange thing in one more strange world?

She was on the trail of something now, and the master was behind her, out of sight. He'd better hurry. He'd better hurry or there'll be waiting to do, watching the thing, whatever it is, steady on until he comes, holding tight back, and that will be hard. Hurry, hurry.

She could hear the whispered whistle of a tune through the receiver at her ear and she knew he was not hurrying but just being happy. She ran on, eager, curious. She did not give the signal for hurry, but she made a hurry sound of her own, and she heard him stop whistling and whisper back into the mike, "So, so, Queen of Venus. The furs are waiting to be picked. No hurry, Baby." But morning was to her for hurry. There was time later to be tired and slow.

That fat-man honeyish smell was about, closer and strong. Her curiosity became two-pronged—this smell or that? What *is* the big thing that watches? She kept to the trail she was on, though. Better to be sure, and this thing was not so elusive, not twisting and doubling back, but up ahead and going where it was going.

She topped a rise and half slid, on thick furred rump, down the other side, splattering ice. She snuffled at the bottom to be sure of the smell again, and then, nose to ground, trotted past a thick and tangled hedgerow.

She was thinking through her nose, now. The world was all smell, crisp air, and sour ice, and turpentine pine … and this animal, a urine and brown grass thing … and then, strong in front of her, honey-furry-fat man.

She felt it looming before she raised her head to look, and there it was, the smell in person, some taller than the master and twice as wide. Counting his doubled suit and all, twice as wide.

This was a fur! Wonderful, wonderful. But she just stood, looking up, mouth open and lips pulled back, the fur on the back of her neck rising more from the suddenness than from fear.

It was silver and black, a tiger-striped thing, and the whitish parts glistened and caught the light as the ice of Jaxa did, and sparkled and dazzled in the same way. And there, in the center of the face, was a large and terrible orange eye, rimmed in black with black radiating lines crossing the forehead and rounding the head. That spot of orange dominated the whole figure, but it was a flat, blind eye, unreal, grown out of fur. At first she saw only that spot of color, but then she noticed under it two small, red glinting eyes and they were kind, not terrible.

This was the time for the call: Come, come and get the great fur, for the richest lady on earth to wear and be dazzling in and, most of all, to pay for. But there was something about the flat, black nose and the tender, bow-shaped lips, and those kind eyes that stopped her from calling. Something masterly. She was full of wondering and indecision and she made no sound at all.

The thing spoke to her then, and its voice was a deep lullaby sound of buzzing cellos. It gestured with a thick, fur-backed hand. It promised, offered, and asked; and she listened, knowing and not knowing.

The words came slowly.

This … is … world.

Here is the sky, the earth, the ice. The heavy arms moved. The hands pointed.

We have watched you, little slave. What have you done that is free today? Take the liberty. Here is the earth for your four-shoed feet, the sky of stars, the ice to drink. Do something free today. Do, do.

Nice voice, she thought, nice thing. It gives and gives ... something.

Her ears pointed forward, then to the side, one and then the other, and then forward again. She cocked her head, but the real meaning would not come clear. She poked at the air with her nose.

Say that again, her whole body said. I almost have it. I *feel* it. Say it once more and maybe then the sense of it will come.

But the creature turned and started away quickly, very quickly for such a big thing. It seemed to shimmer itself away until the glitter was only the glitter of the ice and the black was only the thick, flat branches.

The master was close. She could hear his crackling steps coming up behind her.

She whined softly, more to herself than to him.

"Ho, Queenie. Have you lost it?" She sniffed the ground again. The honey-furry smell was strong. She sniffed beyond, zigzagging. The trail was there. "Go to it, Baby." She loped off to a sound like Chinese wind chimes, businesslike again. Her tail hung guiltily, though, and she kept her head low. She had missed an important signal. She'd waited until it was too late. But was the thing a master? Or a fur? She wanted to do the right thing. She always tried and tried for that, but now she was confused.

She was getting close to whatever it was she trailed, but the hovering smell was still there too, though not close. She thought of gifts. She knew that much from the slow, lullaby words, and gifts made her think of bones and meat, not the dry fishy biscuit she always got on trips like this. A trickle of drool flowed from the side of her mouth and froze in a silver thread across her shoulder.

She slowed. The thing she trailed must be *there*, just behind the next row of trees. She made a sound in her throat ... ready, steady ... and she advanced until she was sure. She sensed the shape. She didn't really see it ... mostly it was the smell and something more in the tinkling glassware noises. She gave the signal and stood still, a furry, square imitation of a pointer. Come, hurry. This waiting is the hardest part.

He followed, beamed to her radio. "Steady, Baby. Hold that pose. Good girl, good girl!" There was only the slightest twitch of her tail as she wagged it, answering him in her mind.

He came up behind her and then passed, crouched, holding the rifle-rod before him, elbows bent. He knelt then, and waited as if at a point of his own, rod to shoulder. Slowly he turned with the moving shadow of the beast, and shot, twice in quick succession.

They ran forward then, together, and it was what she had expected—a deerlike thing, dainty hoofs, proud head, and spotted in three colors, large gray-green rounds on tawny yellow, with tufts of that same glittering silver scattered over.

The master took out a flat-bladed knife. He began to whistle out loud as he cut off the handsome head. His face was flushed.

She sat down nearby, mouth open in a kind of smile, and she watched his face as he worked. The warm smell made the drool come at the sides of her mouth and drip out to freeze on the ice and on her paws, but she sat quietly, only watching.

Between the whistlings he grunted, and swore, and talked to himself, and finally he had the skin and the head in a tight inside-out bundle.

Then he came to her and patted her sides with a flat, slap sound, and he scratched behind her ears and held a biscuit for her on his thick-gloved palm. She swallowed it whole and then watched him as he squatted on his heels and ate one almost like it.

Then he got up and slung the bundle of skin and head across his back. "I'll take this one, Baby. Come on, let's get one more something before lunch." He waved her to the right. "We'll make a big circle," he said.

She trotted out, glad she was not carrying anything. She found a strong smell at a patch of discolored ice and urinated on it. She sniffed and growled at a furry, mammal-smelling bird that landed in the trees above her and sent a shower of ice slivers down on her head. She zigzagged and then turned and bit, lips drawn back in mock rage, at a branch that scraped her side.

She followed for a while the chattery sound of water streaming along under the ice, and left it where an oily, lambish smell crossed. Almost immediately she came upon them—six small, greenish balls of wool with floppy, woolly feet. The honey-fat man smell was strong here too, but she signaled for the lambs, the "Come and shoot" sound, and she stood again waiting for the master.

"*Good* girl!" His voice has special praise. "By God, this place is a gold mine. Hold it, Queen of Venus. Whatever it is, don't let go."

There was a fifty-yard clear view here and she stood in plain sight of the little creatures, but they didn't notice. The master came slowly and cautiously, and knelt beside her. Just as he did, there appeared at the far end of the clearing a glittering silver and black tiger-striped creature.

She heard the sharp inward breath of the master and she felt the tenseness come to him. There was a new, faint whiff of sour sweat, and a special way of breathing. What she felt from him made the fur rise along her back with a mixture of excitement and fear.

The tiger thing held a small packet in one hand and was peering into it and pulling at the opening in it with a blunt finger. Suddenly there was a sweep of motion beside her and five fast, frantic pops sounded sharp in her ear. Two came after the honey-fat man had already fallen and lay like a huge, decorated sack.

The master ran forward and she came at his heels. They both stopped, not too close, and she watched the master looking at the big, dead, tiger head with the terrible eye. The master was breathing hard. His face was red and puffy. He didn't whistle or talk. After a time he took out his knife. He tested the blade, making a small, bloody thread of a mark on his left thumb. Then he walked closer, and she stood, and watched him, and whispered a questioning whine.

He stooped by the honey-fat master and it was that small, partly opened packet that he cut viciously through the center. Small round chunks fell out, bite-sized chunks of dried meat, and a cheesy substance, and some broken bits of clear, bluish ice.

The master kicked at them. His face was not red anymore, but pale. His mouth was open in a grin that was not a grin.

He went about the skinning then.

He did not keep the flat-faced, heavy head nor the blunt-fingered hands.

The master had to make a sliding thing of two of the widest kind of flat branches to carry the new heavy fur, as well as the head and the skin of the deer. Then he started directly for the ship.

It was past eating time but she looked at his restless eyes and did not ask about it. She walked in front of him, staying close. She looked back often, watching him pull the sled by the string across his shoulder and she knew, by the way he held the rod before him in both hands, that she should be wary.

Sometimes the damp-looking, inside-out bundle hooked on things, and the master would curse in a whisper and pull at it. She could see the bundle made him tired, and she wished he would stop for a rest and food as they usually did long before this time.

They went slowly, and the smell of honey-fat master hovered as it had from the beginning. They crossed the trails of many animals. They even saw another deer run off, but she knew that it was not a time for chasing.

Then another big silver and black tiger stood exactly before them. It appeared suddenly, as if actually it had been standing there all the time, and they had not been near enough to pick it out from its glistening background.

It just stood and looked and dared, and the master held his rifle rod with both hands and looked too, and she stood between them glancing from one face to the other. She knew, after a moment, that the master would not shoot, and it seemed the tiger thing knew too, for it turned to look at her and it raised its arms and spread its fingers as if grasping at the forest on each side. It swayed a bit, like bigness off balance, and then it spoke in its tight-strung, cello tones. The words and the tone seemed the same as before.

Little slave, what have you done that is free today? Remember this is world. Do something free today. Do, do.

She knew that what it said was important to it, something she should understand, a giving and a taking away. It watched her, and she looked back with wide eyes, wanting to do the right thing, but not knowing what.

The tiger-fat master turned then, this time slowly, and left a wide back for the master and her to see, and then it half turned, throwing a quick glance at the two of them over the heavy humped shoulder. Then it moved slowly away into the trees and ice, and the master still held the rifle rod with two hands and did not move.

The evening wind began to blow, and there sounded about them that sound of a million chandeliers tinkling like gigantic wind chimes. A furry bird, the size of a shrew and as fast, flew by between them with a miniature shriek.

She watched the master's face and, when he was ready, she went along beside him. The soft sounds the honey-fat master had made echoed in her mind but had no meaning.

That night the master stretched the big skin on a frame and afterward he watched the dazzle of it. He didn't talk to her. She watched him a while and then she turned around three times on her rug and lay down.

The next morning the master was slow, reluctant to go out. He studied charts of other places, round or hourglass-shaped maps with yellow dots and labels, and he drank his coffee standing up looking at them. But finally they did go out, squinting into the ringing air.

It was her world. More each day, right feel, right temperature, lovely smells. She darted on ahead as usual, yet not too far today, and sometimes she stopped and waited and looked at the master's face as he came up. And sometimes she would whine a question before she went on … Why don't you walk brisk, brisk, and call me Queen of Venus, or Bitch of Betelgeuse? Why don't you sniff like I do? Sniff, and you will be happy … And she would run on again.

Trails were easy to find, and once more she found the oily lamb smell, and once more came upon them quickly. The master strode up beside her and raised his rifle rod … but a moment later he turned, carelessly, letting himself make a loud noise, and the lambs ran. He made a face, and spat upon the ice. "Come on Queenie. Let's get out of here. I'm sick of this place."

He turned and made the signal to go back, pointing with his thumb above his head in two jerks of motion.

But why, why? This is morning now and our world. She wagged her tail and gave a short bark, and looked at him, dancing a little on her back paws, begging with her whole body.

"Come on," he said.

She turned then, and took her place at his heel, head low, but eyes looking up at him, wondering if she had done something wrong, and wanting to be right, and noticed, and loved because he was troubled and preoccupied.

They'd gone only a few minutes on the way back when he stopped suddenly in the middle of a step, slowly put both feet flat upon the ground and stood like a soldier at a stiff, off-balance attention. There, lying in the way before them, was the huge, orange-eyed head and in front of it, as if at the end of outstretched arms, lay two leathery hands, the hairless palms up.

She made a growl deep in her throat and the master made a noise almost exactly like hers. She waited for him, standing as he stood, not moving, feeling his tenseness coming in to her. Yet it was just a head and two hands of no value, old ones they had had before and thrown away.

He turned and she saw a wild look in his eyes. He walked with deliberate steps, and she followed, in a wide circle about the spot. When they had skirted the place, he began to walk very fast.

They were not far from the ship. She could see its flat blackness as they drew nearer to the clearing, the burned, iceless pit of spewed and blackened earth. And then she saw that the silver tiger masters were there, nine of them in a wide circle, each with the honey-damp fur smell, but each with a separate particular sweetness.

The master was still walking very fast, eyes down to watch his footing, and he did not see them until he was in the circle before them all, as they stood there like nine upright bears in tiger suits.

He stopped and made a whisper of a groan, and he let the rifle rod fall low in one hand so that it hung loose with the end almost touching the ground. He looked from one to the other and she looked at him, watching his pale eyes move along the circle.

"Stay," he said, and then he began to go toward the ship at an awkward limp, running and walking at the same time, banging the rifle rod handle against the air lock as he entered.

He had said, "Stay." She sat watching the ship door and moving her front paws up and down because she wanted to be walking after him. He was gone only a minute, though, and when he came back it was without the rod and he was holding the great fur with cut pieces of thongs dangling like ribbons along its edges where it had been tied to the stretching frame. He went at that same run-walk, unbalanced by the heavy bundle, to one of them along the circle. Three gathered together before him and refused to take it back. They pushed it, bunched loosely, back across his arms and to it they added another large and heavy package in a parchment bag, and the master stood, with his legs wide to hold it all.

Then one honey-fat master motioned with a fur-backed hand to the ship and the bundles, and then to the ship and the master, and then to the sky. He made two sharp sounds once, and then again. And another made two different sounds, and she felt the feeling of them ... Take your things and go home. Take them, these and these, and go.

They turned to her then and one spoke and made a wide gesture. *This is world. The sky, the earth, the ice.*

They wanted her to stay. They gave her ... was it their world? But what good was a world?

She wagged her tail hesitantly, lowered her head, and looked up at them ... I do want to do right, to please everybody, everybody, but ... Then she followed the master into the ship.

The locks rumbled shut. She took her place, flat on her side, take-off position. The master snapped the flat plastic sheet over her, covering head and all and, in a few minutes, they roared off.

Afterward he opened the parchment bag. She knew what was in it. She knew he knew too, but she knew by the smell. He opened it and dumped out the head and the hands.

She saw him almost put the big head out the waste chute, but he didn't. He took it into the place where he kept good heads and some odd paws or hoofs, and he put it by the others there.

Even she knew this head was different. The others were slantbrowed like she was and most had jutting snouts. This one was bigger even than the big ones, with its heavy, ruffed fur and huge eye staring, and more grand than any of them, more terrible ... and yet a flat face, with a delicate black nose and tender lips. The tenderest lips of all.

1. Take a few minutes to record in your journal your first impressions of the story. You might choose one focus from the following:
   - your feelings for the characters in the story;
   - the most vivid or memorable portions of the story;
   - thoughts and questions you have about the characters and setting.

   Share your impressions in a small group.
2. For each of the following, develop character sketches and note if (and, if so, how) your view changed of the character(s):
   - the dog;
   - her master;
   - the "honey-fat men."

   What phrases from the story best describe each?
3. Explain the conclusion of the story. Why did the honey-fat men take to the hunter the head and hands of his kill? Why did the hunter act as he did?
4. As told from the dog's viewpoint, the story leaves many ambiguities. Why would the author choose this point of view? What comments does the story seem to make? Explain.
5. In a small group, improvise the scene in which the honey-fat men decide to visit the hunter. Share your scene with the class.
6. Choose one of the following activities:
   a) Write the ship log entry that the hunter would write after take-off.
   b) Reflect upon, perhaps research, then present your ideas about an issue that the story encouraged you to consider or reconsider.

4

Theme and Interpretation

After seeing a movie with friends or family, we might spend some time sharing our responses to the movie—discussing the characters, the chase scene, special effects, and so on. As our discussion progresses, we might consider such questions as, "Well, so what? What was it all about? What does it say to me?" Similarly, after reading a story, we respond to various elements, details, and techniques of the story, but we also consider what to us is the theme, the central idea or the focus of the story.

In stories written chiefly to entertain readers, themes tend to get little attention; they are usually clichéd and familiar, such as "Crime doesn't pay" in an action-packed police story. However, in stories written to change us, to make us think deeply, to offer a comment on life, writers often present less familiar ideas. In such stories, themes are of great significance—for both writers and readers.

Because each reader is unique, one story will affect each of us differently, particularly on our first reading. Some readers, for example, might identify strongly with a character's predicament and actions, while other readers might be merely curious about the outcome of the conflict. By sharing and refining many responses to that story, we can move toward fuller interpretations and greater understandings of theme.

We must be careful not to regard the search for theme as an obligation to reduce every story to a single observation about life. Rather, an understanding of theme should emerge naturally from our individual interpretations of the story. Stating theme is a way for us to share, clarify, and compare our interpretations of a story. Having done that, we can examine how the parts of that story work together to communicate theme. Then, we might consider how significant the story is for us and for other readers. The final question for each reader, then, might be this: "What, in my life, does this story illuminate?"

The four stories in this unit will challenge readers to interpret stories and to reflect upon their themes. Shirley Jackson's powerful story, "The Lottery," explores tradition and change in society as well as the actions of groups and individuals. A group's actions and motivations are also the subject of Graham Greene's "The Destructors"; in it a gang destroys a home that had been spared by World War II. In "Invitations," a series of social invitations first attract, then repel the protagonist. Just as she questions her values and the expectations of society, so may we. The final story, "The Pigeons in St. Louis Square," juxtaposes human change and fragility with nature and its recurring cycles.

All four stories provide pathways to deeper understanding of ourselves, others around us, and life in general.

Shirley Jackson

The Lottery

"It's not the way it used to be," Old Man Warner said clearly. "People ain't the way they used to be."

The morning of June 27th was clear and sunny, with the fresh warmth of a full-summer day; the flowers were blossoming profusely and the grass was richly green. The people of the village began to gather in the square, between the post office and the bank, around ten o'clock; in some towns there were so many people that the lottery took two days and had to be started on June 26th, but in this village, where there were only about three hundred people, the whole lottery took less than two hours, so it could begin at ten o'clock in the morning and still be through in time to allow the villagers to get home for noon dinner.

The children assembled first, of course. School was recently over for the summer, and the feeling of liberty sat uneasily on most of them; they tended to gather together quietly for a while before they broke into boisterous play, and their talk was still of the classroom and the teacher, of books and reprimands. Bobby Martin had already stuffed his pockets full of stones, and the other boys soon followed his example, selecting the smoothest and roundest stones; Bobby and Harry Jones and Dickie Delacroix—the villagers pronounced this name "Dellacroy"—eventually made a great pile of stones in one corner of the square and guarded it against the raids of the other boys. The girls stood aside, talking among themselves, looking over their shoulders at the boys, and the very small children rolled in the dust or clung to the hands of their older brothers or sisters.

Soon the men began to gather, surveying their own children, speaking of planting and rain, tractors and taxes. They stood together, away from the pile of stones in the corner, and their jokes were quiet and they smiled rather than laughed. The women, wearing faded house dresses and sweaters, came shortly after their menfolk. They greeted one another and exchanged bits of gossip as they went to join their husbands. Soon the women, standing by their husbands, began to call to their children, and the children came reluctantly, having to be called four or five times. Bobby Martin ducked under his mother's grasping hand and ran, laughing, back to the pile of stones. His father spoke up sharply, and Bobby came quickly and took his place between his father and his oldest brother.

The lottery was conducted—as were the square dances, the teen-age club, the Halloween program—by Mr. Summers, who had time and energy to devote to civic activities. He was a round-faced, jovial man and he ran the coal business, and people were sorry for him, because he had no children and his wife was a scold. When he arrived in the square, carrying the black wooden box, there was a murmur of conversation among the villagers, and he waved and called, "Little late today, folks." The postmaster, Mr. Graves, followed him, carrying a three-legged stool, and the stool was put in the center of the square and Mr. Summers set the black box down on it. The villagers kept their distance, leaving a space between themselves and the stool, and when Mr. Summers said, "Some of you fellows want to give me a hand?" there was a hesitation before two men, Mr. Martin and his oldest son, Baxter, came forward to hold the box steady on the stool while Mr. Summers stirred up the papers inside it.

The original paraphernalia for the lottery had been lost long ago, and the black box now resting on the stool had been put into use even before Old Man Warner, the oldest man in town, was born. Mr. Summers spoke frequently to the villagers about making a new box, but no one liked to upset even as much tradition as was represented by the black box. There was a story that the present box had been made with some pieces of the box that had preceded it, the one that had been constructed when the first people settled down to make a village here. Every year, after the lottery, Mr. Summers began talking again about a new box, but every year the subject was allowed to fade off without anything being done. The black box grew shabbier each year; by now it was no longer completely black but splintered badly along one side to show the original wood color, and in some places faded or stained.

Mr. Martin and his oldest son, Baxter, held the black box securely on the stool until Mr. Summers had stirred the papers thoroughly with his hand. Because so much of the ritual had been forgotten or discarded, Mr. Summers had been successful in having slips of paper substituted for the chips of wood that had been used for generations. Chips of wood, Mr. Summers had argued, had been very well when the village was tiny, but now that the population was more than three hundred and likely to keep on growing, it was necessary to use something that would fit more easily into the black box. The night before the lottery, Mr. Summers and Mr. Graves made up the slips of paper and put them in the box, and it was then taken to the safe of Mr. Summers' coal company and locked up until Mr. Summers was ready to take it to the square next morning. The rest of the year, the box was put away, sometimes one place, sometimes another; it had spent one year in Mr. Graves's barn and another year underfoot in the post office, and sometimes it was set on a shelf in the Martin grocery and left there.

There was a great deal of fussing to be done before Mr. Summers declared the lottery open. There were the lists to make up—of heads of families, heads of households in each family, members of each household in each family. There was the proper swearing-in of Mr. Summers by the postmaster, as the official of the lottery; at one time, some people remembered, there had been a recital of some sort, performed by the official of the lottery, a perfunctory, tuneless chant that had been rattled off duly each year; some people believed that the official of the lottery used to stand just so when he said or sang it, others believed that he was supposed to walk among the people, but years and years ago this part of the ritual had been allowed to lapse. There had been, also, a ritual salute, which the official of the lottery had had to use in addressing each person who came up to draw from the box, but this also had changed with time, until now it was felt necessary only for the official to speak to each person approaching. Mr. Summers was very good at all this; in his clean white shirt and blue jeans, with one hand resting carelessly on the black box, he seemed very proper and important as he talked interminably to Mr. Graves and the Martins.

Just as Mr. Summers finally left off talking and turned to the assembled villagers, Mrs. Hutchinson came hurriedly along the path to the square, her sweater thrown over her shoulders, and slid into place in the back of the crowd. "Clean forgot what day it was," she said to Mrs. Delacroix, who stood next to her, and they both laughed softly. "Thought my old man was out back stacking wood," Mrs. Hutchinson went on, "and then I looked out the window and the kids were gone, and then I remembered it was the twenty-seventh and came a-running." She dried her hands on her apron, and Mrs. Delacroix said, "You're in time, though. They're still talking away up there."

Mrs. Hutchinson craned her neck to see through the crowd and found her husband and children standing near the front. She tapped Mrs. Delacroix on the arm as a farewell and began to make her way through the crowd. The people separated good-humoredly to let her through; two or three people said, in voices just loud enough to be heard across the crowd, "Here comes your Missus, Hutchinson," and "Bill, she made it after all." Mrs. Hutchinson reached her husband, and Mr. Summers, who had been waiting, said cheerfully, "Thought we were going to have to get on without you, Tessie." Mrs. Hutchinson said, grinning, "Wouldn't have me leave m'dishes in the sink, now, would you, Joe?" and soft laughter ran through the crowd as the people stirred back into position after Mrs. Hutchinson's arrival.

"Well, now," Mr. Summers said soberly, "guess we better get started, get this over with, so's we can go back to work. Anybody ain't here?"

"Dunbar," several people said. "Dunbar, Dunbar."

Mr. Summers consulted his list. "Clyde Dunbar," he said. "That's right. He's broke his leg, hasn't he? Who's drawing for him?"

"Me, I guess," a woman said, and Mr. Summers turned to look at her. "Wife draws for her husband," Mr. Summers said. "Don't you have a grown boy to do it for you, Janey?" Although Mr. Summers and everyone else in the village knew the answer perfectly well, it was the business of the official of the lottery to ask such questions formally. Mr. Summers waited with an expression of polite interest while Mrs. Dunbar answered.

"Horace's not but sixteen yet," Mrs. Dunbar said regretfully. "Guess I gotta fill in for the old man this year."

"Right," Mr. Summers said. He made a note on the list he was holding. Then he asked, "Watson boy drawing this year?"

A tall boy in the crowd raised his hand. "Here," he said. "I'm drawing for m'mother and me." He blinked his eyes nervously and ducked his head as several voices in the crowd said things like "Good fellow, Jack," and "Glad to see your mother's got a man to do it."

"Well," Mr. Summers said, "guess that's everyone. Old Man Warner make it?"

"Here," a voice said, and Mr. Summers nodded.

A sudden hush fell on the crowd as Mr. Summers cleared his throat and looked at the list. "All ready?" he called. "Now, I'll read the names—heads of families first—and the men come up and take a paper out of the box. Keep the paper folded in your hand without looking at it until everyone has had a turn. Everything clear?"

The people had done it so many times that they only half listened to the directions; most of them were quiet, wetting their lips, not looking around. Then Mr. Summers raised one hand high and said, "Adams." A man disengaged himself from the crowd and came forward. "Hi, Steve," Mr. Summers said, and Mr. Adams said, "Hi, Joe." They grinned at one another humorlessly and nervously. Then Mr. Adams reached into the black box and took out a folded paper. He held it firmly by one corner as he turned and went hastily back to his place in the crowd, where he stood a little apart from his family, not looking down at his hand.

"Allen," Mr. Summer said. "Anderson.... Bentham."

"Seems like there's no time at all between lotteries any more," Mrs. Delacroix said to Mrs. Graves in the back row. "Seems like we got through with the last one only last week."

"Time sure goes fast," Mrs. Graves said.

"Clark.... Delacroix."

"There goes my old man," Mrs. Delacroix said. She held her breath while her husband went forward.

"Dunbar," Mr. Summers said, and Mrs. Dunbar went steadily to the box while one of the women said, "Go on, Janey," and another said, "There she goes."

"We're next," Mrs. Graves said. She watched while Mr. Graves came around from the side of the box, greeted Mr. Summers gravely, and selected a slip of paper from the box. By now, all through the crowd there were men holding the small folded papers in their large hands, turning them over and over nervously. Mrs. Dunbar and her two sons stood together, Mrs. Dunbar holding the slip of paper.

"Harburt.... Hutchinson."

"Get up there, Bill," Mrs. Hutchinson said, and the people near her laughed.

"Jones."

"They do say," Mr. Adams said to Old Man Warner, who stood next to him, "that over in the north village they're talking of giving up the lottery."

Old Man Warner snorted. "Pack of crazy fools," he said. "Listening to the young folks, nothing's good enough for *them.* Next thing you know, they'll be wanting to go back to living in caves, nobody work any more, live *that* way for a while. Used to be a saying about 'Lottery in June, corn be heavy soon.' First thing you know, we'd all be eating stewed chickweed and acorns. There's *always* been a lottery," he added petulantly. "Bad enough to see young Joe Summers up there joking with everybody."

"Some places have already quit lotteries," Mrs. Adams said.

"Nothing but trouble in *that,*" Old Man Warner said stoutly. "Pack of young fools."

"Martin." And Bobby Martin watched his father go forward.

"Overdyke.... Percy."

"I wish they'd hurry," Mrs. Dunbar said to her older son. "I wish they'd hurry."

"They're almost through," her son said.

"You get ready to run tell Dad," Mrs. Dunbar said.

Mr. Summers called his own name and then stepped forward precisely and selected a slip from the box. Then he called, "Warner."

"Seventy-seventh year I been in the lottery," Old Man Warner said as he went through the crowd. "Seventy-seventh time."

"Watson." The tall boy came awkwardly through the crowd. Someone said, "Don't be nervous, Jack," and Mr. Summers said, "Take your time, son."

"Zanini."

After that, there was a long pause, a breathless pause, unt Mr. Summers, holding his slip of paper in the air, said, "A[illegible] fellows." For a minute, no one moved, and then all the slips of paper were opened. Suddenly, all the women began to speak at once, saying, "Who is it?" "Who's got it?" "Is it the Dunbars?" "Is it the Watsons?" Then the voices began to say, "It's Hutchinson. It's Bill," "Bill Hutchinson's got it."

"Go tell your father," Mrs. Dunbar said to her older son.

People began to look around to see the Hutchinsons. Bill Hutchinson was standing quiet, staring down at the paper in his hand. Suddenly, Tessie Hutchinson shouted to Mr. Summers, "You didn't give him time enough to take any paper he wanted. I saw you. It wasn't fair."

"Be a good sport, Tessie," Mrs. Delacroix called, and Mrs. Graves said, "All of us took the same chance."

"Shut up, Tessie," Bill Hutchinson said.

"Well, everyone," Mr. Summers said, "that was done pretty fast, and now we've got to be hurrying a little more to get done in time." He consulted his next list. "Bill," he said, "you draw for the Hutchinson family. You got any other households in the Hutchinsons?"

"There's Don and Eva," Mrs. Hutchinson yelled. "Make *them* take their chance!"

"Daughters draw with their husbands' families, Tessie," Mr. Summers said gently. "You know that as well as anyone else."

"It wasn't *fair*," Tessie said.

"I guess not, Joe," Bill Hutchinson said regretfully. "My daughter draws with her husband's family, that's only fair. And I've got no other family except the kids."

"Then, as far as drawing for families is concerned, it's you," Mr. Summers said in explanation, "and as far as drawing for households is concerned, that's you, too. Right?"

"Right," Bill Hutchinson said.

"How many kids, Bill?" Mr. Summers asked formally.

"Three," Bill Hutchinson said. "There's Bill, Jr., and Nancy, and little Dave. And Tessie and me."

"All right, then," Mr. Summers said. "Harry, you got their tickets back?"

Mr. Graves nodded and held up the slips of paper. "Put them in the box, then," Mr. Summers directed. "Take Bill's and put it in."

"I think we ought to start over," Mrs. Hutchinson said, as quietly as she could. "I tell you it wasn't *fair.* You didn't give him time enough to choose. *Every*body saw that."

Mr. Graves had selected the five slips and put them in the box, and he dropped all the papers but those onto the ground, where the breeze caught them and lifted them off.

"Listen, everybody," Mrs. Hutchinson was saying to the people around her.

"Ready, Bill?" Mr. Summers asked, and Bill Hutchinson, with one quick glance around at his wife and children, nodded.

"Remember," Mr. Summers said, "take the slips and keep them folded until each person has taken one. Harry, you help little Dave." Mr. Graves took the hand of the little boy, who came willingly with him up to the box. "Take a paper out of the box, Davy," Mr. Summers said. Davy put his hand into the box and laughed. "Take just *one* paper," Mr. Summers said. "Harry, you hold it for him." Mr. Graves took the child's hand and removed the folded paper from the tight fist and held it while little Dave stood next to him and looked up at him wonderingly.

"Nancy next," Mr. Summers said. Nancy was twelve, and her school friends breathed heavily as she went forward, switching her skirt, and took a slip daintily from the box. "Bill, Jr.," Mr. Summers said, and Billy, his face red and his feet over-large, nearly knocked the box over as he got a paper out. "Tessie," Mr. Summers said. She hesitated for a minute, looking around defiantly, and then set her lips and went up to the box. She snatched a paper out and held it behind her.

"Bill," Mr. Summers said, and Bill Hutchinson reached into the box and felt around, bringing his hand out at last with the slip of paper in it.

The crowd was quiet. A girl whispered, "I hope it's not Nancy," and the sound of the whisper reached the edges of the crowd.

"It's not the way it used to be," Old Man Warner said clearly. "People ain't the way they used to be."

"All right," Mr. Summers said. "Open the papers. Harry, you open little Dave's."

Mr. Graves opened the slip of paper and there was a general sigh through the crowd as he held it up and everyone could see that it was blank. Nancy and Bill, Jr., opened theirs at the same time, and both beamed and laughed, turning around to the crowd and holding their slips of paper above their heads.

"Tessie," Mr. Summers said. There was a pause, and then Mr. Summers looked at Bill Hutchinson, and Bill unfolded his paper and showed it. It was blank.

"It's Tessie," Mr. Summers said, and his voice was hushed. "Show us her paper, Bill."

Bill Hutchinson went over to his wife and forced the slip of paper out of her hand. It had a black spot on it, the black spot Mr. Summers had made the night before with the heavy pencil in the coal-company office. Bill Hutchinson held it up, and there was a stir in the crowd.

"All right, folks," Mr. Summers said. "Let's finish quickly."

Although the villagers had forgotten the ritual and lost the original black box, they still remembered to use stones. The pile of stones the boys had made earlier was ready; there were stones on the ground with the blowing scraps of paper that had come out of the box. Mrs. Delacroix selected a stone so large she had to pick it up with both hands and turned to Mrs. Dunbar. "Come on," she said. "Hurry up."

Mrs. Dunbar had small stones in both hands, and she said, gasping for breath, "I can't run at all. You'll have to go ahead and I'll catch up with you."

The children had stones already, and someone gave little Davy Hutchinson a few pebbles.

Tessie Hutchinson was in the center of a cleared space by now, and she held her hands out desperately as the villagers moved in on her. "It isn't fair," she said. A stone hit her on the side of the head.

Old Man Warner was saying, "Come on, come on, everyone." Steve Adams was in the front of the crowd of villagers, with Mrs. Graves beside him.

"It isn't fair, it isn't right," Mrs. Hutchinson screamed, and then they were upon her.

1. In your response journal, record your thoughts, feelings, or reactions to the story. You might choose one focus from the following:
   - your feelings about the story's ending;
   - any questions you would like to ask the author;
   - any events, other stories, or movies that "The Lottery" brings to mind.

   In a small group, share and discuss your journal entries. Summarize for the class key points of your discussion.
2. The story begins with the suggestion of idyllic country life. With a partner, note the ominous signs which accumulate, foreshadowing later conflicts.
3. The impact of the story depends on Jackson creating a recognizable, congenial setting, then placing within it a horrifying event. What is her purpose in doing this? What social comments does Jackson seem to be making?
4. Ironically, Tessie Hutchinson is the "winner" of the lottery. Discuss
   - how Tessie first views the lottery and the changes in her views;
   - Old Man Warner's views;
   - the views implicit in the actions of other villages.

   Suggest the reasons for each view.
5. Examine the many symbols in the story. How does Jackson use symbolism to express theme?
6. Choose between the following activities:
   a) Consider the ritual sacrifice of Tessie. For what is she being sacrificed? Is she a scapegoat? List similar activities you have you heard of from the distant past, the recent past, and the present (e.g., bullfighting). Critically examine one and present your information and opinions to the class.
   b) Consider the theme of the story. Do you agree or disagree with it? Why? Support your argument with examples from current events, history, literature, and/or mass media.

Note: For the author's thoughts and a critic's essay, see pages 273 and 284 in the unit "Perspectives on Story."

Graham Greene

The Destructors

"We'd be like worms, don't you see, in an apple. When we came out again there'd be nothing there ..."

1

It was on the eve of August Bank Holiday that the latest recruit became the leader of the Wormsley Common Gang. No one was surprised except Mike, but Mike at the age of nine was surprised by everything. "If you don't shut your mouth," somebody once said to him, "you'll get a frog down it." After that Mike had kept his teeth tightly clamped except when the surprise was too great.

The new recruit had been with the gang since the beginning of the summer holidays, and there were possibilities about his brooding silence that all recognised. He never wasted a word even to tell his name until that was required of him by the rules. When he said "Trevor" it was a statement of fact, not as it would have been with the others a statement of shame or defiance. Nor did anyone laugh except Mike, who finding himself without support and meeting the dark gaze of the newcomer opened his mouth and was quiet again. There was every reason why T., as he was afterwards referred to, should have been an object of mockery—there was his name (and they substituted the initial because otherwise they had no excuse not to laugh at it), the fact that his father, a former architect and present clerk, had "come down in the world" and that his mother considered herself better than the neighbours. What but an odd quality of danger, of the unpredictable, established him in the gang without any ignoble ceremony of initiation?

The gang met every morning in an impromptu car-park, the site of the last bomb of the first blitz. The leader, who was known as

Blackie, claimed to have heard it fall, and no one was precise enough in his dates to point out that he would have been one year old and fast asleep on the down platform of Wormsley Common Underground Station. On one side of the car-park leant the first occupied house, No. 3, of the shattered Northwood Terrace—literally leant, for it had suffered from the blast of the bomb and the side walls were supported on wooden struts. A smaller bomb and some incendiaries had fallen beyond, so that the house stuck up like a jagged tooth and carried on the further wall relics of its neighbour, a dado, the remains of a fireplace. T., whose words were almost confined to voting "Yes" or "No" to the plan of operations proposed each day by Blackie, once startled the whole gang by saying broodingly, "Wren built that house, father says."

"Who's Wren?"

"The man who built St. Paul's."

"Who cares?" Blackie said. "It's only Old Misery's."

Old Misery—whose real name was Thomas—had once been a builder and decorator. He lived alone in the crippled house, doing for himself: once a week you could see him coming back across the common with bread and vegetables, and once as the boys played in the car-park he put his head over the smashed wall of his garden and looked at them.

"Been to the loo," one of the boys said, for it was common knowledge that since the bombs fell something had gone wrong with the pipes of the house and Old Misery was too mean to spend money on the property. He could do the redecorating himself at cost price, but he had never learnt plumbing. The loo was a wooden shed at the bottom of the narrow garden with a star-shaped hole in the door: it had escaped the blast which had smashed the house next door and sucked out the window-frames of No. 3.

The next time the gang became aware of Mr. Thomas was more surprising. Blackie, Mike and a thin yellow boy, who for some reason was called by his surname Summers, met him on the common coming back from the market. Mr. Thomas stopped them. He said glumly, "You belong to the lot that play in the car-park?"

Mike was about to answer when Blackie stopped him. As the leader he had responsibilities. "Suppose we are?" he said ambiguously.

"I got some chocolates," Mr.Thomas said. "Don't like 'em myself. Here you are. Not enough to go round, I don't suppose. There never is," he added with sombre conviction. He handed over three packets of Smarties.

The gang were puzzled and perturbed by this action and tried to explain it away. "Bet someone dropped them and he picked 'em up," somebody suggested.

"Pinched 'em and then got in a bleeding funk," another thought aloud.

"It's a bribe," Summers said. "He wants us to stop bouncing balls on his wall."

"We'll show him we don't take bribes," Blackie said, and they sacrificed the whole morning to the game of bouncing that only Mike was young enough to enjoy. There was no sign from Mr. Thomas.

Next day T. astonished them all. He was late at the rendezvous, and the voting for that day's exploit took place without him. At Blackie's suggestion the gang was to disperse in pairs, take buses at random and see how many free rides could be snatched from unwary conductors (the operation was to be carried out in pairs to avoid cheating). They were drawing lots for their companions when T. arrived.

"Where you been, T.?" Blackie asked. "You can't vote now. You know the rules."

"I've been *there*," T. said. He looked at the ground, as though he had thoughts to hide.

"Where?"

"At Old Misery's." Mike's mouth opened and then hurriedly closed again with a click. He had remembered the frog.

"At Old Misery's?" Blackie said. There was nothing in the rules against it, but he had a sensation that T. was treading on dangerous ground. He asked hopefully, "Did you break in?"

"No. I rang the bell."

"And what did you say?"

"I said I wanted to see his house."

"What did he do?"

"He showed it me."

"Pinch anything?"

"No."

"What did you do it for then?"

The gang had gathered round: it was as though an impromptu court were about to form and to try some case of deviation. T. said, "It's a beautiful house," and still watching the ground, meeting no one's eyes, he licked his lips first one way, then the other.

"What do you mean, a beautiful house?" Blackie asked with scorn.

"It's got a staircase two hundred years old like a corkscrew. Nothing holds it up."

"What do you mean, nothing holds it up. Does it float?"

"It's to do with opposite forces, Old Misery said."

"What else?"

"There's panelling."

"Like in the Blue Boar?"

"Two hundred years old."

"Is Old Misery two hundred years old?"

Mike laughed suddenly and then was quiet again. The meeting was in a serious mood. For the first time since T. had strolled into the car-park on the first day of the holidays his position was in danger. It only needed a single use of his real name and the gang would be at his heels.

"What did you do it for?" Blackie asked. He was just, he had no jealousy, he was anxious to retain T. in the gang if he could. It was the word "beautiful" that worried him—that belonged to a class world that you could still see parodied at the Wormsley Common Empire by a man wearing a top hat and a monocle, with a haw-haw accent. He was tempted to say, "My dear Trevor, old chap," and unleash his hell hounds. "If you'd broken in," he said sadly—that indeed would have been an exploit worthy of the gang.

"This was better," T. said. "I found out things." He continued to stare at his feet, not meeting anybody's eye, as though he were absorbed in some dream he was unwilling—or ashamed—to share.

"What things?"

"Old Misery's going to be away all tomorrow and Bank Holiday."

Blackie said with relief, "You mean we could break in?"

"And pinch things?" somebody asked.

Blackie said, "Nobody's going to pinch things. Breaking in—that's good enough, isn't it? We don't want any court stuff."

"I don't want to pinch anything," T. said. "I've got a better idea."

"What is it?"

T. raised eyes, as grey and disturbed as the drab August day. "We'll pull it down," he said. "We'll destroy it."

Blackie gave a single hoot of laughter and then, like Mike, fell quiet, daunted by the serious implacable gaze. "What'd the police be doing all the time?" he said.

"They'd never know. We'd do it from inside. I've found a way in." He said with a sort of intensity, "We'd be like worms, don't you see, in an apple. When we came out again there'd be nothing there, no staircase, no panels, nothing but just walls, and then we'd make the walls fall down—somehow."

"We'd go to jug," Blackie said.

"Who's to prove? and anyway we wouldn't have pinched anything." He added without the smallest flicker of glee, "There wouldn't be anything to pinch after we'd finished."

"I've never heard of going to prison for breaking things," Summers said.

"There wouldn't be time," Blackie said. "I've seen housebreakers at work."

"There are twelve of us," T. said. "We'd organise."

"None of us know how …"

"I know," T. said. He looked across at Blackie, "Have you got a better plan?"

"Today," Mike said tactlessly, "we're pinching free rides…."

"Free rides," T. said. "You can stand down, Blackie, if you'd rather…."

"The gang's got to vote."

"Put it up then."

Blackie said uneasily, "It's proposed that tomorrow and Monday we destroy Old Misery's house."

"Here, here," said a fat boy called Joe.

"Who's in favour?"

T. said, "It's carried."

"How do we start?" Summers asked.

"He'll tell you," Blackie said. It was the end of his leadership. He went away to the back of the car-park and began to kick a stone, dribbling it this way and that. There was only one old Morris in the park, for few cars were left there except lorries: without an attendant there was no safety. He took a flying kick at the car and scraped a little paint off the rear mudguard. Beyond, paying no more attention to him than to a stranger, the gang had gathered round T.; Blackie was dimly aware of the fickleness of favour. He thought of going home, of never returning, of letting them all discover the hollowness of T.'s leadership, but suppose after all what T. proposed was possible—nothing like it had ever been done before. The fame of the Wormsley Common car-park gang would surely reach around London. There would be headlines in the papers. Even the grown-up gangs who ran the betting at the all-in wrestling and the barrow-boys would hear with respect of how Old Misery's house had been destroyed. Driven by the pure, simple and altruistic ambition of fame for the gang, Blackie came back to where T. stood in the shadow of Misery's wall.

T. was giving orders with decision: it was as though this plan had been with him all his life, pondered through the seasons, now in his fifteenth year crystallised with the pain of puberty. "You," he said to Mike, "bring some big nails, the biggest you can find, and a hammer. Anyone else who can better bring a hammer and a screw-driver. We'll need plenty of them. Chisels too. We can't have too many chisels. Can anybody bring a saw?"

"I can," Mike said.

"Not a child's saw," T. said. "A real saw."

Blackie realised he had raised his hand like any ordinary member of the gang.

"Right, you bring one, Blackie. But now there's a difficulty. We want a hacksaw."

"What's a hacksaw?" someone asked.

"You can get 'em at Woolworth's," Summer said.

The fat boy called Joe said gloomily, "I knew it would end in a collection."

"I'll get one myself," T. said. "I don't want your money. But I can't buy a sledge-hammer."

Blackie said, "They are working on No. 15. I know where they'll leave their stuff for Bank Holiday."

"Then that's all," T. said. "We meet here at nine sharp."

"I've got to go to church," Mike said.

"Come over the wall and whistle. We'll let you in."

2

On Sunday morning all were punctual except Blackie, even Mike. Mike had had a stroke of luck. His mother felt ill, his father was tired after Saturday night, and he was told to go to church alone with many warnings of what would happen if he strayed. Blackie had had difficulty in smuggling out the saw, and then in finding the sledge-hammer at the back of No. 15. He approached the house from a lane at the rear of the garden, for fear of the policeman's beat along the main road. The tired evergreens kept off a stormy sun: another wet Bank Holiday was being prepared over the Atlantic, beginning in swirls of dust under the trees. Blackie climbed the wall into Misery's garden.

There was no sign of anybody anywhere. The loo stood like a tomb in a neglected graveyard. The curtains were drawn. The house slept. Blackie lumbered nearer with the saw and the sledgehammer. Perhaps after all nobody had turned up: the plan had been a wild invention: they had woken wiser. But when he came close to the back door he could hear a confusion of sound, hardly louder than a hive in swarm: a clickety-clack, a bang bang bang, a scraping, a creaking, a sudden painful crack. He thought: it's true, and whistled.

They opened the back door to him and he came in. He had at once the impression of organisation, very different from the old happy-go-lucky ways under his leadership. For a while he wandered up and down stairs looking for T. Nobody addressed him: he had a sense of great urgency, and already he could begin to see the plan. The interior of the house was being carefully demolished without touching the outer walls. Summers with hammer and chisel was ripping out the skirting-boards in the ground floor dining-room: he had already smashed the panels of the door. In the same room Joe was heaving up the parquet blocks, exposing the soft wood floor-boards over the cellar. Coils of wire came out of the damaged skirting and Mike sat happily on the floor, clipping the wires.

On the curved stairs two of the gang were working hard with an inadequate child's saw on the banisters—when they saw Blackie's big saw they signalled for it wordlessly. When he next saw them a quarter of the banisters had been dropped into the hall. He found T. at last in the bathroom—he sat moodily in the least cared-for room in the house, listening to the sounds coming up from below.

"You've really done it," Blackie said with awe. "What's going to happen?"

"We've only just begun," T. said. He looked at the sledge-hammer and gave his instructions. "You stay here and break the bath and the wash-basin. Don't bother about the pipes. They come later."

Mike appeared at the door. "I've finished the wire, T.," he said.

"Good. You've just got to go wandering round now. The kitchen's in the basement. Smash all the china and glass and bottles you can lay hold of. Don't turn on the taps—we don't want a flood—yet. Then go into all the rooms and turn out drawers. If they are locked get one of the others to break them open. Tear up any papers you find and smash all the ornaments. Better take a carving-knife with you from the kitchen. The bedroom's opposite here. Open the pillows and tear up the sheets. That's enough for the moment. And you, Blackie, when you've finished in here crack the plaster in the passage up with your sledge-hammer."

"What are you going to do?" Blackie asked.

"I'm looking for something special," T. said.

It was nearly lunch-time before Blackie had finished and went in search of T. Chaos had advanced. The kitchen was a shambles of broken glass and china. The dining-room was stripped of parquet, the skirting was up, the door had been taken off its hinges, and the destroyers had moved up a floor. Streaks of light came in through the closed shutters where they worked with the seriousness of creators—and destruction after all is a form of creation. A kind of imagination had seen this house as it had now become.

Mike said, "I've got to go home for dinner."

"Who else?" T. asked, but all the others on one excuse or another had brought provisions with them.

They squatted in the ruins of the room and swapped unwanted sandwiches. Half an hour for lunch and they were at work again. By the time Mike returned, they were on the top floor, and by six the superficial damage was completed. The doors were all off, all the skirtings raised, the furniture pillaged and ripped and smashed—no one could have slept in the house except on a bed of broken plaster. T. gave his orders—eight o'clock next morning, and to escape notice they climbed singly over the garden wall, into the car-park. Only Blackie and T. were left: the light had nearly gone, and when they touched a switch, nothing worked—Mike had done his job thoroughly.

"Did you find anything special?" Blackie asked.

T. nodded. "Come over here," he said, "and look." Out of both pockets he drew bundles of pound notes. "Old Misery's savings," he said. "Mike ripped out the mattress, but he missed them."

"What are you going to do? Share them?"

"We aren't thieves," T. said. "Nobody's going to steal anything from this house. I kept these for you and me—a celebration." He knelt down on the floor and counted them out—there were seventy in all. "We'll burn them," he said, "one by one," and taking it in turns they held a note upwards and lit the top corner, so that the flame burnt slowly towards their fingers. The grey ash floated above them and fell on their heads like age. "I'd like to see Old Misery's face when we are through," T. said.

"You hate him a lot?" Blackie asked.

"Of course I don't hate him," T. said. "There'd be no fun if I hated him." The last burning note illuminated his brooding face. "All this hate and love," he said, "it's soft, it's hooey. There's only things, Blackie," and he looked round the room crowded with the unfamiliar shadows of half things, broken things, former things. "I'll race you home, Blackie," he said.

3

Next morning the serious destruction started. Two were missing—Mike and another boy whose parents were off to Southend and Brighton in spite of the slow warm drops that had begun to fall and the rumble of thunder in the estuary like the first guns of the old blitz. "We've got to hurry," T. said.

Summers was restive. "Haven't we done enough?" he said. "I've been given a bob for slot machines. This is like work."

"We've hardly started," T. said. "Why, there's all the floors left, and the stairs. We haven't taken out a single window. You voted like the others. We are going to *destroy* this house. There won't be anything left when we've finished."

They began again on the first floor picking up the top floorboards next the outer wall, leaving the joists exposed. Then they sawed through the joists and retreated into the hall, as what was left of the floor heeled and sank. They had learnt with practise, and the second floor collapsed more easily. By the evening an odd exhilaration seized them as they looked down the great hollow of the house. They ran risks and made mistakes: when they thought of the windows it was too late to reach them. "Cor," Joe said, and dropped a penny down into the dry rubble-filled well. It cracked and span among the broken glass.

"Why did we start this?" Summers asked with astonishment; T. was already on the ground, digging at the rubble, clearing a space along the outer wall. "Turn on the taps," he said. "It's too dark for anyone to see now, and in the morning it won't matter." The water overtook them on the stairs and fell through the floorless rooms.

It was then they heard Mike's whistle at the back. "Something's wrong," Blackie said. They could hear his urgent breathing as they unlocked the door.

"The bogies?" Summers asked.

"Old Misery," Mike said. "He's on his way." He put his head between his knees and retched. "Ran all the way," he said with pride.

"But why?" T. said. "He told me ..." He protested with the fury of the child he had never been, "It isn't fair."

"He was down at Southend," Mike said, "and he was on the train coming back. Said it was too cold and wet." He paused and gazed at the water. "My, you've had a storm here. Is the roof leaking?"

"How long will he be?"

"Five minutes. I gave Ma the slip and ran."

"We better clear," Summers said. "We've done enough, anyway."

"Oh no, we haven't. Anybody could do this—" "this" was the shattered hollowed house with nothing left but the walls. Yet walls could be preserved. Façades were valuable. They could build inside again more beautifully than before. This could again be a home. He said angrily, "We've got to finish. Don't move. Let me think."

"There's no time," a boy said.

"There's got to be a way," T. said. "We couldn't have got thus far..."

"We've done a lot," Blackie said.

"No. No, we haven't. Somebody watch the front."

"We can't do any more."

"He may come in at the back."

"Watch the back too." T. began to plead. "Just give me a minute and I'll fix it. I swear I'll fix it." But his authority had gone with his ambiguity. He was only one of the gang. "Please," he said.

"Please," Summers mimicked him, and then suddenly struck home with the fatal name. "Run along home, Trevor."

T. stood with his back to the rubble like a boxer knocked groggy against the ropes. He had no words as his dreams shook and slid. Then Blackie acted before the gang had time to laugh, pushing Summers backward. "I'll watch the front, T.," he said, and cautiously he opened the shutters of the hall. The grey wet common stretched ahead, and the lamps gleamed in the puddles. "Someone's coming, T. No, it's not him. What's your plan, T.?"

"Tell Mike to go out to the loo and hide close beside it. When he hears me whistle he's got to count ten and start to shout."

"Shout what?"

"Oh, 'Help', anything."

"You hear, Mike," Blackie said. He was the leader again. He took a quick look between the shutters. "He's coming, T."

"Quick, Mike. The loo. Stay here, Blackie, all of you till I yell."

"Where are you going, T.?"

"Don't worry. I'll see to this. I said I would, didn't I?"

Old Misery came limping off the common. He had mud on his shoes and he stopped to scrape them on the pavement's edge. He didn't want to soil his house, which stood jagged and dark between the bomb-sites, saved so narrowly, as he believed, from destruction. Even the fanlight had been left unbroken by the bomb's blast. Somewhere somebody whistled. Old Misery looked sharply round. He didn't trust whistles. A child was shouting: it seemed to come from his own garden. Then a boy ran into the road from the car-park. "Mr. Thomas," he called, "Mr. Thomas."

"What is it?"

"I'm terribly sorry, Mr. Thomas. One of us got taken short, and we thought you wouldn't mind, and now he can't get out."

"What do you mean, boy?"

"He's got stuck in your loo."

"He'd no business ... Haven't I seen you before?"

"You showed me your house."

"So I did. So I did. That doesn't give you the right to ..."

"Do hurry, Mr. Thomas. He'll suffocate."

"Nonsense. He can't suffocate. Wait till I put my bag in."

"I'll carry your bag."

"Oh no, you don't. I carry my own."

"This way, Mr. Thomas."

"I can't get in the garden that way. I've got to go through the house."

"But you *can* get in the garden this way, Mr. Thomas. We often do."

"You often do?" He followed the boy with a scandalised fascination. "When? What right? ..."

"Do you see ...? the wall's low."

"I'm not going to climb walls into my own garden. It's absurd."

"This is how we do it. One foot here, one foot there, and over." The boy's face peered down, an arm shot out, and Mr. Thomas found his bag taken and deposited on the other side of the wall.

"Give me back my bag," Mr. Thomas said. From the loo a boy yelled and yelled. "I'll call the police."

"Your bag's all right, Mr. Thomas. Look. One foot there. On your right. Now just above. To your left." Mr. Thomas climbed over this own garden wall. "Here's your bag, Mr. Thomas."

"I'll have the wall built up," Mr. Thomas said, "I'll not have you boys coming over here, using my loo." He stumbled on the path, but the boy caught his elbow and supported him. "Thank you, thank you, my boy," he murmured automatically. Somebody shouted again through the dark. "I'm coming, I'm coming," Mr. Thomas called. He said to the boy beside him, "I'm not unreasonable. Been a boy myself. As long as things are done regular. I don't mind you playing round the place Saturday mornings. Sometimes I like company. Only it's got to be regular. One of you asks leave and I say Yes. Sometimes I'll say No. Won't feel like it. And you come in at the front door and out at the back. No garden walls."

"Do get him out, Mr. Thomas."

"He won't come to any harm in my loo," Mr. Thomas said, stumbling slowly down the garden. "Oh, my rheumatics," he said. "Always get 'em on Bank Holiday. I've got to go careful. There's loose stones here. Give me your hand. Do you know what my horoscope said yesterday? 'Abstain from any dealings in first half of week. Danger of serious crash.' That might be on this path," Mr. Thomas said. "They speak in parables and double meanings." He paused at the door of the loo. "What's the matter in there?" he called. There was no reply.

"Perhaps he's fainted," the boy said.

"Not in my loo. Here, you, come out," Mr. Thomas said, and giving a great jerk at the door he nearly fell on his back when it swung easily open. A hand first supported him and then pushed him hard. His head hit the opposite wall and he sat heavily down. His bag hit his feet. A hand whipped the key out of the lock and the door slammed. "Let me out," he called, and heard the key turn in the lock. "A serious crash," he thought, and felt dithery and confused and old.

A voice spoke to him softly through the star-shaped hole in the door. "Don't worry, Mr. Thomas," it said, "we won't hurt you, not if you stay quiet."

Mr. Thomas put his head between his hands and pondered. He had noticed that there was only one lorry in the car-park, and he felt certain that the driver would not come for it before the morning. Nobody could hear him from the road in front, and the lane at the back was seldom used. Anyone who passed there would be hurrying home and would not pause for what they would certainly take to be drunken cries. And if he did call "Help," who, on a lonely Bank Holiday evening, would have the courage to investigate? Mr. Thomas sat on the loo and pondered with the wisdom of age.

After a while it seemed to him that there were sounds in the silence—they were faint and came from the direction of his house. He stood up and peered through the ventilation-hole—between the cracks in one of the shutters he saw a light, not the light of a lamp, but the wavering light that a candle might give. Then he thought he heard the sound of hammering and scraping and chipping. He thought of burglars—perhaps they had employed the boy as a scout, but why should burglars engage in what sounded more and more like a stealthy form of carpentry? Mr. Thomas let out an experimental yell, but nobody answered. The noise could not even have reached his enemies.

4

Mike had gone home to bed, but the rest stayed. The question of leadership no longer concerned the gang. With nails, chisels, screwdrivers, anything that was sharp and penetrating they moved around the inner walls worrying at the mortar between the bricks. They started too high, and it was Blackie who hit on the damp course and realised the work could be halved if they weakened the joints immediately above. It was a long, tiring, unamusing job, but at last it was finished. The gutted house stood there balanced on a few inches of mortar between the damp course and the bricks.

There remained the most dangerous task of all, out in the open at the edge of the bomb-site. Summers was sent to watch the road for passers-by, and Mr. Thomas, sitting on the loo, heard clearly now the sound of sawing. It no longer came from his house, and that a little reassured him. He felt less concerned. Perhaps the other noises too had no significance.

A voice spoke to him through the hole. "Mr. Thomas."

"Let me out," Mr. Thomas said sternly.

"Here's a blanket," the voice said, and a long grey sausage was worked through the hole and fell in swathes over Mr. Thomas's head.

"There's nothing personal," the voice said. "We want you to be comfortable to-night."

"To-night," Mr. Thomas repeated incredulously.

"Catch," the voice said. "Penny buns—we've buttered them, and sausage-rolls. We don't want you to starve, Mr. Thomas."

Mr. Thomas pleaded desperately. "A joke's a joke, boy. Let me out and I won't say a thing. I've got rheumatics. I got to sleep comfortable."

"You wouldn't be comfortable, not in your house, you wouldn't. Not now."

"What do you mean, boy?" but the footsteps receded. There was only the silence of night: no sound of sawing. Mr. Thomas tried one more yell, but he was daunted and rebuked by the silence—a long way off an owl hooted and made away again on its muffled flight through the soundless world.

At seven next morning the driver came to fetch his lorry. He climbed into the seat and tried to start the engine. He was vaguely aware of a voice shouting, but it didn't concern him. At last the engine responded and he backed the lorry until it touched the great wooden shore that supported Mr. Thomas's house. That way he could drive right out and down the street without reversing. The lorry moved forward, was momentarily checked as though something were pulling it from behind, and then went on to the sound of a long rumbling crash. The driver was astonished to see bricks bouncing ahead of him, while stones hit the roof of his cab. He put on his brakes. When he climbed out the whole landscape had suddenly altered. There was no house beside the car-park, only a hill of rubble. He went round and examined the back of his car for damage, and found a rope tied there that was still twisted at the other end round part of a wooden strut.

The driver again became aware of somebody shouting. It came from the wooden erection which was the nearest thing to a house in that desolation of broken brick. The driver climbed the smashed wall and unlocked the door. Mr. Thomas came out of the loo.

He was wearing a grey blanket to which flakes of pastry adhered. He gave a sobbing cry. "My house," he said. "Where's my house?"

"Search me," the driver said. His eye lit on the remains of a bath and what had once been a dresser and he began to laugh. There wasn't anything left anywhere.

"How dare you laugh," Mr. Thomas said. "It was my house. My house."

"I'm sorry," the driver said, making heroic efforts, but when he remembered the sudden check to his lorry, the crash of bricks falling, he became convulsed again. One moment the house had stood there with such dignity between the bomb-sites like a man in a top hat, and then, bang, crash, there wasn't anything left—not anything. He said, "I'm sorry. I can't help it, Mr. Thomas. There's nothing personal, but you got to admit it's funny."

1. In your response journal, record your thoughts, feelings, or reactions to the story. You might choose one focus from the following:
   - how you feel about the "practical joke" and the lorry driver's response;
   - how you feel about Old Misery;
   - parallels you see between this story and other stories, movies, television shows, real events you know of, etc.

   In a small group, share and discuss your journal entries. Summarize for the class key points of your discussion.
2. In a small group, discuss the gang's activities, rules and codes of behavior, and leaders. Summarize your ideas, draw conclusions about gangs, and present them to the class. (You might consider your own experiences in peer groups as part of this activity.)
3. Examine the details of time and place given in the story. Why did the author set the story in a post-war, London neighborhood? What is the purpose of the allusions to St. Paul's Cathedral and Christopher Wren?
4. What do you consider to be the theme of the story? Give supporting quotations and references.
5. Examine the four sections of the story. With a partner, discuss the purpose of each of part, referring to plot, characters, and conflicts.
6. Choose one of the following activities:
   a) Write a newspaper story about the prank.
   b) Roleplay scenes in which the boys are questioned by police about their motives.
   c) In an informal discussion or a dramatization (of a meeting of social workers and parents, of a trial, etc.), explore what should happen to the gang members.

Carol Shields

Invitations

What mattered was that she had been invited.

On Monday she looked in her mailbox, although she had no reason to expect a letter so soon. But there it was, a small, square card. She held it in her two hands, testing its weight.

It was an invitation to an exhibition of drawings at a private gallery. The name of the artist was only faintly familiar to her, and she couldn't decide if she'd ever seen his work or not. She tried to imagine what kind of drawings she was being invited to view—would they be primitive or abstract or what was sometimes called "magic realism"? She summoned these categories to mind and then decided it didn't matter. What mattered was that she had been invited.

The invitation pleased her, though she wasn't such a fool as to think she'd been specifically singled out because of her aesthetic sensitivity or because of her knowledge of modern graphics or even because of the pleasure of her company. The address on the card had been typed; her name, in fact, was misspelled, the last two letters transposed. Somewhere, no doubt, she'd turned up on a mailing list—that was all.

She would wear a certain printed velvet skirt she had and with it a black turtleneck sweater. No one would expect her to buy a drawing or even to comment on the exhibition. It was necessary only to accept a glass of wine and a cube of orange cheese and stand for a minute or two in front of each drawing, nodding comprehendingly and perhaps murmuring something properly neutral into the air such as "nicely detailed" or "wonderful sense of space." There was a good chance no one would even speak to her, but it would be better than spending Saturday evening in her new apartment, sitting in an armchair with a book and feeling loneliness drink her drop by drop.

The previous tenant had left behind a single item, which was a paperback copy of Jane Austen's *Mansfield Park*, a book that, oddly enough, she had always intended to read. She couldn't help feeling there had been something deliberate—and something imperative, too—about this abandoned book, as though it had been specifically intended for her and that she was being enjoined to take it seriously. But how much better it would be to be going *out*; how much easier it would be to say, should anyone ask, that on Saturday evening she would be attending an opening of an interesting new exhibition.

On Tuesday she was again taken by surprise, for in her mailbox there was another invitation, this time for a cocktail party given by a distant friend of a friend, someone she'd never met but whose name she dimly remembered having heard. It was a disappointment that the party was being held on the same night as the gallery opening and that, furthermore, it was at the same hour. For a minute she entertained the possibility of attending both functions, galloping breathlessly from one to the other. But no, it was not feasible; the two parties were at opposite ends of the city. It was a great pity, she felt, since invitations are few and far between when one moves to a new address. She would have to make a choice.

Of course she would choose the cocktail party. The gallery opening, now that she stopped to think about it, was no more than a commercial venture, an enticement to buyers and patrons. It would be fraudulent of her to attend when she'd no intention of buying a picture, and besides, she was drawn to cocktail parties. She was attracted, in fact, to parties of all kinds, seeing them as an opportunity to possess, for a few hours at least, a life that was denser, more concentrated and more vigorous than the usual spun-out wastes of time that had to be scratched endlessly for substance. She could still wear her certain velvet skirt, but with a pretty red satin blouse she'd recently acquired.

On Wednesday, strangely, she received a third invitation—and it, too, was for Saturday evening. This time the invitation was handwritten, a rather charming note which she read through quickly three times. She was being invited to a small buffet supper. There

would be only a dozen or so guests, it was explained. The author of a new biography would be there, and so would the subject of the biography who was, by chance, also a biographer. A particular balding computer scientist would be in attendance along with his wife, who was celebrated for her anti-nuclear stance and for her involvement in Navajo rugs. There would be a professor of history and also a professor of histology, as well as a person renowned for his love of Black Forest cakes and cheese pastries. There would be a famous character actor whose face was familiar, if not his name, and also the hairdresser who'd invented the Gidget cut and raised razor cuts to their present *haute* status.

Of course she could not say no. How much more congenial to go to a supper party than to peer at violent works of art and mutter, "Interesting, interesting," and how much more rewarding than standing about with a drink and a salty canapé and trying to make conversation with a room full of strangers. Her green silk dress would be suitable, if not precisely perfect, and she could gamble safely enough on the fact that no one would have seen it before.

Thursday's mail brought still another invitation, also unfortunately for Saturday evening. She smiled, remembering how her mother used to say, "It never rains but it pours." The invitation, which was for a formal dinner party, was printed on fine paper, and there was a handwritten note at the bottom. "We do hope you can make it," the note said. "Of course we know you by reputation and we've been looking forward to meeting you for years."

It had been some time since she'd attended a formal dinner party, and she was flattered to be sent an invitation with a handwritten note at the bottom. It pleased her to imagine a large, vaulted dining room and parade of courses elegantly served, each with a different wine. The gleam of light through cut glass would sparkle on polished linen and on the faces of the luminaries gathered around the table. Her green silk, with perhaps the double strand of pearls, would be festive enough, but at the same time subdued and formal.

She wasn't entirely surprised to look into her mailbox on Friday and see that she'd been sent yet another invitation. The paper was a heavy, creamy stock and came enclosed in a thick double envelope. There was to be a reception—a *gala* it was called—at the top of a large downtown hotel on Saturday evening. The guest of honor, she read, was to be herself.

She felt a lurch of happiness. Such an honor! But a moment later her euphoria gave way to panic, and when she sat down to collect herself, she discovered she was trembling not with excitement but with fear.

On Saturday she surveyed the five invitations which were arranged in a circle on her coffee table. These missives, so richly welcoming, persuading and honoring, had pleased her at first, then puzzled her. And now she felt for the first time directly threatened. Something or someone was conspiring to consume a portion of her life, of herself, in fact—entering her apartment and taking possession of her Saturday evening just as a thief might enter and carry off her stereo equipment or her lovely double rope of pearls or a deep slice of her dorsal flesh.

She decided to stay home instead with a cup of coffee and her adventitiously acquired copy of *Mansfield Park*. Already it was dark, and she switched on the small reading lamp by her chair. The shade of the lamp was made of a pale, ivory-yellow material, and the light that shone through it had the warm quality of very old gold.

It happened that people passing her window on their way to various parties and public gatherings that night were moved to see her, a woman sitting calmly in an arc of lamplight, turning over—one by one—the soft pages of a thick book. Clearly she was lost in what she was reading, for she never once glanced up. Her look of solitary containment and the oblique angle with which the light struck the left side of her face made her seem piercingly lovely. One of her hands, curved like a comma, lay on her lap; the other, slowly, thoughtfully, turned over the pages.

Those who passed by and saw her were seized by a twist of pain, which was really a kind of nostalgia for their childhood and for a simplified time when they, too, had been bonded to the books they read and to certain golden rooms which they remembered as being complete and as perfect as stage settings. They felt resentment, too, at the cold rain and the buffeting wind and the price of taxis and the hostility of their hosts. They felt embarrassed by their own small, proffered utterances and by the expanded social rubric they had come to inhabit.

As they moved to and fro in large, brightly-lit rooms, so high up in glittering towers that they felt they were clinging to the sides of cliffs, their feet began to ache and exhaustion overcame them. Soon it was past midnight, no longer the same day, but the next and the next. New widths of time clamored to be filled, though something it seemed, some image of possibility, begged to be remembered.

Outside, the wind blew and blew. The sky slipped sideways, turning first yellow, then a mournful, treasonous purple, as though time itself was drowning in a waterfall of shame.

1. In your response journal, record your thoughts, feelings, or reactions to the story. You might choose one focus from the following:
   - similar feelings and experiences you have had;
   - any advice or insights you could offer the narrator;
   - words or phrases that stood out for you.

   In a small group, share and discuss your journal entries. Summarize for the class key points of your discussion.
2. In a small group, review the motivation, conflict, climax, and *dénouement* of the story.
3. Focus on the last six paragraphs of the story. How does the author use images and impressions to suggest change in the main character? What contrasts are made? What do you think is the "image of possibility" in the second last paragraph? Why does it seem to go unremembered?
4. What statement does the author seem to be making? Support your ideas with examples from the text and references to personal experience.
5. Read Robert Frost's poem "The Road Not Taken" and compare Frost's and Shield's views of individual choices.
6. Choose one of the following activities:
   a) Write the "invitation" that the author and the narrator seem to be offering the reader/individual in society.
   b) Write a free verse poem describing the character's new-found freedom.
   c) Describe a choice you once made which was similar to that of the narrator.

Yvette Naubert

The Pigeons in St. Louis Square

Time can never be turned back;
nothing can resist it.

Their heads bobbing, taking mechanical little steps, they walk around the benches, the alleys, and scratch about for seeds existing only in their memory. At this early morning hour, labourers, workmen, and women factory workers rush across the square and hurry over to St. Denis Street or Sherbrooke station. The pigeons know these regular passers-by very well, all these people who ignore them and hurry along, turning their worries over in their minds instead of throwing them to the winds like useless seeds. But the pigeons don't care; it's not yet time for the old man to arrive so they peacefully go about their own business. These winged citizens, bold enough to venture out into the middle of the street, deaf to abuse and screaming tires, are not frightened by cars. Noise is so familiar to them that they would be even more fearful of a prolonged silence; perhaps the absence of human beings in St. Louis Square would turn their world upside down. They fly onto the benches, walk along the back rests, leave their droppings everywhere. They explore the alleys, sit on the edge of the silent fountain, not understanding why the bowl is empty, bathe in the bottom of the basin in the little puddles left by the rain. The history of this restless cosmopolitan place where so many races and nationalities rub elbows, where so many dispossessed persons often take up temporary residence, is transmitted from one generation to the next, from beak to feather, so to speak. At one time it had been a privileged place, with polite customs and quiet scenes filled with a harmony which had disappeared forever. The changes in the lives of men scarcely have any effect on the pigeons who like only the giver of seeds, whatever his nationality or social position.

The old gabled stone houses with their turrets, bay windows and elaborate balconies have surrounded St. Louis Square for such a long time that the pigeons have no memory of them ever being constructed. They were there when the pigeons took possession of the domain and what existed before that was lost in a night too long for a pigeon's memory. The fronts of several of these old houses have been modernised but others have been left to slide without a struggle down the slope of ravaging time.

Branches upon branches have been added to the trees; their roots have become more firmly anchored in the soil but they are still the same maples, the same elms which have sheltered for so many seasons the non-migrant birds and the others who leave as summer draws to a close, not to return for a long time afterwards, their feathers puffed up by the wind, their wings dusted with space. The trees are places of refuge; thanks to them we can see that spring has changed into summer or that winter, always anxious to settle in but not to leave again, is jostling autumn a little too much. Besides, winter is never completely forgotten. The memory of the struggle against the cold and the snow, the search for food, which is always scarce in winter, is conserved in a corner of the mind. But today, the sun is shining on the new leaves and the air smells like spring.

Nevertheless, the old man doesn't arrive and the pigeons are fidgeting. The dinner hour has long since passed. An old lady settles down on the bench where the old man usually sits. Out of a big black bag she brings not seeds but knitting. The wary pigeons circle around the bench, each time coming closer, but seeds do not often rain down from ladies who knit. Regular visitors as long as the weather is nice, they disappear for a long time, sometimes forever, as soon as the first frost comes. This early rising old lady is dressed in black from head to toe: a black kerchief around her head, and buttoned over a cotton dress the colour of many bereavements, a black cardigan protects her heavy shape from the cold air. Dark lines of pain are concealed in the wrinkles on her face. There is nothing white on her except for her hair and the wool hanging down from her fingers like a long worm the pigeons know is inedible. She willingly escapes from the present; in her mind's eye she sees another continent, a different country, a Portuguese village where the incessant sun of poverty shines.

Just the day before, this corner of the bench where the expatriate old lady is delving back into her past was occupied by the old man whose life had unfolded in the bosom of this country, of this city. He comes back every day to sit in front of the home where he had spent his youth and reflect upon his childhood. He doesn't have to cross the ocean to find memories; only a hundred feet separate him from them. The home where he was born and grew up is right there in front of him and his melancholy thoughts. But he had to reconstruct it in some measure to bring the past to life again because the hand of man had played havoc with it. Man is always in a hurry to change, destroy, and start over again, while the birds go on as usual. The first and second floors have been transformed into apartments; the one on the second floor is for rent. New tribes of nomads, tenants go in and out without really understanding what attracted them to this house and what made them leave it again. For the most part, they are young, they refuse stability which seems to them to be retrograde and bad and they nurture their insecurity as if it were a delicate flower. But the little balcony around which the old man's own father had put a wrought iron railing hasn't changed; perhaps it remembers a little boy with long curls and a young woman embroidering in the fresh air.

The ground floor lost its elegant entrance as did the vestibule where the coat and hat stand stood with its copper coat hooks and its mirror which often reflected women in heavy hats adorned with flowers, fruits, and birds. The walls were knocked down and the lovely oak panelling covered in grey paint in order to accommodate the offices of a real estate broker. The old man wasn't looking at the remodelled house; he was seeing the other one, the home of his memories which couldn't be drowned in a can of paint.

In the neighbouring streets echo the sounds of unofficial languages. They are the languages of a multitude of displaced men and women who have come from countries often far removed from one another and are surprised to find themselves neighbours in the same city. It seems that human beings leave their homes more willingly than the pigeons, these birds for whom distances are measured by the time it takes to return to the nest.

The horizon of these non-migratory pigeons is marked by the buildings around St. Louis Square. They are not racists, nor are they xenophobes. The language which calls them is always harmonious and the hand that throws them seeds or peanuts always pleasant. But no other voice sounds the same as the old man's, always the first to arrive, the most faithful to the daily rendezvous. The seeds he sows taste of tenderness and understanding. Only deep cooing, guttural sounds and clicks of the tongue which the birds understand perfectly are exchanged between him and the pigeons. The old man never acknowledges anyone else. The familiar faces have disappeared long ago. He haunts the square to feed the winged creatures and to contemplate from afar a certain house he hasn't been in for years but which he knows better than anyone else. Was he afraid of reviving forgotten memories? Besides, what was the use? Nothing can start over again. Time can never be turned back; nothing can resist it. In the remodelled house, the old man would no longer hear anything but the breath of ghosts, the flight of spirits, the sighs of those who are lost forever. Would he only find the room where long ago a woman cried out in childbirth? Shortly afterward the midwife presented her with a son, today an old man trying to remember. Years went by; dark days and death came into the house and stayed until the residence passed into the hands of strangers.

And yet the man didn't come to look for the bad memories but for the memory of the happy days of his childhood and his youth. It sparkled in his mind like an unchanging crystal. Perhaps he also came to try to understand and accept the present which embarrasses him like an unknown, incomprehensible language. Tossed about in the tumult of the present, he finds a precarious stability in the past.

Every morning before he arrives, the pigeons gather in a particular spot on St. Denis Street. They leave the rooftops, the trees, and their perch on the fountain and stand watch. As soon as he appears at the corner of the square near St. Denis Street, they rush up to him either taking quick little steps or flying, perch on his arms, his shoulders and his head. They eat out of his hand. The seeds rain down in large quantities. It is the best time of the day. But today the sun follows its upward course in the sky, the old man doesn't appear and the pigeons are puzzled.

The "Montreal Chinese School" stands at the corner of Clarke St. and Prince Arthur St. (On one side of the square there is one French name after the other; on the other side, English names decorate the street signs of the area developed after the conquest.) From the open windows of the school nasal voices reciting a lesson can be heard. Coming and going relatively peacefully, the pigeons find this reassuring as long as the children are inside. In the past, a very long time ago, a small boy used to amuse himself around the fountain which, at that time, had a jet of water singing in it all summer long. He used to float boats in the basin, trundle a hoop around in the alleys and scare the pigeons, ancestors of those of today. The trees were not so bushy then and birds fed in the streets after the horses had passed by. On Sunday morning, distinguished people used to cross through the square, missals in hand, and in the evening after vespers, they strolled quietly under the trees. In good weather, maids in their starched aprons and bonnets took the babies out for walks in their huge carriages in the afternoon.

Times had really changed; no one is more conscious of that than the nostalgic old man. Now, not only strangers, but foreigners invade the place every day. The horses had long ago disappeared. Only the pigeons remain. They come and go, flutter about and scratch for food, concerned about the absence of the old man.

The postman makes his rounds, his bag over his shoulder, a stack of letters in his hand. The stack of letters diminishes, the sack empties, but it never contains even one seed. And too, the postman is not the most likeable person who comes around during the day and it's the same with the delivery men. They are all people in a hurry whose quick-moving feet have to be avoided.

A dangerous time for the pigeons is when the sun is at its zenith; the students from the "Montreal Chinese School" disperse and other school children run across the square uttering their war cries. The birds take to their nests and look after their young or seek refuge in the trees or on the silent fountain. The old lady in black sticks a long knitting needle into her knitting which disappears into the black bag. She slowly walks away, her back stooped but her legs still solid, her attention held by some memory stronger than the others. Cooking odours from continental kitchens waft through the air and children's cries, the same in any language and all latitudes, burst forth through the open windows.

The pigeons explore the alleys and the meagre grass. Sometimes under a leaf carried by the wind there is a surprise, a seed forgotten from the day before. The shadows of the trees are lost in the trees themselves; the sun illuminates everything from on high and nothing escapes its light. And too, the pigeons couldn't possibly miss seeing the old man if he were to take the notion to come at this unusual time.

Although they have heard his story many times, they don't tire of it; it's the life of a gentle man who has loved a lot. The ordinary story of an old man whose heart has never grown weary of loving, who was driven out of his paternal home by misfortune and who returns, lonesome, to reminisce about happy times in this very spot where they took place. The pigeons, who have never left this corner, understand that people come back to it and, in remembrance of the past, throw them the best possible seeds.

But, little by little, the light gives way to darkness and young mothers appear in the alleys with their beloved little children. The pigeons don't have a very great affection for them. When they are out of their carriages or push-carts, these monsters fight with the birds over the coveted peanuts. Only the arrival of the old man would reestablish the equilibrium of the day gently drawing to a close. Slow-moving men with a lost look in their eyes sit down on the unoccupied benches. Others stand around in groups, fearing the solitude of old people left to themselves. Men who are still young go from bench to bench searching for something they wouldn't dare admit. Boys and girls are stretched out on the grass and seem to take root in the soil as soon as they sit down. Motionless or slow-moving, floating in an artificial dream that only takes them to the threshold of their being, they challenge established society with their refusal which in turn engenders immobility. Sometimes they accompany the nonchalant flight of the pigeons on the guitar. Then a young man, lying down, throws a peanut or two in such a serious way, as if it's the last act he will ever perform.

On the bench where the old lady had been sitting that morning, a woman and two men using unknown words, are launched into a passionate discussion in which they express fear for this enormous country, for this crowded city which is less miraculous than they had believed. The school children with their almond eyes add the strange music of the Chinese language to the noise and the sound, and for a quarter of an hour, St. Louis Square is transformed into an oriental garden. In the fading light, more and more of the boys and girls who are coming in increasing numbers to live in the neighbourhood around the square, gather around the monument to Octave Cremazie and his Carillon soldier dying in his flag. They don't venerate him any more than do the pigeons who leave their droppings on the heads of the poet and the hero he eulogized in his forgotten verses. But the old man never went near the monument without remembering its inauguration day on June 24, 1906. In his white suit with a sailor's collar and hat, his buttoned shoes, holding his father's hand, he listened to the long boring speeches which prevented him from running about in the alleys. The speeches have long since been forgotten but not the year 1906 nor June 24 since it was the last time his father held his hand in his.

However, when nearly everything was invaded by the darkness, the tumult of a brawl breaks out among the obsessed young people. Immediately, men in black appear, brandishing long clubs. Then the young people, who had been lying in a horizontal position, assume the vertical and flee as if their legs were made only for that purpose. These nocturnal pursuits are now part of the daily existence and that's how the pigeons know that times have changed.

The street lights have been lit for a while and a few dreamers linger in the reestablished silence. Silhouettes which look like the gallows cut across St. Louis Square, permeated by the gentle night. To be sure, the lovers drifting around in the square frosted by the moonlight are experiencing the perfect love. But the pigeons don't see any of these people, nor a few hours earlier did they notice a long black vehicle move along St. Louis Square on St. Denis Street and go away, carrying off the last witness to a time which has gone forever.

Tomorrow, and for a few days yet, the pigeons will wait for the old man. They will be on the lookout at the time he usually appears. But he will not come, will never come again and the pigeons will end up forgetting him completely.

Now they sleep, heads tucked under their wings.

translated by Margaret Rose

1. In your response journal, record your thoughts, feelings, or reactions to the story. You might choose one focus from the following:
   - images that were especially vivid for you;
   - a pattern you noticed in the details or events of the story;
   - thoughts that come to mind about change.

   In a small group, share and discuss your journal entries. Summarize for the class key points of your discussion.
2. Discuss both the references to time and to seasons and the ways in which the author uses time in her story.
3. Develop brief character sketches of the pigeons, the old man, and other human beings in the story. Comment on the role of each. Support your ideas with details from the story.
4. Where does the story take place? Consider the significance of this setting for the story.
5. Discuss the various images and the theme of the story. How do the unusual focus and perspective of the story enable the author to accomplish her purpose?
6. Choose one of the following activities:
   a) Consider how a portion of the story could be filmed and write the script (indicating camera shots and angles, etc.).
   b) Write a memoir about a place for which you have strong feelings. Be sure you include enough detail to create a vivid sense of the place and why it means so much to you. (You may illustrate your writing with a photograph or drawing of the place.)
   c) Write a stream-of-consciousness narrative for either the old man or the old woman.

5

Irony and Symbol

Often when first reading a short story, we respond to the main character's thoughts, feelings, and actions. Then, we might examine the tools the writer used to make the story "work." Two tools that writers frequently use are irony and symbol. Both can deepen the meaning and increase the impact of the story.

Irony involves contrast between two elements. As readers, we may see a difference between what a character says and what he or she means, between what a character says or believes and what we know to be true, or between what is taking place and what would be more appropriate according to our expectations. These three forms of irony—verbal, dramatic, and situational—are common to media such as television and literature. Of the three, the form that most often provides depth of meaning and impact in literature is situational irony.

Many times in our lives we recognize differences between what is happening and what might be expected or seem more appropriate. Sometimes irony is simply humorous to us, such as when someone's inappropriate clothing makes us laugh. Other times, irony can provoke thought, such as when violence at a protest for peace makes us contemplate values and actions. It is for this thoughtful response that situational irony is often used in short stories.

Another writer's tool—symbol—compresses meaning within stories. A symbol is an object or action that, by its position and importance in a story, gains meaning in addition to what it represents literally. Use of flowers as a central image in a story, for example, might lead us to consider the characteristics of flowers. We might be led to recognize that flowers have only temporary lives in full glory, before they shrivel up and die. If the main character has lived a life of brief glory and concern with beauty, we might see a parallel to the flowers and decide that the story makes use of symbol. The story, then, gains meaning on several levels and is made especially powerful through the use of symbols to reinforce the story's theme. The symbol of flowers serves as "shorthand" for the writer.

When reconsidering a story and thinking about possible symbols, we must be cautious. A very determined reader might see every action and object in a story as a symbol. So, how do we know what symbols a writer intends? First, the symbolic object or action receives deliberate emphasis through repetition or positioning in the story. Second, seeing the object or action as a symbol enhances the interpretation of the story and does not contradict it. Our explorations of the meanings of symbols will take us further into the story, not away from it.

The selections in this unit contain irony and symbols. In "Just Lather, That's All," we meet a barber who has the choice between shaving a murderous captain and killing him. Edgar Allan Poe's "The Masque of the Red Death" gains vividness and depth through the use of color symbolism and dramatic irony. In "Holding Things Together," the narrator's unhappiness with her marriage and her burden of stereotyped expectations are conveyed to us not only directly, but also indirectly and symbolically through her anxieties about her car. The final story, "The Rocking-Horse Winner," prompts reflection on the symbolic meaning of the rocking horse and the ironic, bitter rewards of placing materialism over love and family relationships.

Each of the stories is challenging and thought-provoking, with a vividness and depth of meaning created, in part, using the tools of irony and symbol.

Hernando Téllez

Just Lather, That's All

"Not one of them comes out of this alive, not one."

He said nothing when he entered. I was passing the best of my razors back and forth on a strop. When I recognized him I started to tremble. But he didn't notice. Hoping to conceal my emotion, I continued sharpening the razor. I tested it on the meat of my thumb, and then held it up to the light. At that moment he took off the bullet-studded belt that his gun holster dangled from. He hung it up on a wall hook and placed his military cap over it. Then he turned to me, loosening the knot of his tie, and said, "It's hot as hell. Give me a shave." He sat in the chair.

I estimated he had a four-day beard. The four days taken up by the latest expedition in search of our troops. His face seemed reddened, burned by the sun. Carefully, I began to prepare the soap. I cut off a few slices, dropped them into the cup, mixed in a bit of warm water, and began to stir with the brush. Immediately the foam began to rise. "The other boys in the group should have this much beard, too." I continued stirring the lather.

"But we did all right, you know. We got the main ones. We brought back some dead, and we've got some others still alive. But pretty soon they'll all be dead."

"How many did you catch?" I asked.

"Fourteen. We had to go pretty deep into the woods to find them. But we'll get even. Not one of them comes out of this alive, not one."

He leaned back on the chair when he saw me with the lather-covered brush in my hand. I still had to put the sheet on him. No doubt about it, I was upset. I took a sheet out of a drawer and knotted it around my customer's neck. He wouldn't stop talking. He probably thought I was in sympathy with his party.

"The town must have learned a lesson from what we did the other day," he said.

"Yes," I replied, securing the knot at the base of his dark, sweaty neck.

"That was a fine show, eh?"

"Very good," I answered, turning back for the brush. The man closed his eyes with a gesture of fatigue and sat waiting for the cool caress of the soap. I had never had him so close to me. The day he ordered the whole town to file into the patio of the school to see the four rebels hanging there, I came face to face with him for an instant. But the sight of the mutilated bodies kept me from noticing the face of the man who had directed it all, the face I was now about to take into my hands. It was not an unpleasant face, certainly. And the beard, which made him seem a bit older than he was, didn't suit him badly at all. His name was Torres. Captain Torres. A man of imagination, because who else would have thought of hanging the naked rebels and then holding target practice on certain parts of their bodies? I began to apply the first layer of soap. With his eyes closed, he continued. "Without any effort I could go straight to sleep," he said, "but there's plenty to do this afternoon." I stopped the lathering and asked with a feigned lack of interest: "A firing squad?" "Something like that, but a little slower." I got on with the job of lathering his beard. My hands started trembling again. The man could not possibly realize it, and this was in my favor. But I would have preferred that he hadn't come. It was likely that many of our faction had seen him enter. And an enemy under one's roof imposes certain conditions. I would be obliged to shave that beard like any other one, carefully, gently, like that of any customer, taking pains to see that no single pore emitted a drop of blood. Being careful to see that the little tufts of hair did not lead the blade astray. Seeing that his skin ended up clean, soft, and healthy, so that passing the back of my hand over it I couldn't feel a hair. Yes, I was secretly a rebel, but I was also a conscientious barber, and proud of the preciseness of my profession. And this four-days' growth of beard was a fitting challenge.

I took the razor, opened up the two protective arms, exposed the blade and began the job, from one of the sideburns downward. The razor responded beautifully. His beard was inflexible and hard, not too long, but thick. Bit by bit the skin emerged. The razor rasped along, making its customary sound as fluffs of lather mixed with bits of hair gathered along the blade. I paused a moment to clean it, then took up the strop again to sharpen the razor, because I'm a barber who does things properly. The man, who had kept his eyes closed, opened them now, removed one of his hands from under the sheet, felt the spot on his face where the soap had been cleared off, and said, "Come to the school today at six o'clock." "The same thing as the other day?" I asked horrified. "It could be better," he replied. "What do you plan to do?" "I don't know yet. But we'll amuse ourselves." Once more he leaned back and closed his eyes. I approached him with the razor poised. "Do you plan to punish them all?" I ventured timidly. "All." The soap was drying on his face. I had to hurry. In the mirror I looked toward the street. It was the same as ever: the grocery store with two or three customers in it. Then I glanced at the clock: two-twenty in the afternoon. The razor continued on its downward stroke. Now from the other sideburn down. A thick, blue beard. He should have let it grow like some poets or priests do. It would suit him well. A lot of people wouldn't recognize him. Much to his benefit, I thought, as I attempted to cover the neck area smoothly. There, for sure, the razor had to be handled masterfully, since the hair, although softer, grew into little swirls. A curly beard. One of the tiny pores could be opened up and issue forth its pearl of blood. A good barber such as I prides himself on never allowing this to happen to a client. And this was a first-class client. How many of us had he ordered shot? How many of us had he ordered mutilated? It was better not to think about it. Torres did not know that I was his enemy. He did not know it nor did the rest. It was a secret shared by very few, precisely so that I could inform the revolutionaries of what Torres was doing in the town and of what he was planning each time he undertook a rebel-hunting excursion. So it was going to be very difficult to explain that I had him right in my hands and let him go peacefully—alive and shaved.

The beard was now almost completely gone. He seemed younger, less burdened by years than when he had arrived. I suppose this always happens with men who visit barber shops. Under the stroke of my razor Torres was being rejuvenated—rejuvenated because I am a good barber, the best in the town, if I may say so. A little more lather here, under his chin, on his Adam's apple, on this big vein. How hot it is getting! Torres must be sweating as much as I. But he is not afraid. He is a calm man, who is not even thinking about what he is going to do with the prisoners this afternoon. On the other hand I, with this razor in my hands, stroking and re-stroking this skin, trying to keep blood from oozing from these pores, can't even think clearly. Damn him for coming, because I'm a revolutionary and not a murderer. And how easy it would be to kill him. And he deserves it. Does he? No! What the devil! No one deserves to have someone else make the sacrifice of becoming a murderer. What do you gain by it? Nothing. Others come along and still others, and the first ones kill the second ones and they the next ones and it goes on like this until everything is a sea of blood. I could cut this throat just so, zip! zip! I wouldn't give him time to complain and since he has his eyes closed he wouldn't see the glistening knife blade or my glistening eyes. But I'm trembling like a real murderer. Out of his neck a gush of blood would spout onto the sheet, on the chair, on my hands, on the floor. I would have to close the door. And the blood would keep inching along the floor, warm, ineradicable, uncontainable, until it reached the street, like a little scarlet stream. I'm sure that one solid stroke, one deep incision, would prevent any pain. He wouldn't suffer. But what would I do with the body? Where would I hide it? I would have to flee, leaving all I have behind, and take refuge far away, far, far away. But they would follow until they found me. "Captain Torres' murderer. He slit his throat while he was shaving him—a coward." And then on the other side. "The avenger of us all. A name to remember. (And here they would mention my name.) He was the town barber. No one knew he was defending our cause."

And what of all this? Murderer or hero? My destiny depends on the edge of this blade. I can turn my hand a bit more, press a little harder on the razor, and sink it in. The skin would give way like silk, like rubber, like the strop. There is nothing more tender than human skin and the blood is always there, ready to pour forth. A blade like this doesn't fail. It is my best. But I don't want to be a murderer, no sir. You came to me for a shave. And I perform my work honorably.... I don't want blood on my hands. Just lather, that's all. You are an executioner and I am only a barber. Each person has his own place in the scheme of things. That's right. His own place.

Now his chin had been stroked clean and smooth. The man sat up and looked into the mirror. He rubbed his hands over his skin and felt it fresh, like new.

"Thanks," he said. He went to the hanger for his belt, pistol and cap. I must have been very pale; my shirt felt soaked. Torres finished adjusting the buckle, straightened his pistol in the holster and after automatically smoothing down his hair, he put on the cap. From his pants pocket he took out several coins to pay me for my services. And he began to head toward the door. In the doorway he paused for a moment, and turning to me he said:

"They told me that you'd kill me. I came to find out. But killing isn't easy. You can take my word for it." And he headed on down the street.

translated by Donald A. Yates

1. Take a few minutes to jot down your first impressions. If you wish, you might choose one focus from the following on which to write:
   - your thoughts and feelings about the ending;
   - the character you admire most and why;
   - questions you have.

   Share your writing with two or three classmates.
2. Initially, Torres seems ignorant of the danger he is in. At the end of the story, he reveals otherwise. Why, then, does he go to the barber's?
3. The barber realizes he could easily kill Torres, but decides against it. What are the reasons for this change? What is your opinion of his decision?
4. Comment upon the razor as a symbol in the story.
5. State the story's theme. For support, choose sentences from the story that come closest to the theme. Do you agree with the author's ideas about violence, action, change, evil? Explain.
6. Choose one of the following activities:
   a) Write Torres' report to one of his superiors.
   b) Roleplay the supper conversation that night between the barber and a family member or friend.
   c) Write the warning or explanation the barber might give to other rebels.

Edgar Allan Poe

The Masque of the Red Death

"Who dares to insult us with this blasphemous mockery?"

The "Red Death" had long devastated the country. No pestilence had ever been so fatal, or so hideous. Blood was its Avatar and its seal—the redness and the horror of blood. There were sharp pains, and sudden dizziness, and then profuse bleeding at the pores, with dissolution. The scarlet stains upon the body and especially upon the face of the victim, were the pest ban which shut him out from the aid and from the sympathy of his fellow-men. And the whole seizure, progress, and termination of the disease, were the incidents of half an hour.

But the Prince Prospero was happy and dauntless and sagacious. When his dominions were half depopulated, he summoned to his presence a thousand hale and light-hearted friends from among the knights and dames of his court, and with these retired to the deep seclusion of one of his castellated abbeys. This was an extensive and magnificent structure, the creation of the prince's own eccentric yet august taste. A strong and lofty wall girdled it in. This wall had gates of iron. The courtiers, having entered, brought furnaces and massy hammers and welded the bolts. They resolved to leave means neither of ingress nor egress to the sudden impulses of despair or of frenzy from within. The abbey was amply provisioned. With such precautions the courtiers might bid defiance to contagion. The external world could take care of itself. In the meantime it was folly to grieve, or to think. The prince had provided all the appliances of pleasure. There were buffoons, there were improvisatori, there were ballet-dancers, there were musicians, there was Beauty, there was wine. All these and security were within. Without was the "Red Death."

It was toward the close of the fifth or sixth month of his seclusion, and while the pestilence raged most furiously abroad, that the Prince Prospero entertained his thousand friends at a masked ball of the most unusual magnificence.

It was a voluptuous scene, that masquerade. But first let me tell of the rooms in which it was held. There were seven—an imperial suite. In many palaces, however, such suites form a long and straight vista, while the folding doors slide back nearly to the walls on either hand, so that the view of the whole extent is scarcely impeded. Here the case was very different; as might have been expected from the duke's love of the *bizarre*. The apartments were so irregularly disposed that the vision embraced but little more than one at a time. There was a sharp turn at every twenty or thirty yards, and at each turn a novel effect. To the right and left, in the middle of each wall, a tall and narrow Gothic window looked out upon a closed corridor which pursued the windings of the suite. These windows were of stained glass whose color varied in accordance with the prevailing hue of the decorations of the chamber into which it opened. That at the eastern extremity was hung, for example, in blue—and vividly blue were its windows. The second chamber was purple in its ornaments and tapestries, and here the panes were purple. The third was green throughout, and so were the casements. The fourth was furnished and lighted with orange—the fifth with white—the sixth with violet. The seventh apartment was closely shrouded in black velvet tapestries that hung all over the ceiling and down the walls, falling in heavy folds upon a carpet of the same material and hue. But in this chamber only, the color of the windows failed to correspond with the decorations. The panes here were scarlet—a deep blood color. Now in no one of the seven apartments was there any lamp or candelabrum, amid the profusion of golden ornaments that lay scattered to and fro or depended from the roof. There was no light of any kind emanating from lamp or candle within the suite of chambers. But in the corridors that followed the suite, there stood, opposite to each window, a heavy tripod, bearing a brazier of fire, that projected its rays through the tinted glass and so glaringly illumined the room. And thus were produced a multitude of gaudy and fantastic appearances. But in the western or black chamber the effect of the fire-light that streamed upon the dark hangings through the blood-tinted panes was ghastly in the extreme, and produced so wild a look upon the countenances of those who entered, that there were few of the company bold enough to set foot within its precincts at all.

It was in this apartment, also, that there stood against the western wall, a gigantic clock of ebony. Its pendulum swung to and fro with a dull, heavy, monotonous clang; and when the minute-hand made the circuit of the face, and the hour was to be stricken, there came from the brazen lungs of the clock a sound which was clear and loud and deep and exceedingly musical, but of so peculiar a note and emphasis that, at each lapse of an hour, the musicians of the orchestra were constrained to pause, momentarily, in their performance, to hearken to the sound; and thus the waltzers perforce ceased their evolutions; and there was a brief disconcert of the whole gay company; and, while the chimes of the clock yet rang, it was observed that the giddiest grew pale, and the more aged and sedate passed their hands over their brows as if in confused revery or meditation. But when the echoes had fully ceased, a light laughter at once pervaded the assembly; the musicians looked at each other and smiled as if at their own nervousness and folly, and made whispering vows, each to the other, that the next chiming of the clock should produce in them no similar emotion; and then, after the lapse of sixty minutes (which embrace three thousand and six hundred seconds of the Time that flies), there came yet another chiming of the clock, and then were the same disconcert and tremulousness and meditation as before.

But, in spite of these things, it was a gay and magnificent revel. The tastes of the duke were peculiar. He had a fine eye for colors and effects. He disregarded the *decora* of mere fashion. His plans were bold and fiery, and his conceptions glowed with barbaric lustre. There are some who would have thought him mad. His followers felt that he was not. It was necessary to hear and see and touch him to be *sure* that he was not.

He had directed, in great part, the movable embellishments of the seven chambers, upon occasion of this great *fête*; and it was his own guiding taste which had given character to the masqueraders. Be sure they were grotesque. There were much glare and glitter and

piquancy and phantasm—much of what has been since seen in "Hernani." There were arabesque figures with unsuited limbs and appointments. There were delirious fancies such as the madman fashions. There were much of the beautiful, much of the wanton, much of the *bizarre*, something of the terrible, and not a little of that which might have excited disgust. To and fro in the seven chambers there stalked, in fact, a multitude of dreams. And these—the dreams—writhed in and about, taking hue from the rooms, and causing the wild music of the orchestra to seem as the echo of their steps. And, anon, there strikes the ebony clock which stands in the hall of the velvet. And then, for a moment, all is still, and all is silent save the voice of the clock. The dreams are stiff-frozen as they stand. But the echoes of the chime die away—they have endured but an instant—and a light, half-subdued laughter floats after them as they depart. And now again the music swells, and the dreams live, and writhe to and fro more merrily than ever, taking hue from the many-tinted windows through which stream the rays from the tripods. But to the chamber which lies most westwardly of the seven there are now none of the maskers who venture; for the night is waning away; and there flows a ruddier light through the blood-colored panes; and the blackness of the sable drapery appals; and to him whose foot falls upon the sable carpet, there comes from the near clock of ebony a muffled peal more solemnly emphatic than any which reaches *their* ears who indulge in the more remote gaieties of the other apartments.

But these other apartments were densely crowded, and in them beat feverishly the heart of life. And the revel went whirlingly on, until at length there commenced the sounding of midnight upon the clock. And then the music ceased, as I have told; and the evolutions of the waltzers were quieted; and there was an uneasy cessation all things as before. But now there were twelve strokes to be sounded by the bell of the clock; and thus it happened, perhaps that more of thought crept, with more of time, into the meditations of the thoughtful among those who revelled. And thus too, it happened, perhaps, that before the last echoes of the last chime had utterly sunk into silence, there were many individuals in the crowd who had found leisure to become aware of the presence of a masked figure which had arrested the attention of no single individual before. And the rumor of this new presence having spread itself whisperingly around, there arose at length from the whole company a buzz, or murmur, expressive of disapprobation and surprise—then, finally, of terror, of horror, and of disgust.

In an assembly of phantasms such as I have painted, it may well be supposed that no ordinary appearance could have excited such sensation. In truth the masquerade license of the night was nearly unlimited; but the figure in question had out-Heroded Herod, and gone beyond the bounds of even the prince's indefinite decorum. There are chords in the hearts of the most reckless which cannot be touched without emotion. Even with the utterly lost, to whom life and death are equally jests, there are matters of which no jest can be made. The whole company, indeed, seemed now deeply to feel that in the costume and bearing of the stranger neither wit nor propriety existed. The figure was tall and gaunt, and shrouded from head to foot in the habiliments of the grave. The mask which concealed the visage was made so nearly to resemble the countenance of a stiffened corpse that the closest scrutiny must have had difficulty in detecting the cheat. And yet all this might have been endured, if not approved, by the mad revellers around. But the mummer had gone so far as to assume the type of the Red Death. His vesture was dabbled in *blood*—and his broad brow, with all the features of the face, was besprinkled with the scarlet horror.

When the eyes of Prince Prospero fell upon this spectral image (which, with a slow and solemn movement, as if more fully to sustain its *rôle*, stalked to and fro among the waltzers) he was seen to be convulsed, in the first moment with a strong shudder either of terror or distaste; but, in the next, his brow reddened with rage.

"Who dares"—he demanded hoarsely of the courtiers who stood near him— "who dares to insult us with this blasphemous mockery? Seize him and unmask him—that we may know whom we have to hang, at sunrise, from the battlements!"

It was in the eastern or blue chamber in which stood the Prince Prospero as he uttered these words. They rang throughout the seven rooms loudly and clearly, for the prince was a bold and robust man, and the music had become hushed at the waving of his hand.

It was in the blue room where stood the prince, with a group of pale courtiers by his side. At first, as he spoke, there was a slight rushing movement of this group in the direction of the intruder, who, at the moment was also near at hand, and now, with deliberate and stately step, made closer approach to the speaker. But from a certain nameless awe with which the mad assumptions of the mummer had inspired the whole party, there were found none who put forth hand to seize him; so that, unimpeded, he passed within a yard of the prince's person; and, while the vast assembly, as if with one impulse, shrank from the centres of the rooms to the walls, he made his way uninterruptedly, but with the same solemn and measured step which had distinguished him from the first, through the blue chamber to the purple—through the purple to the green—through the green to the orange—through this again to the white—and even thence to the violet, ere a decided movement had been made to arrest him. It was then, however, that the Prince Prospero, maddening with rage and the shame of his own momentary cowardice, rushed hurriedly through the six chambers, while none followed him on account of a deadly terror that had seized upon all. He bore aloft a drawn dagger, and had approached, in rapid impetuosity, to within three or four feet of the retreating figure, when the latter, having attained the extremity of the velvet apartment, turned suddenly and confronted his pursuer. There was a sharp cry—and the dagger dropped gleaming upon the sable carpet, upon which, instantly afterward, fell prostrate in death the Prince Prospero. Then, summoning the wild courage of despair, a throng of the revellers at once threw themselves into the black apartment, and, seizing the mummer, whose tall figure stood erect and motionless within the shadow of the ebony clock, gasped in unutterable horror at finding the grave cerements and corpse-like mask, which they handled with so violent a rudeness, untenanted by any tangible form.

And now was acknowledged the presence of the Red Death. He had come like a thief in the night. And one by one dropped the revellers in the blood-bedewed halls of their revel, and died each in the despairing posture of his fall. And the life of the ebony clock went out with that of the last of the gay. And the flames of the tripods expired. And Darkness and Decay and the Red Death held illimitable dominion over all.

1. Take a few minutes to jot down your first impressions. If you wish, you might choose one focus from the following on which to write:
   - images the story brought to mind and what those images left you feeling, seeing, or hearing;
   - whether or not Prince Prospero deserved his fate;
   - the use of color in the story.

   Share your writing with two or three classmates.
2. a) Describe Prince Prospero. Consider the word "hedonism." What details in the story suggest that Prospero's lifestyle is hedonistic? How is Prospero's name ironic? (Check also the allusion to a character in Shakespeare's play *The Tempest*.)
   b) Discuss the Red Death. What do you think the Red Death is? Why is the story called "The *Masque* of the Red Death"?
3. Despite Prospero's attempts to keep the pestilence outside his castle, he fails. Why? What moral does the story offer? Give support from the story for your answer.
4. Colors are used symbolically in the story. Discuss meanings suggested by red, black, and various other room colors.
5. Describe the mood at the beginning of the story and identify some words or phrases that create it. When and how does the mood change?
6. Choose one of the following activities:
   a) Explain how you would film this story.
   b) Stage the story as a pantomime set to music.
   c) Compare this story with Poe's "The Fall of the House of Usher."

Anne Tyler

Holding Things Together

I can't stand to have something go wrong with my car.

He says that when he was ten, a family invited him to the movies and he got all dressed up in a new suit and tie and a blue striped shirt. But he didn't know how to tie the tie, and his father had died the year before and no one else in that household of women—mother, aunt, two sisters—knew how, either. They experimented most of Sunday afternoon, knotting and unknotting it until it was limp and crumpled. Finally, his aunt put it in her purse and caught a bus downtown. Standing in front of the show window at Patterson Brothers Menswear, she tied the tie so that it looked like the one on the mannequin. Then she took the bus home again and fastened the knot to his shirt with two straight pins. All through the movie he held his head at an angle, his hands hovering over his chest, protecting his long, clumsy tie as people squeezed past him to their seats.

There are a lot of questions I would like to ask about this. Couldn't he have gone to a neighbor? Didn't he have a male friend? Why wear a tie to a movie anyhow? At age *ten*?

You'd think at least he would have used a safety pin.

But I don't want to make too much of it. We've been married two years and I know by now: he doesn't like to talk about himself. In fact, I'm surprised he told me that story at all. I'm surprised he even remembered it.

He is forty years old, fifteen years my senior. A high-school principal. A large, pale, tired-looking man going bald. He always dresses formally, even for casual events—a home football game, a picnic—but generally there's something off kilter about his clothing. His lapels are spotted; his trousers are rumpled; his shirt is pricked with cigarette burns. His suit jacket always hangs lower in front, and the points of his collar curl up.

Of course, he knows how to tie a tie by now, but there are other things he's never learned. He can't fix a leaky faucet, for instance. He can't change the storm windows or put on tire chains. Is it because he lost his father so young? I was reared to believe that men take charge; I feel cheated. I do it myself, grumpily, or I call in a professional. I tell him I don't know where he'd be without me to hold things together. This always bothers him, and he walks away from me with his hands jammed into his pockets and his jacket sleeves rucked up to his elbows. Then I feel sorry; I never meant to sound so overbearing.

My car developed a shriek in the brakes and I had to take it to Exxon. This was last April, a beautiful, leafy April morning, but I was too upset to enjoy it. I can't stand to have something go wrong with my car. At the slightest symptom, I despair; I picture being stranded on the roadside, hood raised and white handkerchief fluttering, no one to stop for me but a couple of escaping convicts. Now here I was on my way to work and I heard this long, high shriek as I braked for a stoplight. I turned right around and drove to Exxon, where they know me. The mechanic on duty was Victor—a red-headed man with a carrot tattooed on his forearm. "Oh, Victor, just listen," I told him, and I had him stand out front while I drove back and forth, stopping every few feet. The brakes shrilled, though maybe not quite as loudly as before. I cut the motor and stepped out of the car. "What do you think it might be?" I asked.

He pulled at his nose. I waited. (My husband would have pressured him, supplied too much information, pushed for an immediate answer, but I knew enough to let him take his time.) Finally he said, "Just now start up?"

"Five minutes back," I told him.

"Little as *you* drive, chances are it's nothing at all."

"Yes, but what if I try to stop and can't? When it's the brakes, I get worried, Victor."

"Well, no, just calm down. You go in and have a seat. I'll give her a look."

I went into the office, with its two vinyl chairs and the coffee table stacked with *Popular Mechanics*. Tins of motor oil and bottles of windshield detergent were lined up neatly on the shelves. The tall blond boy named Joel was thumbing through an auto-parts catalogue. "Morning, Mrs. S.," he said. (He's fonder of me than Victor is; I think he likes the way I look. One time he asked where I bought my clothes, so that he could tell his wife.) He said, "Something gone wrong with the car again?"

"Victor's out checking my brakes," I told him. "Every time I slow down, they make this squeaky sound."

"Never mind. Lots of times brakes'll do that," he said.

"Really?"

"Sure. I wouldn't give it a thought."

"Oh, Joel, I hope you're right," I said.

Then I sank onto one of the chairs, and fluffed my skirt around my knees. I felt better already. Smaller boned. Joel was standing in a shaft of sunlight with lazy dust specks drifting around his head, and the chair was warm and smooth, and something gave off a nice leathery smell. When Victor came to get me (it was nothing, after all), I really was sorry to leave. I believe I could have sat there all morning.

My husband drives a Plymouth with a dented left fender, a smashed tail-light, and a BB scar like a little rayed sun on its right rear window. He seems determined just to use his car up—run it into the ground and walk away from it, as if it were something to be beaten into submission. Like his battered suits, or his shoes with the heels worn to lopsided slivers. What is it about him? I myself drive a Ford; I believe it's easiest to get parts for a Ford. It's five years old but it looks brand-new. Even the engine looks new; last year I had it steam-cleaned. Some people don't know you can do that, but you can.

If the weather has been dry, you can see the names of a couple of dozen high-school students written in the dust on my husband's fenders. Not to mention four-letter words, smiling faces, valentines. Inside, there are tattered files and magazines strewn across the seats, and squashed cigarette packs on the floor. The gearshift snaps in an alarming way when he goes into "Drive," and the engine tends to diesel long after he's cut the ignition. Also, his fan belt is loose; every time he makes a sharp turn you can hear a sound like a puppy's whimper. I tell him he ought to get it seen to. "You have to stay on top of these things," I tell him. "A machine is only worth the care you give it."

I feel ridiculous. I feel I'm turning into my father, a thorough, methodical man who wouldn't let me get my driver's license till I'd learned how to change a spare tire. Still, I know I'm right. "What if we're stranded somewhere?" I ask. "What if we're taking a very long trip and the car drops dead in the middle of an eight-lane highway?"

"Why, this is a *fine* car," my husband says.

He's offended, I can tell. He slumps in his seat, steering with only one wrist propped across the top of the wheel. He always drives abysmally—dashing start-ups, sudden swerves, jerky stops. At red lights, he refuses to shift to neutral. I tell him he ought to, but he says it's pointless. "Why get a car that's automatic and then spend your life shifting gears?" he asks.

"To save wear and tear on your transmission, of course."

He groans, and starts off again with a screech. I promise myself I won't say another word. But I can't resist a silent comment: as the car heads toward a curve at sixty miles an hour, I raise a hand deliberately and brace myself against the dashboard.

Last June, my old college roommate came to town and I took her out to lunch. Just the two of us; my husband doesn't like her. (He says she's brassy, loud, opinionated, but I believe he's jealous. Men imagine women are closer than they really are.) I picked her up at her sister-in-law's and drove her to Nardulli's, a little Italian restaurant I hardly ever get to go to. Bee looked wonderful. She wore tight white pants and a loose top, and ropes and ropes of branch coral. During the meal, we had all sorts of things to talk about—our jobs, our husbands, old friends—but by the time our coffee came we had more or less petered out. We drove back in near silence, the comfortable kind. Bee hummed "Star Dust" and let her arm hang loose out the window. I coasted down St. Johns Street, timing the lights perfectly.

Then on Delmore, where I had to turn left, the engine died. For no earthly reason. "Now, what …?" I said. I shifted gears and started up again. We rode smoothly till the stop sign on Furgan Street; then the engine died again. After that, it died every time I slowed down. Red and green warning signals flashed on the instrument panel; horns kept honking behind me. My accelerator foot started shaking. "Oh, Lord, something has gone wrong," I told Bee.

"Maybe you're out of gas," she said.

"Gas? How could it be the gas? It keeps on starting up again, doesn't it? That's ridiculous," I said.

Bee glanced at me but said nothing. I was too frantic to apologize. "Listen, I've got to get to Exxon," I said.

"There's a Texaco station just ahead."

"But Exxon is where they know my car, and it's only two more blocks."

The engine died again. "Thank God we're not out on some highway," I said, and I wiped my eyes on my sleeve. I could feel Bee's sideways stare.

Then just as we rolled into Exxon the car gave a final shudder, like a desert wanderer staggering into an oasis. I jumped out, leaving the door swinging open behind me. I ran into the garage, where Joel was standing under an elevated Volkswagen, whistling and squinting upward with his thumbs hitched through his belt loops. "Joel?" I said. "My car's developed this terrible problem."

He stopped whistling. "Why, hello, Mrs. S.," he said.

"Can't you take a look for me?"

He followed me into the sunlight. I felt better already; he was so slow and peaceful. All the while I was telling him the symptoms, he was just coolly raising the hood, poking around, humming whatever he'd been whistling. "Turn her on," he told me. I slid behind the wheel, started the engine, and stopped it when he signalled. Then I got out and went to look under the hood again. I watched his long, bony fingers, which seemed to have more texture than other people's because of the grime in the creases. He jiggled a little black wire.

"Is it the fuel pump?" I asked him. I'd had a terrible experience once with a fuel pump. (I'm learning auto parts the hard way, the same way soldiers learn geography.)

But Joel said, "Can't tell for sure. Going to bring her on inside. It won't take long."

I told Bee. She got out and we went to the office to wait. In the summer, the leathery smell was stronger than ever. I collapsed on one of the chairs, closed my eyes, and tipped by head back. "I'm sorry," I told Bee. "I just get so upset when my car doesn't work."

"You know what I would do?" said Bee. "Take a course in auto mechanics."

I opened my eyes and looked at her.

"Sure," she said. "That's what I did when our lawn started getting me down. I went over to the college and studied landscape architecture. I got up at six every morning for this course on television. I bought a machine to spread lime on the—"

"Yes," I said, "but I already have so much to—"

"Be adventurous! There aren't any *roles* anymore. Just jump in and do what you feel like."

I thought a minute.

"Bee," I said finally, "tell me the truth. Did you do that because you felt like it? Or because you saw that no one else was going to do it?"

"Hmm?" she said. But by then she had picked up one of the magazines, and was idly flipping pages. It was plain she didn't think the question was important.

After a while, Joel came in, wiping his hands on a rag. "It's the filter," he told me. "You've got to get your filter changed."

"Is that serious?"

"No, we can have her ready by five this afternoon."

Bee said, "I'll call my sister-in-law. She can come pick us up."

"But the car," I said. "I mean, after this will it be as good as ever? Will it run without stalling?"

"No reason why it shouldn't," Joel said.

He wrote my name on a printed form: Mrs. Simmons, in large, competent capitals. At the second line, his pencil paused "Address? Phone?" he said.

"Four four four four Nelson Road. Eight four four, two two four four."

"Four must be your lucky number," he said.

"No, nine."

He looked up. Then he laughed.

"Well, you asked," I told him. Then I laughed too, ignoring Bee's blank stare. I felt young and scatterbrained, but in a pleasant way. It was wonderful to know that by five o'clock everything would be all right again.

Bee's sister-in-law came to get us in a great big lavender Cadillac, and she drove me home. Before I got out, I apologized again to Bee. "Oh, listen," she said, "forget it. But how about later, will you need a ride back to the station?"

"Oh, no. I'm sure Alfred will be home by then," I said.

"Well, if he isn't, now ..."

"I'll call you," I promised.

But I was right. My husband was home in time to take me. Just barely, though: I had to rush him right back out the door. He seemed befuddled, out of step. He drove more sloppily than ever. "*What* did you say went wrong? Last week, your car looked fine," he said. He turned right, bouncing over the curb. He went through a yellow light that was changing to red. At Exxon, he slowed and gazed dimly out the window. "Don't leave till I make sure it's fixed," I said. (You have to tell him these things.) I hopped out and went into the garage, where Joel was spinning a tire on a turntable. He smiled when he saw me. "All set," he said. "Feel better now?"

"I certainly do," I said. Then I turned and waved to my husband, telling him he was free to go. He waved back. His sleeve looked like a used lunch bag. For some reason, it made me sad to see his dusty little car go puttering off into traffic again.

I first met my husband while I was student-teaching at his school. I didn't like teaching at all, as it turned out (now I work in a library), but I thought I should go ahead and get my certificate anyway. Just in case, was how I put it—meaning in case I never married, or was widowed young, or something like that.

Alfred when I met him was exactly the way he is now—shabby, shambling, absentminded. The only difference was that he seemed so authoritative. I heard the teachers talking about him: he was "Mr. Simmons" and he didn't like undisciplined classrooms. When he came to a room to observe, some electricity seemed to pass through the students. They acted more alert. The teacher grew crisper. Now I sit across from him at the supper table and I try and try to see him again in that shine of unquestioned assurance. I squint, giving him distance. He becomes so distraught that he drops his fork. "What's the matter?" he asks. "Have I done something wrong?"

Yet at school, the few times I've been back, I notice that the teachers still make improvements in their posture when they see him coming down the hall.

While we were courting, it never occurred to me to ask what he knew how to do. Could he change the oil? Hang a screen door? Well, of course he could; all men could. And even if he couldn't, what difference did it make? I loved him. I would go weak with love just watching his cuff button spin dizzily from one frayed thread. If he got lost while driving me to a restaurant, I was glad; I hadn't wanted to eat anyhow. I was only waiting for the moment when he would park the car in front of my apartment and take me in his arms. His hands (with their spatulate nails, their pink, uncalloused palms that should have been a warning) seemed to mold me; I curved within them and grew taller, slimmer, prettier. It was hardly the moment to ask if he knew how to replace a wall switch.

Then we married and went to live in a middle-aged house on Coker Street. It was a hard time; my parents thought Alfred was disappointing, and they more or less withdrew themselves. I felt orphaned. I started work in the library, and every evening when I came home (dead tired, feet aching) I had to fix supper, take out the garbage, vacuum, dust. On weekends, I mowed the lawn and pruned the shrubs, and then I washed the woodwork, painted rooms, varnished floors. My husband only watched, from various doorways. I don't mean to imply that he was lazy. It's just that he didn't know how to help. He would gladly take out the garbage for me but forgot to replace the trash-can lid, so dogs would tip the can over and spread the garbage everywhere. He dripped paint, stepped in the varnish, broke a window trying to open it. It turned out that he had never learned how to handle money, and had therefore been assigned one of those special bank tellers who balance checkbooks for rich, helpless widows. Also, he had a cubbyhole in his desk at home that contained nothing but unpaid parking tickets.

Well, I paid the tickets, I took over the checkbook, I drew up a yearly budget. Quizzing him on deductible expenses (my father's task, in my childhood), I felt I was becoming angular, wider shouldered. I developed my father's habit of offering forth one flat, spread hand, palm upward, inviting others to be reasonable. "Well, think, Alfred. Did you buy any stamps? Office supplies? Any books that had to do with your profession?'

"Books?" he would say. "Why, yes, I believe I did."

"How much were they? Do you have the receipts?"

"Oh, no. I must have lost them."

"Five dollars? Ten?"

"I'm not quite sure."

"Think of the titles. Maybe that will help. Fifteen dollars? Twenty? Was it under twenty-five?"

"I just don't *know*, Lucy. Please, does it matter all that much?"

At night, I began to have insomnia. I lay in bed with my hands curled tight, no matter how often I told myself to open them. I felt I was clutching all the strings of the house, keeping it together. Everything depended on me.

"When I start the motor," I told Joel, "it sounds just fine. Then I go faster and I'm waiting for that click, you know? That click that tells me the car's shifted gears? But I don't seem to hear it. And it seems to me the motor whines a little, has the wrong sound; I don't know how to explain it."

"Just hope it's not the transmission," Joel said. "That can get expensive."

We were waiting for a stoplight; he was driving. He was going to test the automatic shift for me. It was August and very hot and sunny (Joel's face was glazed with sweat and his yellow hair had a glittery look), but I didn't open my window. I liked the feeling of soaking in heat; I'd felt cold and anxious all morning. I liked the fact that Joel, waiting serenely for the light, whistled "Let It Be" and drummed his fingers on the steering wheel. My car seemed humble and obedient.

"I hope I don't have to buy a new one," I said.

"You won't," he told me.

The light changed. Joel started right off, but we were following someone—some old lady in a Studebaker who just wouldn't get up any speed. "Shoot," Joel said. He switched lanes. Now we really were travelling, and Joel had his head cocked to hear the sound of the motor. "Well?" he said. "Seems to me like she's shifting just about on schedule."

"No, wait a minute, give it a minute ..."

I was listening too, but I couldn't hear what I heard when I was alone.

We turned off onto a smaller road, a residential street with no traffic lights. Joel stopped the car, then started again and went up to sixty, all the time keeping his head cocked. He braked and shifted to neutral; his knuckles moved beneath the skin like well-oiled machine parts. "Let's run her through again," he said.

The second run carried us to the end of the road—a surprise, a field full of goldenrod and beer cans. He stopped the car and wiped his upper lip with the back of his hand. "Well," he said, gazing out at the field. Behind his eyes (which were long and blue, as clear as windows) I imagined sheets of information, all the facts he knew being reviewed in an orderly way. "No," he said finally, and shook his head. "She seems O.K. to me."

You'd think I'd be relieved, but I wasn't. If something is wrong, it can be fixed; then you know it won't go wrong again for a while. But if nothing's been pinpointed, if it's just this nebulous feeling of *error* in your mind ... I sighed and gripped my purse. Joel looked over at me. "I must be going crazy," I told him.

"Oh, no ..."

"I seem to be taking this car so seriously. Lately, I've stopped driving on freeways. I don't want to be too far from a service station. I've had to give up the League of Women Voters and my favorite supermarket. Even here in town, I only go by routes that have service stations. Streets with nothing but houses make me anxious."

"Shoot, this car's in *fine* shape," he told me, giving the wheel a pat. "You don't have to feel like that."

"I'm worried pretty soon I'll just have to stay at home all day."

That made him laugh. "So what?" he said. "What's so bad about home?"

"I'd lose my job, for one thing."

"Well, I just wish my wife would have your problem," he said. "That's all she does all day—drive around. Drops me off at the station and then drives here, drives there … spends all our money, wears out the baby …"

"But she does have you to call if something goes wrong," I said.

"Where, forty miles out on the Beltway? Out at Korvettes, or K Mart, or Two Guys? And none of what she buys is worth much. All these skimpy sweaters, tacky plastic earrings … I don't begrudge the money, but she could save it up and buy something *good*, like your tan coat—you know your tan coat?—and be a whole lot better off. I tell her that, but think she'll listen?"

"Maybe she's lonely," I said.

"Maybe so," he said, "but I'd sure like a wife who stayed home some. And she doesn't take care of herself—she's so sloppy. She's let her hair grow long, and every time I come home I think, Well, who's this? I mean it never stops being a surprise, I never get used to it. I think, Is this *it*, is this who I'm with, this lady with the stringy hair? It's like I have amnesia. I just can't figure how it all happened."

"No one told us it would be so permanent," I said.

"Why, no," he said. "Not so as to make us believe it."

He looked over at me. His hands fell off the wheel. Outside, I could hear the locusts whirring, pointing up our silence. "Well!" I said, and Joel said, "Well! Victor will be having kittens by now." And he started up the car again, and turned around, and we drove on back to the station.

Last September, I went South to visit my parents for a week. It didn't go well, though. I'd been away too long; something had stiffened between us. I watched my younger sister teasing them at the supper table and I felt more orphaned than ever. My father stayed down in his workshop, taking things apart and putting them back together; my mother and I were so polite it was painful. I was glad when it was time to leave.

Alfred met me at the train station, carrying roses. I was so happy to see him. His crumpled clothes gave me a soothed and trustful feeling; I rested on his smell of old tobacco. "Don't let me leave you again," I told him. He smiled and laid the roses in my arms.

Driving home, he asked about my family: Were they used to the idea of our marriage yet? "Oh, sure," I told him offhandedly. What did my family have to do with us?

He parked in front of our house, with two wheels on the curb. He took my suitcase from the trunk, and we climbed the front steps, holding hands. "You notice I've mowed the grass for you," he said.

I was surprised. I looked around at the lawn—straggly, dotted with the first few leaves of fall. Plainly, something had been chewing at it. I saw the narrow, tufted rows he'd missed. "Why, Alfred!" I said.

He seemed uneasy.

"That's wonderful!" I told him.

"Yes, but—Lucy? I'm not so sure about the lawnmower."

"Lawnmower?"

"I mean, it seems to me that something's wrong with it."

"Oh, well, I'll check it later," I told him.

"It's right over there, if you want to take a look."

In the grass at the side of the house, he meant; he'd left it out. It was an electric mower, and fairly expensive—not a thing you'd leave sitting around. But I didn't tell him so. "What seems to be the trouble?" I asked.

"Well—"

He set my suitcase on the porch and went over to the mower. He turned the mower upside down without unplugging it (I winced but said nothing) and pointed to the blades. "See there?" he said.

Well, they *used* to be blades. Now they were mangled hunks of metal, notched and torn and twisted. I said, "What on earth?" I bent closer. One of the hunks of metal wasn't a blade at all, it turned out, but something flatter and wider. "Why, that's the foot guard," I said. "It's supposed to be attached to the rear of the mower."

"Evidently it came loose," Alfred said.

"Yes, but—what happened, you just went on mowing? You mowed on over your own foot guard and let the blades gnash it up?"

"I didn't realize what was going on," he said.

"But the noise must have been horrendous!"

"Well, I thought it was the … I don't know. I just thought it was having a little spell of some sort, caught a twig or something."

I pictured it exactly: Alfred doggedly pushing on, with terrible shrieks and clatters coming from the mower. It gave me a feeling of despair. I couldn't seem to rise above this. "Oh, Alfred," I said, "can't you do something right? Will I always have to be the one?"

He straightened up and looked at me. His face had grown white. His eyes (ordinarily a mild gray) had widened and darkened; they seemed to be all iris. "I knew you would say that, Lucy," he said.

"If you knew, then why—"

"Nothing I do will satisfy you. You always want everything perfect and you always do it yourself; or stand over me and nag and belittle, find fault with every move I make. You just have to be in control; it's always you that holds the power."

"Is that how you see it?" I said. "Do you think I choose to be this way? Do you think I *want* the power? Take it! Why won't you take it? Do you think I'd hold it if anybody else would? *Take* it!"

And I shook my hands in his face, offering all that was in them, but he merely looked at me with a stoic expression. My hands were left raised before me. I let them drop. I watched him turn to right the mower and unplug it and trundle it toward the garage: a large, sad man in a baggy suit, slumping slightly as he walked.

My car's been running well lately, though I haven't given up worrying. In fact, the last time I went to Exxon it was just to fill the gas tank. I went on a foggy October morning, the first really cold day of fall. Joel was the one on duty. He seemed grim, maybe hung over; and I had a headache from sitting up to watch the late show after Alfred had gone to bed. So all I did was nod, and Joel nodded back and went to start the pump. While the tank was filling, he stood waiting with his arms folded. I stared straight ahead, watching my breath steam the windshield. Then I paid him six dollars and twenty-four cents and put my billfold back in my purse and drove away.

1. Take a few minutes to jot down your first impressions. If you wish, you might choose one focus from the following on which to write:
   - questions or observations about Lucy's relationship with Alfred;
   - what in the story seems realistic and/or unrealistic;
   - ways in which one character reminds you of yourself or of someone else.

   Share your writing with two or three classmates.
2. a) In what way does Lucy's approach to her car reflect her approach to Alfred and her relationship with him? In what way does Alfred's car reflect his character?

   b) What qualities attracted Lucy to Alfred in the first place? What has changed?
3. What does Joel represent for Lucy? Considering the details the author gives about Joel and his life, what does the author seem to suggest?
4. What differences can you see in the way Lucy and Bee respond to conflict? What advice would Bee likely offer Lucy about her relationship with Alfred?
5. In small groups, discuss one of the issues raised by the story (e.g., gender stereotypes).
6. From the perspective of either Alfred or Lucy, write two journal entries—the first made just after their final dialogue in the story, and the second sometime in the future.

D.H. Lawrence

The Rocking-Horse Winner

There was never enough money.

There was a woman who was beautiful, who started with all the advantages, yet she had no luck. She married for love, and the love turned to dust. She had bonny children, yet she felt they had been thrust upon her, and she could not love them. They looked at her coldly, as if they were finding fault with her. And hurriedly she felt she must cover up some fault in herself. Yet what it was that she must cover up she never knew. Nevertheless, when her children were present, she always felt the centre of her heart go hard. This troubled her, and in her manner she was all the more gentle and anxious for her children as if she loved them very much. Only she herself knew that at the centre of her heart was a hard little place that could not feel love, no, not for anybody. Everybody else said of her: "She is such a good mother. She adores her children." Only she herself, and her children themselves, knew it was not so. They read it in each other's eyes.

There were a boy and two little girls. They lived in a pleasant house, with a garden, and they had discreet servants, and felt themselves superior to anyone in the neighbourhood.

Although they lived in style, they felt always an anxiety in the house. There was never enough money. The mother had a small income, and the father had a small income, but not nearly enough for the social position which they had to keep up. The father went into town to some office. But though he had good prospects, these prospects never materialized. There was always the grinding sense of the shortage of money, though the style was always kept up.

At last the mother said: "I will see if I can't make something." But she did not know where to begin. She racked her brains, and tried this thing and the other, but could not find anything successful. The failure made deep lines come into her face. Her children were growing up, they would have to go to school. There must be more money, there must be more money. The father, who was always very handsome and expensive in his tastes, seemed as if he never would be able to do anything worth doing. And the mother, who had a great belief in herself, did not succeed any better, and her tastes were just as expensive.

And so the house came to be haunted by the unspoken phrase: There must be more money! There must be more money! The children could hear it all the time, though nobody said it aloud. They heard it at Christmas, when the expensive and splendid toys filled the nursery. Behind the shining modern rocking horse, behind the smart doll's-house, a voice would start whispering: "There must be more money! There must be more money!" And the children would stop playing, to listen for a moment. They would look into each other's eyes, to see if they had all heard. And each one saw in the eyes of the other two that they too had heard. "There must be more money! There must be more money!"

It came whispering from the springs of the still-swaying rocking horse, and even the horse, bending his wooden, champing head, heard it. The big doll, sitting so pink and smirking in her new pram, could hear it quite plainly, and seemed to be smirking all the more self-consciously because of it. The foolish puppy, too, that took the place of the Teddy bear, he was looking so extraordinarily foolish for no other reason but that he heard the secret whisper all over the house: "There must be more money!"

Yet nobody ever said it aloud. The whisper was everywhere, and therefore no one spoke it. Just as no one ever says: "We are breathing!" in spite of the fact that breath is coming and going all the time.

"Mother," said the boy Paul one day, "why don't we keep a car of our own? Why do we always use uncle's, or else a taxi?"

"Because we're the poor members of the family," said the mother.

"But why are we, mother?"

"Well—I suppose," she said slowly and bitterly, "it's because your father has no luck."

The boy was silent for some time.

"Is luck money, mother?" he asked, rather timidly.

"No, Paul. Not quite. It's what causes you to have money."

"Oh!" said Paul vaguely. "I thought when Uncle Oscar said filthy lucker, it meant money."

"Filthy lucre does mean money," said the mother. "But it's lucre, not luck."

"Oh!" said the boy. "Then what is luck, mother?"

"It's what causes you to have money. If you're lucky you have money. That's why it's better to be born lucky than rich. If you're rich, you may lose your money. But if you're lucky, you will always get more money."

"Oh! Will you? And is father not lucky?"

"Very unlucky, I should say," she said bitterly.

The boy watched her with unsure eyes.

"Why?" he asked.

"I don't know. Nobody ever knows why one person is lucky and another unlucky."

"Don't they? Nobody at all? Does nobody know?"

"Perhaps God. But He never tells."

"He ought to, then. And aren't you lucky either, mother?"

"I can't be, if I married an unlucky husband."

"But by yourself, aren't you?"

"I used to think I was, before I married. Now I think I am very unlucky indeed."

"Why?"

"Well—never mind! Perhaps I'm not really," she said.

The child looked at her, to see if she meant it. But he saw, by the lines of her mouth, that she was only trying to hide something from him.

"Well, anyhow," he said stoutly, "I'm a lucky person."

"Why?" said his mother, with a sudden laugh.

He stared at her. He didn't even know why he had said it.

"God told me," he asserted, brazening it out.

"I hope He did, dear!" she said, again with a laugh, but rather bitter.

"He did, mother!"

"Excellent!" said the mother, using one of her husband's exclamations.

The boy saw she did not believe him; or, rather, that she paid no attention to his assertion. This angered him somewhat, and made him want to compel her attention.

He went off by himself, vaguely, in a childish way, seeking for the clue to "luck." Absorbed, taking no heed of other people, he went about with a sort of stealth, seeking inwardly for luck. He wanted luck, he wanted it, he wanted it. When the two girls were playing dolls in the nursery, he would sit on his big rocking horse, charging madly into space, with a frenzy that made the little girls peer at him uneasily. Wildly the horse careered, the waving dark hair of the boy tossed, his eyes had a strange glare in them. The little girls dared not speak to him.

When he had ridden to the end of his mad little journey, he climbed down and stood in front of his rocking horse, staring fixedly into its lowered face. Its red mouth was slightly open, its big eye was wide and glassy-bright.

"Now!" he would silently command the snorting steed. "Now, take me to where there is luck! Now take me!"

And he would slash the horse on the neck with the little whip he had asked Uncle Oscar for. He knew the horse could take him to where there was luck, if only he forced it. So he would mount again and start on his furious ride, hoping at last to get there. He knew he could get there.

"You'll break your horse, Paul!" said the nurse.

"He's always riding like that! I wish he'd leave off!" said his elder sister Joan.

But he only glared down on them in silence. Nurse gave him up. She could make nothing of him. Anyhow he was growing beyond her.

One day his mother and his Uncle Oscar came in when he was on one of his furious rides. He did not speak to them.

"Hallo, you young jockey! Riding a winner?" said his uncle.

"Aren't you growing too big for a rocking horse? You're not a very little boy any longer, you know," said his mother.

But Paul only gave a blue glare from his big, rather close-set eyes.

He would speak to nobody when he was in full tilt. His mother watched him with an anxious expression on her face.

At last he suddenly stopped forcing his horse into the mechanical gallop, and slid down.

"Well, I got there!" he announced fiercely, his blue eyes still flaring, and his sturdy long legs straddling apart.

"Where did you get to?" asked his mother.

"Where I wanted to go," he flared back at her.

"That's right, son!" said Uncle Oscar. "Don't you stop till you get there. What's the horse's name?"

"He doesn't have a name," said the boy.

"Gets on without all right?" asked the uncle.

"Well, he has different names. He was called Sansovino last week."

"Sansovino, eh? Won the Ascot. How did you know his name?"

"He always talks about horse races with Bassett," said Joan.

The uncle was delighted to find that his small nephew was posted with all the racing news. Bassett, the young gardener, who had been wounded in the left foot in the war and had got his present job through Oscar Cresswell, whose batman he had been, was a perfect blade of the "turf." He lived in the racing events, and the small boy lived with him.

Oscar Cresswell got it all from Bassett.

"Master Paul comes and asks me, so I can't do more than tell him, sir," said Bassett, his face terribly serious, as if he were speaking of religious matters.

"And does he ever put anything on a horse he fancies?"

"Well—I don't want to give him away—he's a young sport, a fine sport, sir. Would you mind asking him yourself? He sort of takes a pleasure in it, and perhaps he'd feel I was giving him away, sir, if you don't mind."

Bassett was serious as a church.

The uncle went back to his nephew, and took him off for a ride in the car.

"Say, Paul, old man, do you ever put anything on a horse?" the uncle asked.

The boy watched the handsome man closely.

"Why, do you think I oughtn't to?" he parried.

"Not a bit of it! I thought perhaps you might give me a tip for the Lincoln."

The car sped on into the country, going down to Uncle Oscar's place in Hampshire.

"Honour bright?" said the nephew.

"Honour bright, son!" said the uncle.

"Well, then, Daffodil."

"Daffodil! I doubt it, sonny. What about Mirza?"

"I only know the winner," said the boy. "That's Daffodil."

"Daffodil, eh?"

There was a pause. Daffodil was an obscure horse comparatively.

"Uncle!"

"Yes, son?"

"You won't let it go any further, will you? I promised Bassett."

"Bassett be damned, old man! What's he got to do with it?"

"We're partners. We've been partners from the first. Uncle, he lent me my first five shillings, which I lost. I promised him, honour bright, it was only between me and him; only you gave me that ten-shilling note I started winning with, so I thought you were lucky. You won't let it go any further, will you?"

The boy gazed at his uncle from those big, hot, blue eyes, set rather close together. The uncle stirred and laughed uneasily.

"Right you are, son! I'll keep your tip private. Daffodil, eh? How much are you putting on him?"

"All except twenty pounds," said the boy. "I keep that in reserve."

The uncle thought it a good joke.

"You keep twenty pounds in reserve, do you, you young romancer? What are you betting, then?"

"I'm betting three hundred," said the boy gravely. "But it's between you and me, Uncle Oscar! Honour bright?"

The uncle burst into a roar of laughter.

"It's between you and me all right, you young Nat Gould," he said, laughing. "But where's your three hundred?"

"Bassett keeps it for me. We're partners."

"You are, are you! And what is Bassett putting on Daffodil?"

"He won't go quite as high as I do, I expect. Perhaps he'll go a hundred and fifty."

"What, pennies?" laughed the uncle.

"Pounds," said the child, with a surprised look at his uncle. "Bassett keeps a bigger reserve than I do."

Between wonder and amusement Uncle Oscar was silent. He pursued the matter no further, but he determined to take his nephew with him to the Lincoln races.

"Now, son," he said, "I'm putting twenty on Mirza, and I'll put five for you on any horse you fancy. What's your pick?"

"Daffodil, uncle."

"No, not the fiver on Daffodil!"

"I should if it was my own fiver," said the child.

"Good! Good! Right you are! A fiver for me and a fiver for you on Daffodil."

The child had never been to a race meeting before, and his eyes were blue fire. He pursed his mouth tight, and watched. A Frenchman just in front had put his money on Lancelot. Wild with excitement, he flayed his arms up and down, yelling "Lancelot! Lancelot!" in his French accent.

Daffodil came in first, Lancelot second, Mirza third. The child, flushed and with eyes blazing, was curiously serene. His uncle brought him four five-pound notes, four to one.

"What am I to do with these?" he cried, waving them before the boy's eyes.

"I suppose we'll talk to Bassett," said the boy. "I expect I have fifteen hundred now; and twenty in reserve; and this twenty."

His uncle studied him for some moments.

"Look here, son!" he said. "You're not serious about Bassett and that fifteen hundred, are you?"

"Yes, I am. But it's between you and me, uncle. Honour bright!"

"Honour bright all right, son! But I must talk to Bassett."

"If you'd like to be a partner, uncle, with Bassett and me, we could all be partners. Only, you'd have to promise, honour bright, uncle, not to let it go beyond us three. Bassett and I are lucky, and you must be lucky, because it was your ten shillings I starting winning with...."

Uncle Oscar took both Bassett and Paul into Richmond Park for an afternoon, and there they talked.

"It's like this, you see, sir," Bassett said. "Master Paul would get me talking about racing events, spinning yarns, you know, sir. And he was always keen on knowing if I'd made or if I'd lost. It's about a year since, now, that I put five shillings on Blush of Dawn for him—and we lost. Then the luck turned, with that ten shillings he had from you, that we put on Singhalese. And since that time, it's been pretty steady, all things considering. What do you say, Master Paul?"

"We're all right when we're sure," said Paul. "It's when we're not quite sure that we go down."

"Oh, but we're careful then," said Bassett.

"But when are you sure?" smiled Uncle Oscar.

"It's Master Paul, sir," said Bassett, in a secret, religious voice. "It's as if he had it from heaven. Like Daffodil, now, for the Lincoln. That was as sure as eggs."

"Did you put anything on Daffodil?" asked Oscar Cresswell.

"Yes, sir, I made my bit."

"And my nephew?"

Bassett was obstinately silent, looking at Paul.

"I made twelve hundred, didn't I, Bassett? I told uncle I was putting three hundred on Daffodil."

"That's right," said Bassett, nodding.

"But where's the money?" asked the uncle.

"I keep it safe locked up, sir. Master Paul he can have it any minute he likes to ask for it."

"What, fifteen hundred pounds?"

"And twenty! and forty, that is, with the twenty he made on the course."

"It's amazing!" said the uncle.

"If Master Paul offers you to be partners, sir, I would, if I were you; if you'll excuse me," said Bassett.

Oscar Cresswell thought about it.

"I'll see the money," he said.

They drove home again, and sure enough, Bassett came round to the garden-house with fifteen hundred pounds in notes. The twenty pounds reserve was left with Joe Glee, in the Turf Commission deposit.

"You see, it's all right, uncle, when I'm sure! Then we go strong, for all we're worth. Don't we, Bassett?"

"We do that, Master Paul."

"And when are you sure?" said the uncle, laughing.

"Oh, well, sometimes I'm absolutely sure, like about Daffodil," said the boy; "and sometimes I have an idea; and sometimes I haven't even an idea, have I, Bassett? Then we're careful, because we mostly go down."

"You do, do you! And when you're sure, like about Daffodil, what makes you sure, sonny?"

"Oh, well, I don't know," said the boy uneasily. "I'm sure, you know, uncle; that's all."

"It's as if he had it from heaven, sir," Bassett reiterated.

"I should say so!" said the uncle.

But he became a partner. And when the Leger was coming on, Paul was "sure" about Lively Spark, which was a quite inconsiderable horse. The boy insisted on putting a thousand on the horse, Bassett went for five hundred, and Oscar Cresswell two hundred. Lively Spark came in first, and the betting had been ten to one against him. Paul had made ten thousand.

"You see," he said, "I was absolutely sure of him."

Even Oscar Cresswell had cleared two thousand.

"Look here, son," he said, "this sort of thing makes me nervous."

"It needn't, uncle! Perhaps I shan't be sure again for a long time."

"But what are you going to do with your money?" asked the uncle.

"Of course," said the boy, "I started it for mother. She said she had no luck, because father is unlucky, so I thought if I was lucky, it might stop whispering."

"What might stop whispering?"

"Our house. I hate our house for whispering."

"What does it whisper?"

"Why—why"—the boy fidgeted—"why, I don't know. But it's always short of money, you know, uncle."

"I know it, son, I know it."

"You know people send mother writs, don't you, uncle?"

"I'm afraid I do," said the uncle.

"And then the house whispers, like people laughing at you behind your back. It's awful, that is! I thought if I was lucky . . ."

"You might stop it," added the uncle.

The boy watched him with big blue eyes that had an uncanny cold fire in them, and he said never a word.

"Well, then!" said the uncle. "What are we doing?"

"I shouldn't like mother to know I was lucky," said the boy.

"Why not, son?"

"She'd stop me."

"I don't think she would."

"Oh!"—and the boy writhed in an odd way—"I don't want her to know, uncle."

"All right, son! We'll manage it without her knowing."

They managed it very easily. Paul, at the other's suggestion, handed over five thousand pounds to his uncle, who deposited it with the family lawyer, who was then to inform Paul's mother that a relative had put five thousand pounds into his hands, which sum was to be paid out a thousand pounds at a time, on the mother's birthday, for the next five years.

"So she'll have a birthday present of a thousand pounds for five successive years," said Uncle Oscar. "I hope it won't make it all the harder for her later."

Paul's mother had her birthday in November. The house had been "whispering" worse than ever lately, and, even in spite of his luck, Paul could not bear up against it. He was very anxious to see the effect of the birthday letter, telling his mother about the thousand pounds.

When there were no visitors, Paul now took his meals with his parents, as he was beyond the nursery control. His mother went into town nearly every day. She had discovered that she had an odd knack of sketching furs and dress materials, so she worked secretly in the studio of a friend who was the chief "artist" for the leading drapers. She drew the figures of ladies in furs and ladies in silk and sequins for the newspaper advertisements. This young woman artist earned several thousand pounds a year, but Paul's mother only made several hundreds, and she was again dissatisfied. She so wanted to be first in something, and she did not succeed, even in making sketches for drapery advertisements.

She was down to breakfast on the morning of her birthday. Paul watched her face as she read her letters. He knew the lawyer's letter. As his mother read it, her face hardened and became more expressionless. Then a cold, determined look came on her mouth. She hid the letter under the pile of others, and said not a word about it.

"Didn't you have anything nice in the post for your birthday, mother?" said Paul.

"Quite moderately nice," she said, her voice cold and absent.

She went away to town without saying more.

But in the afternoon Uncle Oscar appeared. He said Paul's mother had had a long interview with the lawyer, asking if the whole five thousand could be advanced at once, as she was in debt.

"What do you think, uncle?" said the boy.

"I leave it to you, son."

"Oh, let her have it, then! We can get some more with the other," said the boy.

"A bird in the hand is worth two in the bush, laddie!" said Uncle Oscar.

"But I'm sure to know for the Grand National; or the Lincolnshire; or else the Derby. I'm sure to know for one of them" said Paul.

So Uncle Oscar signed the agreement, and Paul's mother touched the whole five thousand. Then something very curious happened. The voices in the house suddenly went mad, like a chorus of frogs on a spring evening. There were certain new furnishings, and Paul had a tutor. He was really going to Eton, his father's school, in the following autumn. There were flowers in the winter, and a blossoming of the luxury Paul's mother had been used to. And yet the voices in the house, behind the sprays of mimosa and almond blossom, and from under the piles of iridescent cushions, simply trilled and screamed in a sort of ecstasy: "There must be more money! Oh-h-h, there must be more money. Oh, now, now-w! Now-w-w—there must be more money!—more than ever! More than ever!"

It frightened Paul terribly. He studied away at his Latin and Greek with his tutors. But his intense hours were spent with Bassett. The Grand National had gone by: he had not "known," and had lost a hundred pounds. Summer was at hand. He was in agony for the Lincoln. But even for the Lincoln he didn't "know" and he lost fifty pounds. He became wild-eyed and strange, as if something were going to explode in him.

"Let it alone, son! Don't you bother about it!" urged Uncle Oscar. But it was as if the boy couldn't really hear what his uncle was saying.

"I've got to know for the Derby! I've got to know for the Derby!" the child reiterated, his big blue eyes blazing with a sort of madness.

His mother noticed how overwrought he was.

"You'd better go to the seaside. Wouldn't you like to go now to the seaside, instead of waiting? I think you'd better," she said, looking down at him anxiously, her heart curiously heavy because of him.

But the child lifted his uncanny blue eyes.

"I couldn't possibly go before the Derby, mother!" he said "I couldn't possibly!"

"Why not?" she said, her voice becoming heavy when she was opposed. "Why not? You can still go from the seaside to see the Derby with your Uncle Oscar, if that's what you wish. No need for you to wait here. Besides, I think you care too much about these races. It's a bad sign. My family has been a gambling family, and you won't know till you grow up how much damage it has done. But it has done damage. I shall have to send Bassett away, and ask Uncle Oscar not to talk racing to you, unless you promise to be reasonable about it; go away to the seaside and forget it. You're all nerves!"

"I'll do what you like, mother, so long as you don't send me away till after the Derby," the boy said.

"Send you away from where? Just from this house?"

"Yes," he said, gazing at her.

"Why, you curious child, what makes you care about this house so much, suddenly? I never knew you loved it."

He gazed at her without speaking. He had a secret within a secret, something he had not divulged, even to Bassett or to Uncle Oscar.

But his mother, after standing undecided and a little bit sullen for some moments, said:

"Very well, then! Don't go to the seaside till after the Derby, if you don't wish it. But promise me you won't let your nerves go to pieces. Promise you won't think so much about horse racing and events, as you call them!"

"Oh, no," said the boy casually. "I won't think much about them, mother. You needn't worry. I wouldn't worry, mother, if I were you."

"If you were me and I were you," said his mother, "I wonder what we should do!"

"But you know you needn't worry, mother, don't you?" the boy repeated.

"I should be awfully glad to know it," she said wearily.

"Oh, well, you can, you know. I mean, you ought to know you needn't worry," he insisted.

"Ought I? Then I'll see about it," she said.

Paul's secret of secrets was his wooden horse, that which had no name. Since he was emancipated from a nurse and a nursery governess, he had had his rocking horse removed to his own bedroom at the top of the house.

"Surely, you're too big for a rocking horse!" his mother had remonstrated.

"Well, you see, mother, till I can have a real horse, I like to have some sort of animal about," had been his quaint answer.

"Do you feel he keeps you company?" she laughed.

"Oh, yes! He's very good, he always keeps me company, when I'm there," said Paul.

So the horse, rather shabby, stood in an arrested prance in the boy's bedroom.

The Derby was drawing near, and the boy grew more and more tense. He hardly heard what was spoken to him, he was very frail, and his eyes were really uncanny. His mother had sudden seizures of uneasiness about him. Sometimes, for half-an-hour, she would feel a sudden anxiety about him that was almost anguish. She wanted to rush to him at once, and know he was safe.

Two nights before the Derby, she was at a big party in town, when one of her rushes of anxiety about her boy, her first-born, gripped her heart till she could hardly speak. She fought with the feeling, might and main, for she believed in common sense. But it was too strong. She had to leave the dance and go downstairs to telephone to the country. The children's nursery governess was terribly surprised and startled at being rung up in the night.

"Are the children all right, Miss Wilmot?"

"Oh, yes, they are quite all right."

"Master Paul? Is he all right?"

"He went to bed as right as a trivet. Shall I run up and look at him?"

"No," said Paul's mother reluctantly. "No! Don't trouble. It's all right. Don't sit up. We shall be home fairly soon." She did not want her son's privacy intruded upon.

"Very good," said the governess.

It was about one o'clock when Paul's mother and father drove up to their house. All was still. Paul's mother went to her room and slipped off her white fur coat. She had told her maid not to wait up for her. She heard her husband downstairs, mixing a whiskey-and-soda.

And then, because of the strange anxiety at her heart, she stole upstairs to her son's room. Noiselessly she went along the upper corridor. Was there a faint noise? What was it?

She stood, with arrested muscles, outside his door, listening. There was a strange, heavy, and yet not loud noise. Her heart stood still. It was a soundless noise, yet rushing and powerful. Something huge, in violent, hushed motion. What was it? What in God's name was it? She ought to know. She felt that she knew the noise. She knew what it was.

Yet she could not place it. She couldn't say what it was. And on and on it went, like a madness.

Softly, frozen with anxiety and fear, she turned the door handle.

The room was dark. Yet in the space near the window, she heard and saw something plunging to and fro. She gazed in fear and amazement.

Then suddenly she switched on the light, and saw her son, in his green pyjamas, madly surging on the rocking horse. The blaze of light suddenly lit him up, as he urged the wooden horse, and lit her up, as she stood, blonde, in her dress of pale green and crystal, in the doorway.

"Paul!" she cried. "Whatever are you doing?"

"It's Malabar!" he screamed, in a powerful, strange voice. "It's Malabar."

His eyes blazed at her for one strange and senseless second, as he ceased urging his wooden horse. Then he fell with a crash to the ground, and she, all her tormented motherhood flooding upon her, rushed to gather him up.

But he was unconscious, and unconscious he remained, with some brain-fever. He talked and tossed, and his mother sat stonily by his side.

"Malabar! It's Malabar! Bassett, Bassett, I know! It's Malabar!"

So the child cried, trying to get up and urge the rocking horse that gave him his inspiration.

"What does he mean by Malabar?" asked the heart-frozen mother.

"I don't know," said the father stonily.

"What does he mean by Malabar?" she asked her brother Oscar.

"It's one of the horses running for the Derby," was the answer.

And, in spite of himself, Oscar Cresswell spoke to Bassett, and himself put a thousand on Malabar: at fourteen to one.

The third day of the illness was critical: they were waiting for a change. The boy, with his rather long, curly hair, was tossing ceaselessly on the pillow. He neither slept nor regained consciousness, and his eyes were like blue stones. His mother sat, feeling her heart had gone, turned actually into a stone.

In the evening, Oscar Cresswell did not come, but Bassett sent a message, saying could he come up for one moment, just one moment? Paul's mother was very angry at the intrusion, but on second thought she agreed. The boy was the same. Perhaps Bassett might bring him to consciousness.

The gardener, a shortish fellow with a little brown moustache, and sharp little brown eyes, tiptoed into the room, touched his imaginary cap to Paul's mother, and stole to the bedside, staring with glittering, smallish eyes, at the tossing, dying child.

"Master Paul!" he whispered. "Master Paul! Malabar come in first all right, a clean win. I did as you told me. You've made over seventy thousand pounds, you have; you've got over eighty thousand. Malabar came in all right, Master Paul."

"Malabar! Malabar! Did I say Malabar, mother? Did I say Malabar? Do you think I'm lucky, mother? I knew Malabar, didn't I? Over eighty thousand pounds! I call that lucky, don't you, mother? Over eighty thousand pounds! I knew, didn't I know I knew? Malabar came in all right. If I ride my horse till I'm sure, then I tell you, Bassett, you can go as high as you like. Did you go for all you were worth, Bassett?"

"I went a thousand on it, Master Paul."

"I never told you, mother, that if I can ride my horse, and get there, then I'm absolutely sure—oh, absolutely! Mother, did I ever tell you? I am lucky."

"No, you never did," said the mother.

But the boy died in the night.

And even as he lay dead, his mother heard her brother's voice saying to her: "My God, Hester, you're eighty-odd thousand to the good and a poor devil of a son to the bad. But, poor devil, poor devil, he's best gone out of a life where he rides his rocking horse to find a winner."

1. Take a few minutes to jot down your first impressions. If you wish, you might choose one focus from the following on which to write:
   - anything you especially like or disliked in the story;
   - questions you have about the characters or events;
   - thoughts prompted by the story about luck, money, and success.

   Share your writing with two or three classmates.
2. Examine the exposition of the story's introduction. How does it set up the various conflicts that follow?
3. Consider the fairy-tale structure of the story. Why do you think Lawrence chose to use it? How does it serve his purpose in the beginning and ending? What fantastic, improbable elements does the story contain?
4. Identify the symbols in the story and explain how they are used throughout the story.
5. How and why is the ending tragic? Need Paul have died? Which characters, if any, deserve criticism for their parts in Paul's death? Defend your answers.
6. Frequently, interpretations of this story support the theme that money and the pursuit of material wealth—at the expense of love and humanity—do not lead to happiness. Do you agree or disagree with this idea? Does the desire for wealth *inevitably* lead to tragedy or unhappiness? Discuss in small groups. Present your group's ideas, conclusions, and/or examples to the class, perhaps in one of the following forms:
   - a debate;
   - an advertising campaign;
   - a speech;
   - a short play or TV "broadcast."

The Texture of Story

Just as we sometimes become fans of a certain group's songs or a filmmaker's movies, we often develop a liking for the writings of particular authors. The content—the characters, conflicts, and events—may be a significant source of our enjoyment; however, the *way* the author writes also contributes to our response. So, for example, we may respond to an emotional conflict brought to life by vivid description and powerful imagery. Thus, the combination of the story *and* the way in which the author tells it can create for the reader a meaningful and memorable reading experience.

The sources of style in a well-written story can be compared to those in an effective movie. The filmmaker works with light and color to establish mood and atmosphere, camera angles to highlight details and feelings, music to heighten the drama in significant scenes, and so on. Similarly, the writer creates the style, or *texture*, of a story by working with diction, sentences, imagery, and figurative language. The writer makes decisions regarding each of these variables based on his or her sense of the story and its purpose.

To step back from a story and consider its style, we can ask ourselves questions such as the following:

- Which words or phrases are most effective? Why?
- Which sentences are most dramatic? especially fluent? poetic?
- Are there any common threads of imagery that weave through the entire story? What patterns has the author used? Why?
- What use does the author make of figurative language?
- What feelings or emotions are at the heart of the story? How does the author's use of words bring out those feelings or emotions?

- Who is telling the story? How is the story's language affected by the choice of narrator?
- In summary, how does the storytelling (or style) complement the basic story?

Style is necessarily complex. Each writer develops a unique style for a story, and each story is an organic whole. So, when we set out to describe or analyze completely the style of a story and its relationship to the story's ideas, we find that the texture of a story is more than the sum of its parts. As readers, we can gain insights into how the story works and what makes it meaningful by looking at the parts, but, in the end, we might reread the story and find there is something more—an elusive quality—that makes the story successful.

The four stories in this unit offer a range of styles and show the positive effect of style on story. The first story, "The Setting Sun and the Rolling World," appeals to readers through its poetic imagery and sensitivity to detail. The contemporary language and informal feeling of "On the Right Track" reflect the youthful narrator's expression and developing self image. The third story, "Rain," offers detailed, sensitive, and lyrical descriptions of people, places, and traditions. Lastly, "Miss Brill" paints with imagery and fine details the world as seen by a romantic, older woman; as a result, the brutal contrast of another perspective can touch us deeply.

Each of the four stories will affect individual readers differently, but each offers a way for us to consider the significant contribution a story's texture makes to the whole selection.

Charles Mungoshi

The Setting Sun and the Rolling World

"You haven't changed your mind?"

Old Musoni raised his dusty eyes from his hoe and the unchanging stony earth he had been tilling and peered into the sky. The white speck whose sound had disturbed his work and thoughts was far out at the edge of the yellow sky, near the horizon. Then it disappeared quickly over the southern rim of the sky and he shook his head. He looked to the west. Soon the sun would go down. He looked over the sunblasted land and saw the shadows creeping east, clearer and taller with every moment that the sun shed each of its rays. Unconsciously wishing for rain and relief, he bent down again to his work and did not see his son, Nhamo, approaching.

Nhamo crouched in the dust near his father and greeted him. The old man half raised his back, leaning against his hoe, and said what had been bothering him all day long.

"You haven't changed your mind?"

"No, father."

There was a moment of silence. Old Musoni scraped earth off his hoe.

"Have you thought about this, son?"

"For weeks, father."

"And you think that's the only way?"

"There is no other way."

The old man felt himself getting angry again. But this would be the last day he would talk to his son. If his son was going away, he must not be angry. It would be equal to a curse. He himself had taken chances before, in his own time, but he felt too much of a father. He had worked and slaved for his family and the land had not betrayed him. He saw nothing now but disaster and death for his son out there in the world. Lions had long since vanished but he knew of worse animals of prey, animals that wore redder claws than the lion's, beasts that would not leave an unprotected homeless boy alone. He thought of the white metal bird and he felt remorse.

"Think again. You will end dead. Think again, of us, of your family. We have a home, poor though it is, but can you think of a day you have gone without?"

"I have thought everything over, father, I am convinced this is the only way out."

"There is no only way out in the world. Except the way of the land, the way of the family."

"The land is overworked and gives nothing now, father. And the family is almost broken up."

The old man got angry. Yes, the land is useless. True, the family tree is uprooted and it dries in the sun. True, many things are happening that haven't happened before, that we did not think would happen, ever. But nothing is more certain to hold you together than the land and a home, a family. And where do you think you are going, a mere beardless kid with the milk not yet dry on your baby nose? What do you think you will do in the great treacherous world where men twice your age have gone and returned with their backs broken—if they returned at all? What do you know of life? What do you know of the false honey bird that leads you the whole day through the forest to a snake's nest? But all he said was: "Look. What have you asked me and I have denied you? What, that I have, have I not given you for the asking?"

"All. You have given me all, father." And here, too, the son felt hampered, patronized, and his pent-up fury rolled through him. It showed on his face but stayed under control. You have given me damn all and nothing. You have sent me to school and told me the importance of education, and now you ask me to throw it on the rubbish heap and scrape for a living on this tired cold shell of the moon. You ask me to forget it and muck around in this slow dance of death with you. I have this one chance of making my own life, once in all eternity, and now you are jealous. You are afraid of your own death. It is, after all, your own death. I shall be around a while yet. I will make my way home if a home is what I need. I am armed more than you think and wiser than you can dream of. But all he said, too, was:

"Really, father, have no fear for me. I will be all right. Give me this chance. Release me from all obligations and pray for me."

There was a spark in the old man's eyes at these words of his son. But just as dust quickly settles over a glittering pebble revealed by the hoe, so a murkiness hid the gleam in the old man's eye. Words are handles made to the smith's fancy and are liable to break under stress. They are too much fat on the hard unbreaking sinews of life.

"Do you know what you are doing, son?"

"Yes."

"Do you know what you will be a day after you leave home?"

"Yes, father."

"A homeless, nameless vagabond living on dust and rat's droppings, living on thank-yous, sleeping up a tree or down a ditch, in the rain, in the sun, in the cold, with nobody to see you, nobody to talk to, nobody at all to tell your dreams to. Do you know what it is to see your hopes come crashing down like an old house out of season and your dreams turning to ash and dung without a tang of salt in your skull? Do you know what it is to live without a single hope of ever seeing good in your own lifetime?" And to himself: Do you know, young bright ambitious son of my loins, the ruins of time and the pains of old age? Do you know how to live beyond a dream, a hope, a faith? Have you seen black despair, my son?

"I know it, father. I know enough to start on. The rest I shall learn as I go on. Maybe I shall learn to come back."

The old man looked at him and felt: Come back where? Nobody comes back to ruins. You will go on, son. Something you don't know will drive you on along deserted plains, past ruins and more ruins, on and on until there is only one ruin left: yourself. You will break down, without tears, son. You are human, too. Listen to the *haya*—the rain bird—and heed its warning of coming storm: plough no more, it says. And what happens if the storm catches you far, far out on the treeless plain? What then, my son?

But he was tired. They had taken over two months discussing all this. Going over the same ground like animals at a drinking place until, like animals, they had driven the water far deep into the stony earth, until they had sapped all the blood out of life and turned it into a grim skeleton, and now they were creating a stampede on the dust, grovelling for water. Mere thoughts. Mere words. And what are words? Trying to grow a fruit tree in the wilderness.

"Go son, with my blessings. I give you nothing. And when you remember what I am saying you will come back. The land is still yours. As long as I am alive you will find a home waiting for you."

"Thank you, father."

"Before you go, see Chiremba. You are going out into the world. You need something to strengthen yourself. Tell him I shall pay him. Have a good journey, son."

"Thank you, father."

Nhamo smiled and felt a great love for his father. But there were things that belonged to his old world that were just lots of humbug on the mind, empty load, useless scrap. He would go to Chiremba but he would burn the charms as soon as he was away from home and its sickening environment. A man stands on his feet and guts. Charms were for you—so was God, though much later. But for us now the world is godless, no charms will work. All that is just the opium you take in the dark in the hope of a light. You don't need that now. You strike a match for a light. Nhamo laughed.

He could be so easily lighthearted. Now his brain worked with a fury only known to visionaries. The psychological ties were now broken, only the biological tied him to his father. He was free. He too remembered the aeroplane which his father had seen just before their talk. Space had no bounds and no ties. Floating laws rule the darkness and he would float with the fiery balls. He was the sun, burning itself out every second and shedding tons of energy which it held in its power, giving it the thrust to drag its brood wherever it wanted to. This was the law that held him: the mystery that his father and ancestors had failed to grasp and which had caused their being wiped off the face of the earth. This thinking reached such a pitch that he began to sing, imitating as intimately as he could Satchmo's voice: "What a wonderful world." It was Satchmo's voice that he turned to when he felt buoyant.

Old Musoni did not look at his son as he left him. Already, his mind was trying to focus at some point in the dark unforeseeable future. Many things could happen and while he still breathed he would see that nothing terribly painful happened to his family, especially to his stubborn last-born, Nhamo. Tomorrow, before sunrise, he would go to see Chiremba and ask him to throw bones over the future of his son. And if there were a couple of ancestors who needed appeasement, he would do it while he was still around.

He noticed that the sun was going down and he scraped the earth off his hoe.

The sun was sinking slowly, bloody red, blunting and blurring all the objects that had looked sharp in the light of day. Soon a chilly wind would blow over the land and the cold cloudless sky would send down beads of frost like white ants over the unprotected land.

1. Working individually, record your initial response to the story. You might choose one focus from the following:
   - thoughts and feelings about the characters;
   - details and/or images that were particularly strong for you;
   - passages that impress you as outstanding writing.

   In a small group, share your response. Summarize your responses for the class.
2. What evidence is there that Old Musoni and Nhamo have discussed this issue before? What reasons does Old Musoni have for his opposition? Why does he fear for Nhamo? How does he show restraint?
3. Review and summarize Nhamo's perspective. What is your opinion of his plan? What predictions do you have for his life after he leaves his father's home? In a small group, discuss your opinions and predictions.
4. Identify three of the strongest metaphors or images in the story. What do they suggest about the conflicts and themes of the story?
5. Consider the mood and perspective implicit in the lyric, "What a wonderful world." In your experience, do teenagers have the same mood and perspective? Answer in a paragraph.
6. a) Consider the event central to the story—a child leaving the family home. Is leaving the family home a necessary stage in growing up? What effects does it often have on parents and children?

   b) Write a poem, song lyric, or anecdote about leaving home. Use a style similar to that of this story.

Dorothy Chisholm

On the Right Track

Kim had some funny ideas but I liked her.

I hate trendy, you know what I mean? That's why when Kim said let's go to Yorkville for lunch one day, my first impulse was to say no. Besides, I didn't have any money. I was trying to save for a trip to Florida so I usually ate at the Burger Barn. Kim would say I ate too much junk food. She was into yogurt and salads.

Anyway, Kim says never mind about the money, I'll lend you some until payday. When I pointed out that it would take two subway tokens to get to Yorkville and back, Kim says never mind the subway, walking is good for you.

I asked Kim what was so great about this cafe in Yorkville and she said there was this terrific guy who ate there. She'd seen him a few times when she went there with Sara. Sara was a girl in our office who quit to have a baby right after I arrived. I sort of replaced her, although she had a lot more responsibility than they'd given me. Anyway, Kim had decided that she had to figure out a way to meet this guy.

Kim was about the only friend I had in the office then. I'd only been there a month and most of the other people in the office were pretty old. Kim had some funny ideas but I liked her. She was really good looking. Golden blond hair and skin that took a great tan. She wore a lot of white, which really showed off her tan and also her terrific figure.

Her name wasn't really Kim. It was Joyce, but she didn't like it and had got everybody to call her Kim. I have to admit it suited her better than Joyce did.

Anyway, she talked me into going to Yorkville for lunch and when we get into this cafe, Kim says the way to save money is not to eat a lot. Order a small salad, she says, because you can fill up on the French bread they put on the table before you even order.

The cafe was one of those small restaurants with a lot of white and chrome and plants all over the place. And everyone is drinking white wine or Perrier water.

Kim asks the waiter if they have any special dishes for dieters. She flashes him this big smile and he says maybe you'd like to try a small salad. So she says she'll have a very small green salad and some Earl Grey tea. I order the same thing.

Well Kim hardly ate anything. She just kept looking around while I ate a whole basket of French bread. I was still hungry when we left and the terrific guy hadn't shown up. Never mind, Kim says, patience is its own reward.

I don't know about patience. I think it was more like determination with Kim. We went back about a week later and, this time, he was there. I had to admit I thought he was pretty good-looking. He was dressed kind of preppy, sort of like the ads in *GQ*. That's *Gentlemen's Quarterly*, which I don't read, but Kim never missed an issue. He was wearing a navy jacket, white shirt, striped tie, Rosedale written all over him.

Not exactly a hunk, but better than okay, I told Kim. She looked at me as if I was sort of ignorant and said that understatement was the essence of good taste or something like that.

Anyway, after she'd finished her salad, Kim said she was going to the washroom and I couldn't believe what she did next. Just as she passes his table, she drops her purse. Talk about corny. But, just the way she did it, for a minute I thought it was an accident. He must have thought so too, because he bends over and picks up the purse. Kim flashes him this great smile and it seems to work because his eyes follow her all the way to the washroom. On the way back she stops and says, haven't I seen you in the Manulife Centre? He says yes, I work in there and Kim says well, by-bye and gives him a little wave.

I couldn't get over her nerve and I also couldn't figure out how she knew the building he worked in. I asked her on the way back to our office, and she says just a lucky guess. I would have found out eventually anyway, she says.

I wondered why she went to all that trouble. She had lots of offers from guys to go out with them. But she turned most of them down because, she said, she knew what she wanted, which was to meet the right type of person. And if you don't get off on the right track, you'll always regret it, she said.

Kim and I started to go to the beach on the week-ends to work on our tans and watch the wind surfers. One day I saw this guy I was in Grade 10 with. Donny. He's pretty good-looking, nice too, and he tells me he's had a hard time finding a job. But he's working, he says, at the Sears warehouse. We talked for awhile and he said he'd give me a call sometime.

Meanwhile, Kim was eyeing this guy in a Ralph Lauren polo shirt and shorts. He was playing frisbee and he had great muscles. On the way home, Kim tells me he has too many muscles. Too much muscle is gross, she says, and probably means he's developed his body instead of his brain.

I told Kim I thought Donny was nice but she says, warehouse, talk about downward mobility. She didn't say it to be mean. She talked like that because she read a lot of magazines. For example, she read *Toronto Life* from cover to cover and she also read *Glamour* and *Cosmo.*

I used to hang out sometimes at this pub near where I lived. I'd go there with Carol, a girl I knew in high school. Kim didn't go to pubs. They're full of jocks, she said. Girls are just another sport to them. She didn't ever go to singles bars, either. Meat markets, she said, they're for losers.

Kim liked to go to expensive boutiques to try on clothes. The first time she asked me to go I told her I couldn't afford to buy anything but she says, don't worry, we're not going to buy anything. We'll just see what we like and then go down to Spadina and get the same thing, only cheaper.

Meanwhile, we kept going to the cafe in Yorkville and sometimes we saw the guy from the Manulife Centre whose name turned out to be Rob. We talked a bit more each time and eventually he and Kim got around to her phone number. But she told him she was just in the process of moving and when she was settled in she'd give him a call.

Which was more or less true because Kim had been trying to talk me into sharing an apartment. She said she was sick of riding the subway all the way from North York and I had to admit it was a long way for me from Etobicoke.

I told Kim I really couldn't afford an apartment but she said we could buy stuff at the Sally Ann and now that she'd finally met Rob we could cut out the lunches in Yorkville. I figured I could put my trip to Florida on hold for a while so I said okay, and Kim found this place in the Annex. It was pretty run down but Kim said when we painted it and put up posters and got some rattan furniture and stuff, it would be great.

My mum said she'd miss me but she understood that I was at an age to be on my own and if I needed anything to just let her know and if it didn't work out she'd always be glad to see me back home.

I don't think Kim had a terrific relationship with her family. I know that when I'd phone and ask for Kim, her mother would always say, just a minute and I'll get Joyce or no, Joyce isn't here. Anyway, Kim's mother told her if she ran out of money, not to bother running back home.

Kim's brother knew a guy who ran a gas station, so he brought his truck around to help us move. My mother gave us some dishes and pots and pans and we took our mattresses but not our beds. Kim said futons were what everybody was using now. Which was okay with me because I figured if this didn't work it would be easier to move.

It was kind of neat having the apartment. Neither of us could cook very well, so we ate a lot of yogurt and frozen stuff and we got some great posters. Kim started to go out with Rob, which was exciting for her. Rob liked to go to concerts and art galleries and to the ROM. Stuff for the mind, Kim said, but we're going to have fun, too. Rob's friend has a boat and we'll go sailing on the lake. When winter comes we'll buy skis, she said, and go to Blue Mountain.

One night when Rob came to take Kim out, she was still in the bedroom putting on her makeup and he starts telling me how much he admires Kim. It must be tough, he says, for her to be in the city on her own, with no family or anything.

Well, this was news to me because, as far as I knew, her family was alive and well in North York. But I didn't say anything.

Another time, Rob asked me if I wanted to go along with them to a concert at Ontario Place. I really wanted to go but I didn't want to horn in on Kim so I said no thanks, I have to wash my hair. I have to admit that sometimes I got pretty lonely in the apartment and if it wasn't for Donny calling a couple of times, it would have been really boring. But there was also a library right around the corner and I started to take books out and I was doing a lot of reading.

One day at the end of the summer Donny asked me to go to the Ex with him, so I asked Kim if she and Rob would like to go with us. Kim says no, the Ex isn't really Rob's style. I felt kind of sorry for her because she used to like the Ex, but I got the feeling that she didn't think Donny had much class. I have to admit he dressed kind of funny. Like, he wasn't much into fashion and he didn't have one of those neat-o haircuts like the guys in *GQ*. He just liked to be comfortable, which was okay with me.

So Donny and I went to the Ex by ourselves and we had a great time going on all the rides and stuff. He also won me this big stuffed bear by knocking over bottles with baseballs. It cost him almost $20 but it was fun riding the street-car home with this huge animal on my lap and everybody saying boy are you lucky. I was kind of glad Kim and Rob weren't with us.

When we got home I invited Donny in for a Coke and Kim and Rob were already there. Kim didn't look too happy and I got the idea they'd had a fight. They'd gone to this movie and Kim tells me and Donny how boring it was. Rob says he thought it was great. The director, he says, was saying something really important. Kim rolls her eyes and says she still thinks it was dumb. I hadn't seen the movie but the way Rob was describing it, I thought it sounded interesting. But I didn't say anything. Rob said he studied this director in a film course at university. He's an auteur, Rob says. I didn't know what an *auteur* was then but I made a note in my head and looked it up the next time I went to the library.

Things were getting kind of heavy so I was glad when Donny told a really funny story about a guy at the Sears warehouse who fell asleep on one of the sofas and a couple of other guys loaded him on a truck. Rob laughed a lot but Kim didn't seem to think it was funny. She'd been kind of ignoring Donny anyway, maybe because he was wearing this funny-looking baseball cap he got at the Ex. Rob was wearing a really nice green polo shirt—the kind with the little alligator on it—and white chinos.

Anyway, Rob and Donny seemed to get along fine. Donny told

Rob he was thinking of going back to school and Rob said that was really wise, that he should get his Grade 13. You need all the education you can get, Rob said. He, himself, was quitting his job at the Manulife Centre and going back for his MBA—to a college in the States.

I looked at Kim and she had a really annoyed look on her face. But Rob didn't notice because he was busy talking to Donny, who was asking him how come he's going for the MBA. Rob says it was his father's idea. If you want to get anywhere in marketing, Rob says, you definitely need an MBA. It will probably take him a year, he says.

I was sort of worried about Kim. She'd always acted so cool about everything. Now, all of a sudden she says, well I don't want to change the subject or anything but why don't we order in a pizza? Which was really weird, because Kim never ate pizza. She said it was fattening and bad for your skin, too.

So we get this giant pizza, all dressed, which lightened things up and we all pigged out on it, even Kim.

Rob went away about a week later and he said he'd write to her, but Kim didn't seem to care much by that time. Well, all this happened last spring and summer and it just shows that you never know how things will turn out.

We had to give up the apartment because the rent went up and by the time we paid it we didn't have enough money to go anywhere. To tell the truth, I didn't mind giving it up. Cooking was a hassle and carrying a big sack of laundry to the coin wash every Saturday was a real drag. My mum was glad to have me back home, but I never found out how Kim's family reacted. She quit her job in the fall and I kind of lost track of her.

Well, last week I was going to visit my girl friend Carol who's living in North York now and I ran into Kim on the street. She's pushing this really cute baby in a carriage. She still looks great although she's put on some weight. It turns out she's married. To her brother's friend. The one who runs the gas station. And when I say, it's really great to see you again, Kim, she says, by the way, I'm Joyce now. Larry likes it better.

Then she asks me how I'm doing and I tell her fine. I've had a raise since she left and I've been given a lot more responsibility, even more than Sara had. They tell me I could have a nice career there. And now that I'm living at home again, I've saved almost enough money for a trip to Europe next year.

Then she says, how's your social life? I tell her I'm going out with Donny a bit and he's got a better job now. Next fall, he's going back to school to take his Grade 13. But it's not serious with Donny and me, I say, because I've got plans of my own.

I didn't tell her that I've been going out with Rob quite a bit, too. Even though he's got his MBA and everything we really have quite a lot in common. But I didn't think it was such a good idea to tell Kim, I mean Joyce, about Rob.

Anyway, she flashes me her great smile and says she's very happy for me and that it sounds like I'm really on the right track.

1. Working individually, record your initial response to the story. You might choose one focus from the following:
   - patterns you see in the story;
   - changes in the various relationships;
   - people, events, TV shows, or movies this story brings to mind.

   In a small group, share your response. Summarize your responses for the class.
2. In a small group, consider the protagonist and Kim/Joyce. How do the characters compare at the beginning of the story? as the story develops? at the end of the story? Why do these changes occur?
3. Consider the significance of the story's title. What does the expression "on the right track" mean? Conversely, what do we mean when we say that someone is "way off track"? Respond, referring to both the story and your experiences.
4. The author uses realistic, informal conversation to develop the texture of the story. Note five portions of conversation that capture the way young people speak. How does each portion help to characterize its speaker?
5. The author also uses specific products and locations (*GQ*, Coke, Florida vacation) to establish social contexts for characters. Choose any five details from the story and explain the relevance for each character.
6. Choose one of the following activities:
   a) Write a story in a similar style (short paragraphs for pacing, extensive conversation) about your home life, family, friends, or school.
   b) Predict the future of any one of the story's characters. Join up with classmates who chose the same character, and develop a detailed portrait of the character (considering work, home life, social life, beliefs, values, consumer habits). Share the results with the class.

Maurice Kenny

Rain

The sun blazes, burning flesh and earth.

I was only visiting that part of the country.

The Pontiac sped along the back road north of Albuquerque toward the Pueblo village of Santa Ana. I rode with an elderly Laguna Indian woman, her younger daughter who had married an Arab, her granddaughter who had married an Englishman and her great-grandson who was then too young to marry.

The road edged the rising mountains to the east and the vast mesa to the west. Through the windshield I spotted an ancient pick-up. Two figures stood near it. As we approached the truck I could see an old Indian couple selling melons. The man held one up to us in silence.

In the Pontiac all three women smoked; the young boy drank a Coke. I was thirsty myself for the sweet juices of those melons.

"They look good."

Too late. The driver passed the truck without a thought.

"What kind of melons are those?" I asked.

The conversation already in progress was so intent upon the trip's purpose, our destination, that no one heard me.

"Those Santa Anas are going to dance a rain, I tell you," the elderly Laguna woman announced emphatically.

"I believe you're right, Grandma," replied the young driver.

"Mercy! Hope they do. This heat's a killer. Good thing the car's air-conditioned, or I'd be wilted for sure."

"The juice of those melons back there would have cooled us off," I offered, but received no response.

"We're gonna see 'em dance, Gramma?"

"We sure are. See them dance the very rain down, Sonny."

I come from rain country. I want rain or snow then to relieve the unbearable heat and the dry sage stench of the desert.

"Alma, when we get there park the car behind the pueblo."

"Right. I'll let you folks out first. And take Sonny with you."

We approached a narrow bridge spanning the Rio Grande River, which was nearly dry. Barely more than a trickle seeped to the Mexican border at Juarez. A long line of cars and trucks waited at the far end of the bridge to cross.

"Folks are leaving!"

"Hope we're not too late!"

"No. Grandma. They dance all afternoon ... same as they do at Laguna."

"Oh! They are going to dance down a rain, I tell you."

The elderly woman's face shone with something like ecstatic joy.

"That's power, Grandma."

"That's power, Alma."

"They got power all right."

"We gonna see 'em dance, Gramma?"

"Yes, Sonny, we are going to see the Santa Anas dance down the rain from the sunny sky up there."

"Is there gonna be a rainbow, Gramma?"

"Rainbows all over the desert."

I come from country where it is not necessary to dance rain or look for rainbows in the sky.

"Alma, you park behind the pueblo. Margo, you go get me a big piece of frybread with honey when we get there. Sonny, you come with me to the plaza. They'll find us. We can't get lost in little Santa Ana. I want to be there up front to see them dance that rain," the great-grandmother proclaimed.

Beyond the adobe village an acre of corn, knee-high, sun-soaked, roots scrambling to the river to suck what tricklets of water remained in the August beds. Overhead the clear sky waited for passing clouds. A citron hue creased the horizon.

We unloaded three metal fold-up chairs and an umbrella from the car trunk. Alma drove off to the parking lot. We others headed for the plaza.

At the pueblo edge a Ferris wheel whirled. Music of a merry-go-round tinkled the afternoon. Sonny's face brightened with surprise, but his grandmother grasped his hand tightly. A smell of burning charcoal seamed the air. Young boys weaved in and out of the strolling crowds selling containers of Coca-Cola from large wooden crates. Children, including Sonny, stared hungrily at the various booths selling cotton candy on plastic sticks. A tongue slid along the rim of a lip. Hundreds of people milled between craft stands and beverage counters, charcoal pits where great cauldrons of bubbling grease singed brown tortilla-like bread. Flies swarmed about the honey pots. A leathery-skinned man wavered through the crowds hawking balloons: purple, the colour of his lips; yellow as the sun; blue as the clear sky; red as the heat of the afternoon.

We waded through the carnival atmosphere.

In the village groups of people loitered in the plaza itself and on the roofs of the squat adobe houses framing the dusty plaza crammed with the curious. Most people had brought folding chairs and umbrellas to ward off the sun's rays and the rain, should it fall. A man raked the dust clean of the central plaza, readying the grounds for the dancers.

People, old friends and new, chattered like mice between bites of greasy frybread with rich honey and sips of Coke. A little girl dressed in bright yellow with matching silk panties showing sat on the dust. A damp spot moved from under her. Two arms reached down and plucked her away as though she were a lemon hanging from a tree.

I was a stranger in that part of the country.

"There's Milly Velarde over there...."

"Jim must have brought her from Cuberio."

"... right under the portico of that adobe, I'm going to bid afternoon."

"Be careful, Mother. These kids might knock you down the way they're running so carelessly. No respect!"

"Can I go?"

"No, Sonny, you stay here with me. Your Mama'll be here in a minute. Doesn't take long to park a car. My, it is hot. I hope these Santa Anas *do* dance rain. I certainly do. Cool us off a little bit."

By then my mouth was clotted with dust. My bare arms, face slowly covered with a fine red film; sweat spotted my shirt.

"Alma! Oh, Alma, over here."

Our driver, the younger woman, had entered the plaza.

Dancers began lining up at the narrow entrance of the plaza between the adobe huts. Women and little girls wore black dresses with red sashes. High wooden tiaras reared from atop their heads over loose black hair. The tiaras had cut-outs of stars and crescent moons. The women carried cedar boughs and boughs were attached to arm bands. The men and young boys were dressed in white kilts with a coyote pelt falling behind, and a wide rope sash circled the waist. Beads hung down their chests. Within turquoise arm bands cedar twigs were entwined. They carried gourd rattles. All the dancers were painted in vermilion.

One older man stood off from the thronging group. He held what appeared a flag pole from which streamed coloured pennants. An old woman, obviously the lead dancer, sucked an orange ice cone. She wore faded green tennis shoes while other dancers were all barefoot. She, however, was dressed as the other women and carried boughs of cedar in her hands as did the other women.

"You want a drink of something?" Alma asked. "It's boiling!"

"Broiling," I nodded.

"Oh, glory, yes, Alma. Get Sonny a Coke, too."

"Can I go with you, Mama?"

"Stay with your grandmother so you don't get lost."

Sadly the little fellow sat down on the dusty earth … with the sounds of the merry-go-round tinkling in his ears.

A heavy-set old man relaxed into a folding chair next to us. His eyes were rheumy. He was blind. A little boy of three or four stood between his grandfather's parted knees. Both were mailed with silver jewellery.

"It was Milly Velarde, Margo! We had a great talk." The elderly grandmother returned. "Says she's losing sight. Cataracts. But wouldn't miss these Santa Anas for the world."

"Cause they always dance rain."

"All knows we need it," pronounced the matriarch.

"Did you get a look at that river? Oh, my! … Look! A hawk."

"A hawk?"

"A red-tail."

"Good sign."

"When they gonna start, Grandma?"

"Soon, Sonny, soon."
"I'm hot, Grandma."
"We're all hot, Sonny."
""Alma isn't here yet, Margo? How long's it take to park a car?"
"She's here. She went to get us a cool drink of something."
The old couple selling the melons along the highway flashed into my mind, my thirst, my heat.
"She'd better hurry. The dancers are lined up to start. And the drummers. Aren't they beautiful?"
"Just beautiful, Mother."
I am a stranger in this rainless country.
I am visiting from a land where it is never necessary to dance rain from the clouds. I thirst for sweet waters of the melons the old woman picked from her wild vines growing on the mesa floor, this dry desert. I am a stranger, but I will wait for the sky to open and flood the plaza, the outer fields with rain. I will wait for the rain to sting my arms, to wet my dry face, to cool my flesh.
"They're about to commence."
A stranger, I spied six men dressed in white shirts and pants join the waiting, anxious dancers immobile assembled into two straight lines … female and male.
"Here comes Alma. You should have gone with her, Sonny. She is burdened with all those Coke containers."
"I wanted to Grandma, but …"
"Not much ice in these things. Won't cool you off much. But they're wet."
"That's what's important," Margo commented.
The chatting, the noise of the plaza hushed low. Only the tinkle of the merry-go-round corrupted the silence. We sat there as if figures in portrait, a photograph.
I remember McIntosh growing on the trees back home in my own grandmother's backyard, and my grandfather's transparents hanging in his now deserted orchard.
I think of spring waters gurgling, spouting from rocky hillsides of low-mountain country of home, north. I think of wading in clear creeks coolly wending their journey toward rivers. I think of rain which will flood those same rivers rushing to the great lake which in turn will empty its belly contents into the sea.

The photo remains static. The sun sweats ... the only movement of the moment. The sun steadily rises in the sky. It swirls before my gaze, my brain. It beats upon my face with hot hands. My shirt grows moist, my face cakes with dust.

I am a stranger in this part of the country. And I am sitting here under this burning sun waiting for the Santa Ana dancers to bring rain onto my hair, the mesa cactus, the river, which is nearly empty, the corn, which is still green yet slowly parching for want of rain and which will die and the people will go into winter without corn.

The photo blurs.

Each June my mother would gather her young brood as though we were a flock of chicks and go off to a distant meadow. She spent the day teaching her children the rites of wild berry picking. She would show us how to squeeze the strawberries and drink the juices under the summer sun, juices which ran between our fingers, down our arms like blood from open wounds, and through the crevice between our usually naked toes. We licked the flesh in laughter, our thirst assuaged. We spent our childhood in berry fields and brambles. My mother, however, remains allergic to strawberries.

Later in the summer she would haul us off to the blackberry brambles, the raspberries whose thorns clutched the skin and stung our hands with nasty bites and tears. Then blueberries, currants, gooseberries, elderberries of the woods. Berry after berry until we had gleaned the land and the wild fruit filled our bellies and filled glass jars for winter on the shelves in the cellar.

Rain sweeps across the hills in spring. Furious April floods the valleys. Meadows run black and treacherous with rainwater. The laundry barrels overflow, cisterns gurgle joyfully. Children play naked in the yard. The stench of enclosure, of winter hibernation, is washed from the flesh. We wait for berrytime.

Eventually, slowly the rivers retrench. Creeks babble again. Hay grows tall to the sun, and chicory wheat, corn, alfalfa shoots to the eye. Squash and bean vines start a steady crawl across the earth. Cows are contented; birds sing. Bears are happy with summer honey. Fox trek across open spaces, tails low to the ground, eyes fixed on a sparrow. Chipmunks race the edge of stone walls of a cemetery. Woodchucks munch grass growing thick and sweet in the open meadow. Then August starts to brown. Wild grapes cluster and purple on vines at the fence.

In my father's pasture an old plum tree hangs heavy with fruit. I taste the sweetness of flesh. It is an old tree, tall and scraggly with few limbs and not many leaves. The dark fruit is delicious. And a pole will bring the fruit down into the hand.

In the winter old men will nibble dried currants and smoke a mixture of sumac and cedar and red willow in their pipes. Women will talk of the largest wild strawberry ever picked thereabouts. Children will crack and chomp the meat of hickory nuts gathered on the floor of the autumn woods. Or pop corn.

The blurred photo swims into focus again.

Sun burns my hair.

I am a stranger here. I have never seen rain danced.

The dancers are about to start.

The drummers are ready.

In the vast, far distance Mount Taylor broods obsidic and tall and heavy against the horizon. A single cloud hovers above the peak. The mountain's sovereign power dominates the desert mesa which appears empty.

The sun blazes, burning flesh and earth.

Men beat drums. The dancers slowly proceed into the plaza. The man lifting the guidon of pennants follows. Two single lines of dancers … women, men follow the lead woman in the green tennis shoes. Their faces are stained red. The men's chests are stained blue. The cedar forests of arms move into the centre of the pueblo. Bare feet kick up puffs of red dust. Men shake rattles. Drummers drum. The guidon lowers. Drummers drum even, loud, incessantly. The sun hovers. Light falls upon Mount Taylor. The dark cloud has moved off the mountain peak. The dark mesa clears. Dancers move across the plaza before a silent horde of people. Minutes pass, perhaps hours. No one counts time because time is neither recognizable nor of any importance. The dancers move, interchanging, stepping forwards, backwards, weaving, drumming the earth with their naked feet. Men slide between women to regroup another line. Rattles shake. The guidon lowers again to the earth, the dry dust, yet refuses to touch the earth. Drums drum.

Brown bodies shine in the sweat of the dance. Paint melts on the flesh. The sun grudgingly moves before the cloud. The photo is animated before the fierce disbelieving eyes of the crowd.

The sweet smell of burning sage permeates the air.

The crowd is still, breathless. Gnats hang onto the fetid air. The cloud moves.

Drums drum.

A shadow crosses the dancers' faces and the crowd under the umbrellas in the adobe pueblo of the mesa.

Drums drum.

The guidon lowers.

Rattles rattle.

I am a stranger in this part of the country.

Rattles rattle.

The guidon lowers but still does not touch the red, dusty earth.

"They sure have power in this pueblo," the matriarch exclaims.

"That's power, Grandmother."

The blind old grandfather sitting with his grandson between his parted knees relaxes in his folding chair, his face to the sky, to the cloud, to the expected rain. He turns the boy's face with his mutton hands to the sky. He mumbles a prayer to himself and then into the ear of the little boy, and to the impending rain. Perhaps he remembers his own youth, his own dance in that plaza years and years before when his feet were strong and supple, not swollen as now, when his rheumy eyes sparkled with expectancy and could watch the cloud move across the quivering mesa to the pueblo, when his hands shook the rattles, the paint smeared and running down his chest naked to the falling pellets of cool rain, and his arms were festooned with the boughs bound in turquoise bands. He smiled a slight grin showing old teeth the colour of dried corn, but the smile changes into a dark frown as his ear catches the din of the carnival outside the plaza with the music of the merry-go-round vying with the beat of the drums, the rattles, and the pounding feet of the dancers. What chance has rain with this mechanical noise frightening the cloud and the spirits of the sky. His own grandchild begging for cotton candy and a swirl on the Ferris wheel. His people stuffing themselves with hot dogs and Cokes. Changes. Everything changes now. He was glad to be blind.

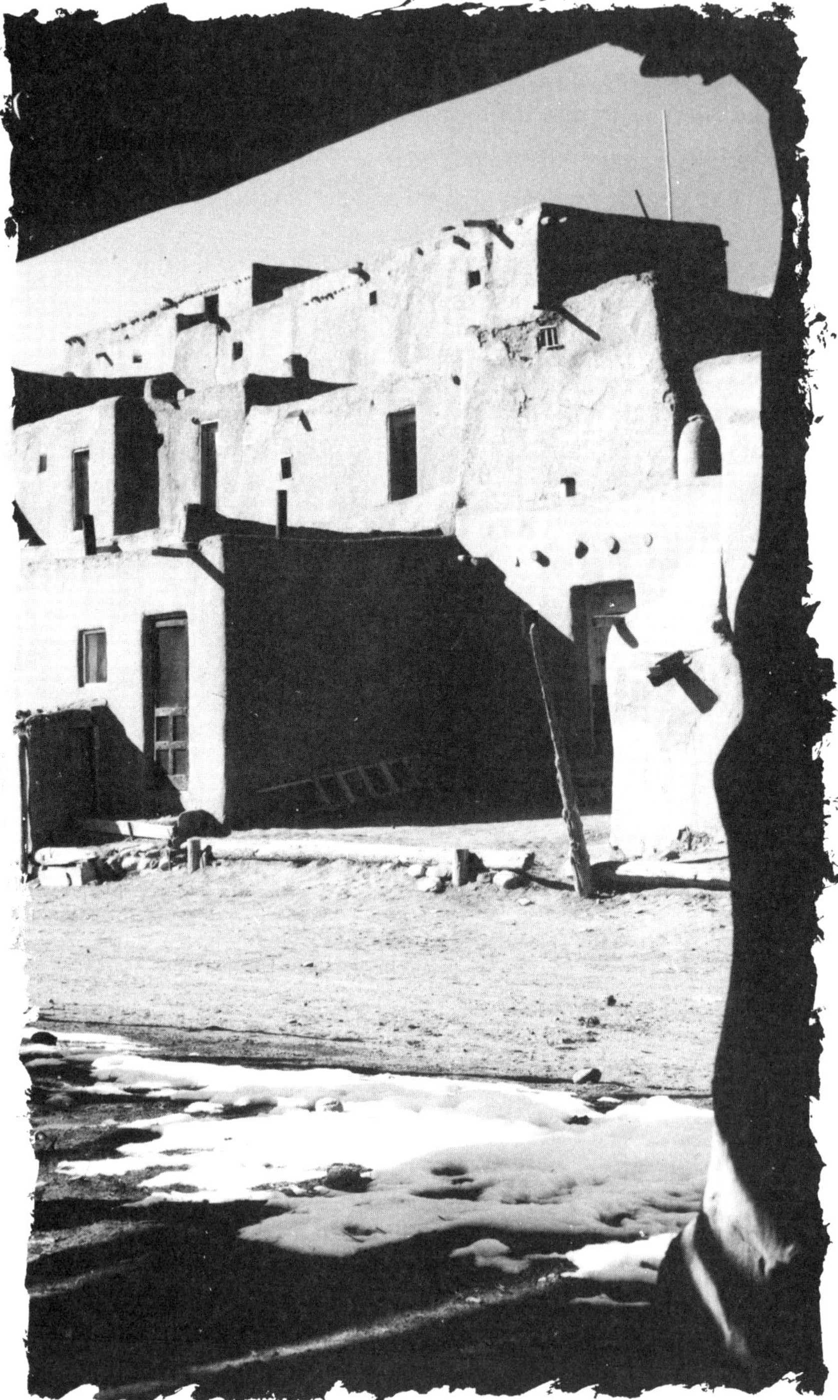

One day soon he would be deaf. Yet, before that biological change he would start the little boy learning the steps, the shake of the rattle, help him to prepare the costume, hunt his coyote, with bow and arrow, and teach him how to forge the bands to bind the cedar to the arm muscle. The boy would learn.

The child stood between the knees of his grandfather shaking a clenched but empty fist as the rain slowly dropped from the sky.

"Power! That's power," the elderly Laguna woman whispered.

The lead dancer in the green tennis shoes falls out of line and accepts a drink of water from a girl at the edge of the plaza.

Feet move and shuffle.

Red and blue paint run sweaty flesh, mingle, drip to the dust puffing up and flying away from the dry earth.

"Power," whisper the voices in the plaza.

The long two lines of dancers stand like falling raindrops caught in the eye of the camera, a photograph.

Whispers breathe across the plaza, the small village of adobe houses with the beat of the drum and the soft shuffle of feet and the rattle of the gourds.

I am a stranger here in this part of the country.

I sniff the burning sage.

I feel the first drop of rain strike my hot cheek, my earlobe, feel it slide through wisps of my hair.

The old woman in the green tennis shoes leads her dancers into the falling rain.

Dust settles. The dancers' feet cake with mud.

Drums drum.

Rattles rattle.

Rain.

The old grandfather is first to stand. He folds his chair, places his hand in the small fist of his grandson, and urges the boy to lead him from the plaza.

At the roadside I buy a melon. The vendor cuts it into small wedges. I suck the sweet juices, and taste my grandmother's McIntosh, my mother's strawberries, my father's plums. I buy three more melons from the couple at the side of the road and take them back to Albuquerque.

"They sure can dance down the rain in that Santa Ana village."

"Sure can, Mother."

"Mama, there's a rainbow."

"The tail …"

And there was.

Down the road a few yards ahead of us walked the old grandfather and the boy in stumbling gate. I watched him turn onto a path leading deep into the mesa as the Pontiac passed and sped on.

I am a stranger to this country. I'm visiting a short while.

1. Working individually, record your initial response to the story. You might choose one focus from the following:
   - details and images that were particularly memorable for you;
   - patterns you see in the story;
   - any questions you have about the story.

   In a small group, share your response. Summarize your responses for the class.
2. In a small group, discuss the characters of the protagonist, the great-grandmother, and the blind, old grandfather.
3. Rather than a story filled with, and dependent upon, action, this selection is more an evocation of people, places, and traditions. Note the portions of the story that were most vivid for you. What makes these portions so vivid? What thoughts, feelings, and images do they bring to mind for you?
4. Much like a refrain in a poem or chorus in a song, the narrator repeats (with variations) "I am a stranger here...." What effect does this repetition have on the reader? Consider the significance of this statement.
5. Examine further the style or texture of the story. Consider why the author made some of the choices that he did—i.e., specific choices in words, phrases, sentence structure, imagery, figurative language, and point of view.
6. Choose one of the following activities:
   a) Recall a special time in your life and write a poem about it. Find a good line to start your poem—e.g., "I am a stranger here," "I was much younger then ..."—and then write the rest.
   b) Using a combination of narration and description, write about a memorable family reunion.
   c) Traveling as a stranger in another land is a familiar pattern in literature. Consider why this might be, and discuss two other examples from literature and/or film.

Katherine Mansfield

Miss Brill

How she loved sitting here, watching it all!
It was like a play.

Although it was so brilliantly fine—the blue sky powdered with gold and great spots of light like white wine splashed over the Jardins Publiques—Miss Brill was glad that she had decided on her fur. The air was motionless, but when you opened your mouth there was just a faint chill, like a chill from a glass of iced water before you sip, and now and again a leaf came drifting—from nowhere, from the sky. Miss Brill put up her hand and touched her fur. Dear little thing! It was nice to feel it again. She had taken it out of its box that afternoon, shaken out the moth powder, given it a good brush, and rubbed the life back into the dim little eyes. "What has been happening to me?" said the sad little eyes. Oh, how sweet it was to see them snap at her again from the red eiderdown! ... But the nose, which was of some black composition, wasn't at all firm. It must have had a knock, somehow. Never mind—a little dab of black sealing-wax when the time came—when it was absolutely necessary.... Little rogue! Yes, she really felt like that about it. Little rogue biting its tail just by her left ear. She could have taken it off and laid it on her lap and stroked it. She felt a tingling in her hands and arms, but that came from walking, she supposed. And when she breathed, something light and sad—no, not sad, exactly—something gentle seemed to move in her bosom.

There were a number of people out this afternoon, far more than last Sunday. And the band sounded louder and gayer. That was because the Season had begun. For although the band played all the year round on Sundays, out of season it was never the same. It was like some one playing with only the family to listen; it didn't care how it played if there weren't any strangers present. Wasn't the conductor wearing a new coat, too? She was sure it was new. He scraped with his foot and flapped his arms like a rooster about to crow, and the bandsmen sitting in the green rotunda blew out their cheeks and glared at the music. Now there came a little "flutey" bit—very pretty!—a little chain of bright drops. She was sure it would be repeated. It was; she lifted her head and smiled.

Only two people shared her "special" seat: a fine old man in a velvet coat, his hands clasped over a huge carved walking-stick, and a big old woman, sitting upright, with a roll of knitting on her embroidered apron. They did not speak. This was disappointing, for Miss Brill always looked forward to the conversation. She had become really quite expert, she thought, at listening as though she didn't listen, at sitting in other people's lives just for a minute while they talked round her.

She glanced, sideways, at the old couple. Perhaps they would go soon. Last Sunday, too, hadn't been as interesting as usual. An Englishman and his wife, he wearing a dreadful Panama hat and she button boots. And she'd gone on the whole time about how she ought to wear spectacles; she knew she needed them; but that it was no good getting any; they'd be sure to break and they'd never keep on. And he'd been so patient. He'd suggested everything—gold rims, the kind that curved round your ears, little pads inside the bridge. No, nothing would please her. "They'll always be sliding down my nose!" Miss Brill had wanted to shake her.

The old people sat on the bench, still as statues. Never mind, there was always the crowd to watch. To and fro, in front of the flower beds and the band rotunda, the couples and groups paraded, stopped to talk, to greet, to buy a handful of flowers from the old beggar who had his tray fixed to the railings. Little children ran among them, swooping and laughing; little boys with big white silk bows under their chins, little girls, little French dolls, dressed up in velvet and lace. And sometimes a tiny staggerer came suddenly rocking into the open from under the trees, stopped, stared, as suddenly sat down "flop," until its small high-stepping mother, like a young hen, rushed scolding to its rescue. Other people sat on the benches and green chairs, but they were nearly always the same, Sunday after Sunday, and—Miss Brill had often noticed—there was something funny about nearly all of them. They were odd, silent, nearly all old, and from the way they stared they looked as though they'd just come from dark little rooms or even—even cupboards!

Behind the rotunda the slender trees with yellow leaves down drooping, and through them just a line of sea, and beyond the blue sky with gold-veined clouds.

Tum-tum-tum tiddle-um! tiddle-um! tum tiddley-um tum ta! blew the band.

Two young girls in red came by and two young soldiers in blue met them, and they laughed and paired and went off arm-in-arm. Two peasant women with funny straw hats passed, gravely, leading beautiful smoke-colored donkeys. A cold, pale nun hurried by. A beautiful woman came along and dropped her bunch of violets, and a little boy ran after to hand them to her, and she took them and threw them away as if they'd been poisoned. Dear me! Miss Brill didn't know whether to admire that or not! And now an ermine toque and a gentleman in gray met just in front of her. He was tall, stiff, dignified, and she was wearing the ermine toque she'd bought when her hair was yellow. Now everything, her hair, her face, even her eyes, was the same color as the shabby ermine, and her hand, in its cleaned glove, lifted to dab her lips, was a tiny yellowish paw. Oh, she was so pleased to see him—delighted! She rather thought they were going to meet that afternoon. She described where she'd been—everywhere, here, there, along by the sea. The day was so charming—didn't he agree? And wouldn't he, perhaps? … But he shook his head, lighted a cigarette, slowly breathed a great deep puff into her face, and, even while she was still talking and laughing, flicked the match away and walked on. The ermine toque was alone; she smiled more brightly than ever. But even the band seemed to know what she was feeling and played more softly, played tenderly, and the drum beat, "The Brute! The Brute!" over and over. What would she do? What was going to happen now? But as Miss Brill wondered, the ermine toque turned, raised her hand as though she'd seen some one else, much nicer, just over there, and pattered away. And the band changed again and played more quickly, more gayly than ever, and the old couple on Miss Brill's seat got up and marched away, and such a funny old man with long whiskers hobbled along in time to the music and was nearly knocked over by four girls walking abreast.

Oh, how fascinating it was! How she enjoyed it! How she loved sitting here, watching it all! It was like a play. It was exactly like a play. Who could believe the sky at the back wasn't painted? But it wasn't till a little brown dog trotted on solemn and then slowly trotted off, like a little "theater" dog, a little dog that had been drugged, that Miss Brill discovered what it was that made it so exciting. They were all on the stage. They weren't only the audience, not only looking on; they were acting. Even she had a part and came every Sunday. No doubt somebody would have noticed if she hadn't been there; she was part of the performance after all. How strange she'd never thought of it like that before! And yet it explained why she made such a point of starting from home at just the same time each week—so as not to be late for the performance—and it also explained why she had quite a queer, shy feeling at telling her English pupils how she spent her Sunday afternoons. No wonder! Miss Brill nearly laughed out loud. She was on the stage. She thought of the old invalid gentleman to whom she read the newspaper four afternoons a week while he slept in the garden. She had got quite used to the frail head on the cotton pillow, the hollowed eyes, the open mouth and the high pinched nose. If he'd been dead she mightn't have noticed for weeks; she wouldn't have minded. But suddenly he knew he was having the paper read to him by an actress! "An actress!" The old head lifted; two points of light quivered in the old eyes. "An actress—are ye?" And Miss Brill smoothed the newspaper as though it were the manuscript of her part and said gently: "Yes, I have been an actress for a long time."

The band had been having a rest. Now they started again. And what they played was warm, sunny, yet there was just a faint chill—a something, what was it?—not sadness—no, not sadness—a something that made you want to sing. The tune lifted, lifted, the light shone; and it seemed to Miss Brill that in another moment all of them, all the whole company, would begin singing. The young ones, the laughing ones who were moving together, they would begin, and the men's voices, very resolute and brave, would join them. And then she too, she too, and the others on the benches—they would come in with a kind of accompaniment—something low, that scarcely rose or fell, something so beautiful—moving.... And Miss Brill's eyes filled with tears and she looked smiling at all the other members of the company. Yes, we understand, we understand, she thought—though what they understood she didn't know.

Just at that moment a boy and a girl came and sat down where the old couple had been. They were beautifully dressed; they were in love. The hero and heroine, of course, just arrived from his father's yacht. And still soundlessly singing, still with that trembling smile, Miss Brill prepared to listen.

"No, not now," said the girl. "Not here, I can't."

"But why? Because of that stupid old thing at the end there?" asked the boy. "Why does she come here at all—who wants her? Why doesn't she keep her silly old mug at home?"

"It's her fu-fur which is so funny," giggled the girl. "It's exactly like a fried whiting."

"Ah, be off with you!" said the boy in an angry whisper. Then: "Tell me, ma petite chère—"

"No, not here," said the girl. "Not *yet.*"

On her way home she usually bought a slice of honeycake at the baker's. It was her Sunday treat. Sometimes there was an almond in her slice, sometimes not. It made a great difference. If there was an almond it was like carrying home a tiny present—a surprise—something that might very well not have been there. She hurried on the almond Sundays and struck the match for the kettle in quite a dashing way.

But today she passed the baker's by, climbed the stairs, went into the little dark room—her room like a cupboard—and sat down on the red eiderdown. She sat there for a long time. The box that the fur came out of was on the bed. She unclasped the necklet quickly; quickly, without looking, laid it inside. But when she put the lid on she thought she heard something crying.

1. Working individually, record your initial response to the story. You might choose one focus from the following:
   - your thoughts and feelings about Miss Brill;
   - anything you might like to say to Miss Brill at the end of the story;
   - a pattern you see in the story's imagery.

   In a small group, share your response. Summarize your responses for the class.
2. What comments by the narrator take the reader into the mind of Miss Brill? What insights into her character are given by the various questions and exclamations?
3. Consider Miss Brill's fantasies. What do they reveal about her needs and fears?
4. What role does the fox fur play in the story? How do you interpret the last line of the story? Why does the story end this way?
5. What seems to have been the author's purpose in writing this story? Support your opinion with references to the story.
6. Choose one of the following activities:
   a) In the form of a collage or brief essay, contrast Miss Brill and her society. (Consider first the historical and social context of the story.)
   b) In the role of Miss Brill, write two diary entries.
   c) Write a character sketch of Miss Brill.

Note: For one critic's response to this story, see page 287 in the unit "Perspectives on Story."

7

Perspectives on Story

There are many ways to talk about, think about, and examine short stories. To the stories in the earlier units, we've had initial personal responses, then shaped and refined them, and developed critical responses. While "personal response" and "critical response" are convenient labels for ways in which readers might consolidate and express their views on a short story, these are only two of the many possible perspectives on story. The possibilities range from the most informal reaction of a casual reader to very formal, scholarly, objective analyses, and can include the writer's perceptions. Each perspective deepens our understanding of a story by taking us further into its meaning.

This unit represents a range of possible readers' *and* writers' perspectives on selected stories in the anthology. In contrast to the unremarkable conception of "The Lottery," the letters in "Biography of a Story" reveal an astonishing range of personal and public reactions to that story. These emotional perspectives juxtapose with the second selection; the scholarly essay "Shirley Jackson's Point of View in 'The Lottery'" guides readers toward a deeper insight into the relationship between the story's structure and meaning. Similarly, "On 'Miss Brill'" is a scholarly analysis of Mansfield's short story. In such analyses, the author typically presents and carefully supports an interpretation of the story which the reader can assess and use to probe further into the story's meaning. The remaining four selections offer writers' perspectives. After reading the powerful and disturbing story "The Yellow Wall Paper," the author's explanation is illuminating. In the same way, the final three selections—Timothy Findley's writing and interview responses—take readers further into the meaning of

"Foxes," a complex, psychological story. Findley's reflections—and Gilman's as well—give us insights into how fiction is created.

Together, the selections in this unit offer a sample of additional perspectives which we may use in shaping, reconsidering, and deepening our understanding of stories.

Shirley Jackson

Biography of a Story

In this excerpt from a lecture, Shirley Jackson recalls her story "The Lottery" and how readers reacted to it when it was first published in The New Yorker *magazine.*

On the morning of June 28, 1948, I walked down to the post office in our little Vermont town to pick up the mail. I was quite casual about it, as I recall—I opened the box, took out a couple of bills and a letter or two, talked to the postmaster for a few minutes, and left, never supposing that it was the last time for months that I was to pick up the mail without an active feeling of panic. By the next week I had had to change my mailbox to the largest one in the post office, and casual conversation with the postmaster was out of the question, because he wasn't speaking to me. June 28, 1948 was the day *The New Yorker* came out with a story of mine in it. It was not my first published story, nor my last, but I have been assured over and over that if it had been the only story I ever wrote or published, there would be people who would not forget my name.

I had written the story three weeks before, on a bright June morning when summer seemed to have come at last, with blue skies and warm sun and no heavenly signs to warn me that my morning's work was anything but just another story. The idea had come to me while I was pushing my daughter up the hill in her stroller—it was, as I say, a warm morning, and thc hill was steep, and beside my daughter the stroller held the day's groceries—and perhaps the effort of the last fifty yards up the hill put an edge to the story; at any rate, I had the idea fairly clearly in my mind when I put my daughter in her playpen and the frozen vegetables in the refrigerator, and, writing the story, I found that it went quickly and easily, moving from beginning to end without pause. As a matter of fact, when I read it over later I decided that except for one or two minor corrections, it needed no changes, and the story I finally typed up and sent off to my agent the next day was almost word for word the original draft. This, as any writer of stories can tell you, is not a usual thing. All I know is that when I came to read the story over I felt strongly that I didn't want to fuss with it. I didn't think it was perfect, but I didn't want to fuss with it. It was, I thought, a serious, straightforward story, and I was pleased and a little surprised at the ease with which it had been written; I was reasonably proud of it, and hoped that my agent would sell it to some magazine and I would have the gratification of seeing it in print.

My agent did not care for the story, but—as she said in her note at the time—her job was to sell it, not to like it. She sent it at once to *The New Yorker*, and about a week after the story had been written I received a telephone call from the fiction editor of *The New Yorker*; it was quite clear that he did not really care for the story, either, but *The New Yorker* was going to buy it. He asked for one change—that the date mentioned in the story be changed to coincide with the date of the issue of the magazine in which the story would appear, and I said of course. He then asked, hesitantly, if I had any particular interpretation of my own for the story; Mr. Harold Ross, then the editor of *The New Yorker*, was not altogether sure that he understood the story, and wondered if I cared to enlarge upon its meaning. I said no. Mr. Ross, he said, thought that the story might be puzzling to some people, and in case anyone telephoned the magazine, as sometimes happened, or wrote in asking about the story, was there anything in particular I wanted them to say? No, I said, nothing in particular; it was just a story I wrote.

I had no more preparation than that. I went on picking up the mail every morning, pushing my daughter up and down the hill in her stroller, anticipating pleasurably the check from *The New Yorker*, and shopping for groceries. The weather stayed nice and it looked as though it was going to be a good summer. Then, on June 28, *The New Yorker* came out with my story.

Things began mildly enough with a note from a friend at *The New Yorker*: "Your story has kicked up quite a fuss around the office," he wrote. I was flattered; it's nice to think that your friends notice what you write. Later that day there was a call from one of the magazine's editors; they had had a couple of people phone in about my story, he said, and was there anything I particularly wanted him to say if there were any more calls? No, I said, nothing particular; anything he chose to say was perfectly all right with me; it was just a story.

I was further puzzled by a cryptic note from another friend: "Heard a man talking about a story of yours on the bus this morning," she wrote. "Very exciting. I wanted to tell him I knew the author, but after I heard what he was saying I decided I'd better not."

One of the most terrifying aspects of publishing stories and books is the realization that they are going to be read, and read by strangers. I had never fully realized this before, although I had of course in my imagination dwelt lovingly upon the thought of the millions and millions of people who were going to be uplifted and enriched and delighted by the stories I wrote. It had simply never occurred to me that these millions and millions of people might be so far from being uplifted that they would sit down and write me letters I was downright scared to open; of the three-hundred-odd letters that I received that summer I can count only thirteen that spoke kindly to me, and they were mostly from friends. Even my mother scolded me: "Dad and I did not care at all for your story in *The New Yorker*," she wrote sternly; "it does seem, dear, that this gloomy kind of story is what all you young people think about these days. Why don't you write something to cheer people up?"

By mid-July I had begun to perceive that I was very lucky indeed to be safely in Vermont, where no one in our small town had ever heard of *The New Yorker*, much less read my story. Millions of people, and my mother, had taken a pronounced dislike to me.

The magazine kept no track of telephone calls, but all letters addressed to me care of the magazine were forwarded directly to me for answering; and all letters addressed to the magazine (some of them addressed to Harold Ross personally—these were the most vehement) were answered at the magazine and then the letters were sent me in great batches, along with carbons of the answers written at the magazine. I have all the letters still, and if they could be considered to give any accurate cross section of the reading public of *The New Yorker*, or even the reading public of one issue of *The New Yorker*, I would stop writing now.

Judging from these letters, people who read stories are gullible, rude, frequently illiterate, and horribly afraid of being laughed at. Many of the writers were positive that *The New Yorker* was going to ridicule them in print, and the most cautious letters were headed, in capital letters: NOT FOR PUBLICATION or PLEASE DO NOT PRINT THIS LETTER, or, at best, THIS LETTER MAY BE PUBLISHED AT YOUR USUAL RATES OF PAYMENT. Anonymous letters, of which there were a few, were destroyed. *The New Yorker* never published any comment of any kind about the story in the magazine, but did issue one publicity release saying that the story had received more mail than any piece of fiction they had ever published; this was after the newspapers had gotten into the act, in midsummer, with a front-page story in the San Francisco *Chronicle* begging to know what the story meant, and a series of columns in New York and Chicago papers pointing out that *New Yorker* subscriptions were being canceled right and left.

Curiously, there are three main themes which dominate the letters of that first summer—three themes which might be identified as bewilderment, speculation, and plain old-fashioned abuse. In the years since then, during which the story has been anthologized, dramatized, televised, and even—in one completely mystifying transformation—made into a ballet, the tenor of letters I receive has changed. I am addressed more politely, as a rule, and the letters largely confine themselves to questions like what does this story mean? The general tone of the early letters, however, was a kind of wide-eyed, shocked innocence. People at first were not so much concerned with what the story meant; what they wanted to know was where these lotteries were held, and whether they could go there and watch. Listen to these quotations:

(KANSAS) Will you please tell me the locale and the year of the custom?

(NEW YORK) To a reader who has only a fleeting knowledge of traditional rites in various parts of the country (I presume the plot was laid in the United States)

I found the cruelty of the ceremony outrageous, if not unbelievable. It may be just a custom or ritual which I am not familiar with.

(NEVADA) Although we recognize the story to be fiction, is it possible that it is based on fact?

(TEXAS) What I would like to know, if you don't mind enlightening me, is in what part of the United States this organized, apparently legal lynching is practiced? Could it be that in New England or in equally enlightened regions, mass sadism is still part and parcel of the ordinary citizen's life?

(NEW YORK) We have not read about it in *In Fact.*

(NEW YORK) Is it based on reality? Do these practices still continue in back-country England, the human sacrifice for the rich harvest? It's a frightening thought.

(OHIO) I think your story is based on fact. Am I right? As a psychiatrist I am fascinated by the psychodynamic possibilities suggested by this anachronistic ritual.

(CANADA) Can the lottery be some barbaric event, a hang-over from the Middle Ages perhaps, which is still carried on in the States? In what part of the country does it take place?

(OREGON) Is there a witchcraft hangover somewhere in these United States that we Far Westerners have missed?

As I say, if I thought this was a valid cross section of the reading public, I would give up writing. During this time, when I was carrying home some ten or twelve letters a day, and receiving a weekly package from *The New Yorker*, I got one letter which troubled me a good deal. It was from California, short, pleasant, and very informal. The man who wrote it clearly expected that I would recognize his name and his reputation, which I didn't. I puzzled over this letter for a day or two before I answered it, because of course it is always irritating to be on the edge of recognizing a name and have it escape you. I was pretty sure that it was someone who had written a book I had read or a book whose review I had read or a story in a recent magazine or possibly even—since I come originally from California—someone with whom I had gone to high school. Finally, since I had to answer the letter, I decided that something carefully complimentary and noncommittal would be best. One day, after I had mailed him my letter, some friends also from California stopped in and asked—as everyone was asking then—what new letters had come. I showed them the letter from my mysterious not-quite-remembered correspondent. Good heavens, they said, was this really a letter from *him*? Tell me who he is, I said desperately, just tell me who he is. Why, how could anyone forget? It had been all over the California papers for weeks, and in the New York papers, too; he had just been barely acquitted of murdering his wife with an ax. With a kind of awful realization creeping over me I went and looked up the carbon of the letter I had written him, my noncommittal letter. "Thank you very much for your kind letter about my story," I had written. "I admire *your* work, too."

The second major theme which dominates the letters is what I call speculation. These letters were from the people who sat down and figured out a meaning for the story, or a reason for writing it, and wrote in proudly to explain, or else wrote in to explain why they could not possibly believe the story had any meaning at all.

(NEW JERSEY) Surely it is only a bad dream the author had?

(CALIFORNIA) The main idea which has been evolved is that the author has tried to challenge the logic of our society's releasing its aggressions through the channel of minority prejudice by presenting an equally logical (or possibly more logical) method of selecting a scapegoat. The complete horror of the cold-blooded method of choosing a victim parallels our own culture's devices for handling deep-seated hostilities.

(VIRGINIA) I would list my questions about the story but it would be like trying to talk in an unknown language so far as I am concerned. The only thing that occurs to me is that perhaps the author meant we should not be too hard on our presidential nominees.

(CONNECTICUT) Is *The New Yorker* only maintaining further its policy of intellectual leg-pulling?

(NEW ORLEANS) I wish Mrs. Hutchinson had been queen for a day or something nice like that before they stoned the poor frightened creature.

(ILLINOIS) If it is simply a fictitious example of man's innate cruelty, it isn't a very good one. Man, stupid and cruel as he is, has always had sense enough to imagine or invent a charge against the objects of his persecution: the Christian martyrs, the New England witches, the Jews and Negroes. But nobody had anything against Mrs. Hutchinson, and they only wanted to get through quickly so they could go home for lunch.

(MISSOURI) In this story you show the perversion of democracy.

(NEW YORK) Were you saying that people will accept any evil as long as it doesn't touch them personally?

(CANADA) My only comment is "what the hell"?

(VIRGINIA) The printers left out three lines of type somewhere.

(INDIANA) When I first read the story in my issue, I felt that there was no moral significance present, that the story was just terrifying, and that was all. However, there has to be a reason why it is so alarming to so many people. I feel that the only solution, the only reason it bothered so many people is that it shows the power of society over the individual. We saw the ease with which society can crush any single one of us. At the same time, we saw that society need have no rational reason for crushing the one, or the few, or sometimes the many.

Far and away the most emphatic letter writers were those who took this opportunity of indulging themselves in good old-fashioned name-calling. Since I am making no attempt whatsoever to interpret the motives of my correspondents, and would not if I could, I will not try now to say what I think of people who write nasty letters to other people who just write stories. I will only read some of their comments.

(NEW YORK) I expect a personal apology from the author.

(CALIFORNIA; this from a world-famous anthropologist) If the author's intent was to symbolize into complete mystification and at the same time be gratuitously disagreeable, she certainly succeeded.

(MICHIGAN) It certainly is modern.

Now, a complete letter, from Illinois.

Editor:

Never has it been my lot to read so cunningly vicious a story as that published in your last issue for June. I tremble to think of the fate of American letters if that piece indicated the taste of the editors of a magazine I had considered distinguished. It has made me wonder what you had in mind when accepting it for publication. Certainly not the entertainment of the reader and if not entertainment, what? The strokes of genius were of course apparent in the story mentioned, but of a perverted genius whose efforts achieved a terrible malformation. You have betrayed a trust with your readers by giving them such a bestial selection. Unaware, the reader was led into a casual tale of the village folk, becoming conscious only gradually of the rising tension, till the shock of the unwholesome conclusion, skillful though it was wrought, left him with total disgust for the story and with disillusionment in the magazine publishing it.

I speak of my own reaction. If that is not the reaction of the majority of your readers I miss my guess. Ethics and uplift are apparently not in your repertoire, nor are they expected, but as editors it is your responsibility to have a sounder and saner criterion for stories than the one which passed on "The Lottery."

Heretofore mine has been almost a stockholder's pride in *The New Yorker*. I shared my copy with my friends as I do the other possessions which I most enjoy. When your latest issue arrived, my new distaste kept me from removing the brown paper wrapping, and into the wastebasket it went. Since I can't conceive that I'll develop interest in it again, save the results of your efforts that indignity every week and cancel my subscription immediately.

Another letter, this one from Indiana.

Sir:

Thanks for letting us take a look at the nauseating and fiction-less bit of print which appeared in a recent issue. I gather that we read the literal translation.

The process of moving set us back a few weeks, but unfortunately your magazine and Miss Jackson's consistently correct spelling and punctuation caught up with us.

We are pleased to think that perhaps her story recalled happier days for you; days when you were able to hurl flat skipping stones at your aged grandmother. Not for any particular reason, of course, but because the village postmaster good-naturedly placed them in your hands, or because your chubby fingers felt good as they gripped the stone.

Our quarrel is not with Miss Jackson's amazingly clear style or reportorial observation. It is not with the strong motives exhibited by the native stone-throwers, or with

> the undertones and overtones which apparently we missed along the way.
>
> It is simply that we read the piece before and not after supper. We are hammering together a few paragraphs on running the head of our kindly neighbour through the electric eggbeater, and will mail same when we have untangled her top-piece. This should give your many readers a low chuckle or at least provide the sophisticates with an inner glow. Also it might interest you to know that my wife and I are gathering up the smoothest, roundest stones in our yard and piling them up on the corner in small, neat pyramids. We're sentimentalists that way.

I have frequently wondered if this last letter is a practical joke; it is certainly not impossible, although I hope not, because it is quite my favorite letter of all "Lottery" correspondence. It was mailed to *The New Yorker*, from Los Angeles, and written in pencil, on a sheet of lined paper torn from a pad; the spelling is atrocious.

> Dear Sir:
>
> The June 26 copy of your magazine fell into my hands in the Los Angeles railroad station yesterday. Although I donnot read your magazine very often I took this copy home to my folks and they had to agree with me that you speak straightforward to your readers.
>
> My Aunt Ellise before she became priestess of the Exalted Rollers used to tell us a story just like "The Lottery" by Shirley Jackson. I don't know if Miss Jackson is a member of the Exalted Rollers but with her round stone sure ought to be. There is a few points in her prophecy on which Aunt Ellise and me don't agree.
>
> The Exalted Rollers donnot believe in the ballot box but believe that the true gospel of the redeeming light will become accepted by all when the prophecy comes true. It does seem likely to me that our sins will bring us punishment though a great scouraging war with the

> devil's toy (the atomic bomb). I don't think we will have to sacrifice humin beings fore atonement.
>
> Our brothers feel that Miss Jackson is a true prophet and disciple of the true gospel of the redeeming light. When will the next revelations be published?
>
> Yours in the spirit.

Of all the questions ever asked me about "The Lottery," I feel that there is only one which I can answer fearlessly and honestly, and that is the question which closes this gentleman's letter. When will the next revelations be published, he wants to know, and I answer roundly, never. I am out of the lottery business for good.

Edgar V. Roberts

Shirley Jackson's Dramatic Point of View in "The Lottery"

This essay offers a critical response to Jackson's famous story.

The dramatic point of view in Shirley Jackson's story "The Lottery" is essential to the success with which the author is able to render horror in the midst of the ordinary. The story is not just a horror story; it could also be called a surprise story, an allegory, and a portrayal of human obtuseness, passivity, and cruelty. But the validity of all other claims for "The Lottery" hinges on the author's establishing the horror as stemming from a seemingly everyday, matter-of-fact situation—a situation that could not easily be maintained if another point of view was used. The success of Shirley Jackson's rendering of horror is achieved through her rudimentary but expert characterization, her almost clinically detached selection of details, and her deceivingly simple diction.

The villagers are depicted as ordinary folks attending a normal, festive event—in contrast to the real horror of their ultimate activity. Because of the dramatic point of view within the context of a brief narrative, Jackson prevents all but the most essential aspects of character from emerging. She chooses to see things from the outside, almost as though she is adopting the pose of a villager who is detached and emotionally uninvolved with the events that are unfolding. Her speaker thus records details about the villagers and reveals a certain knowledge of local gossip. The speaker presents enough background information about Mr. Summers, for example, to permit the conclusion that he is a middle-aged, pillar-of-society type who is the usual community leader. Tessie Hutchinson is the principal character in the story, but we learn little more about her than that she is chatty, illiterate, and relatively inarticulate—all facts that are essential to her behavior at the end of the story when she objects not to the lottery itself but to the "unfairness" of the drawing. So it is also with the other characters—and there are surprisingly quite a few—who appear in the story. Their brief conversations are recorded but no more. We see them from a distance, as we would likely see any representative group of human beings in a gathering that is too formal to permit intimacy. This distant, reportorial method of illustrating character is fundamental to the dramatic point of view, and the twist of cruelty at the end depends on the method.

While the dramatic point of view could theoretically permit the introduction of many details, Jackson's method in "The Lottery" is to concentrate almost clinically on only those details that bring out the horror. Because her speaker is removed from the immediate emotions of the scene, we learn just enough detail, but no more. At the beginning of the story there must be at least some information about the background of the lottery so that the reader can make some sense out of it, but there should be absolutely no disclosure about the consequences of drawing the black spot. Thus, the speaker establishes that the villagers are gathering rocks, but includes no mention of why. The short saying "Lottery in June, corn be heavy soon" is mentioned as a remnant of a more ritualistic kind of scape-goatism, but the speaker does not go into any sort of explanation (page 152). All such references are at first presented innocently, and it is only after reading the ending that a reader can feel their sinister qualities.

Without exaggeration, if there had been more detail in the story, contrast could not have been brought out so well. The selection of some other point of view would inevitably have required more detail. A first-person speaker, for example, could not have been credible if he had not explained the situation in advance, or at least if he had not described some attitude that would have anticipated the conclusion. An omniscient narrator would necessarily have expressed some commentary on the re-actions of the townsfolk. But the dramatic point of view permits just enough detail to inform the reader, but not so much as to spoil the surprise conclusion.

Appropriate to the conclusion, and to the graceless, simple, unquestioning, overly conservative nature of the villagers, is the diction. The language is uncolored and unemotional, sufficiently descriptive but not elaborate. When Tessie Hutchinson appears, she dries "her hands on her apron" (page 150)—a description that is functional and no more. Much of this sort of diction may be seen as a means by which Jackson uses point of view to delay the reader's understanding of what is happening. The piles of stones, for example, are to be used in the ritual stoning of Tessie Hutchinson, yet one could never draw this conclusion when they are first described:

> Bobby Martin had already stuffed his pockets full of stones, and the other boys soon followed his example, selecting the smoothest and roundest stones; Bobby and Harry Jones and Dickie Delacroix—the villagers pronounced this name "Dellacroy"—eventually made a great pile of stones in one corner of the square and guarded it against raids of the other boys. (page 147)

The speaker's references to the nicknames, and to the association of the stones with apparently normal boyhood games, both divert the reader's attention and obscure the horror of the fact that within two hours the stones will be used to kill someone. Even at the end, Tessie Hutchinson's son Davy is given a few "pebbles"; the implication of this word is that the boy is going to a game!

Because of such masterly control over point of view, it is obvious that Jackson has created a supremely successful story. Her objective is to establish a superficial appearance of reality, which she maintains up to the last few paragraphs. Indeed, she is so successful that a possible response to the conclusion is that "such a killing could not take place among such common, earthy folks as the story presents." Yet it is because of this reality that a reader sees the validity of Jackson's vision. Horror is not to be found on moors and in haunted castles, but among the people we see everyday, like the villagers in Tessie Hutchinson's hometown. The story thus expands, and supports many applications to human life in general. Without Jackson's skill in controlling point of view, there could be little of this power of suggestion, and it would not be possible to claim such success for the story.

Kate Fullbrook

On "Miss Brill"

A feminist literary critic assesses this classic story by an influential writer.

If Katherine Mansfield's stories about women psychologically alone in the smart sets of London and New Zealand are painful, those written about women left outside the protective screens of men, money and class are often devastating in their emotional impact. Along with her contemporary, Jean Rhys, Katherine Mansfield has a reputation for her stories of the *femme seule*, and many of her late stories fit into this category. This sub-genre is in many ways a continuation of the nineteenth-century "governess" novel—we are close to the conventions of *Jane Eyre* here—with the change that there is no hope for a happy ending, no matter how qualified, no chance that the excluded woman will be fitted back, on any terms, into the relationships that are meant to define and enclose her life.

Katherine Mansfield's "Miss Brill", written in 1920, is probably her most famous sketch of a woman alone. As she explained in a letter, she worked to put the story together in terms of "a musical composition—trying to get it nearer and nearer to the expression of Miss Brill—until it fitted her".[1] Once again, Katherine Mansfield's mature narrative method operates in the story as the writing strives to convey the experience of Miss Brill through the presentation of events in the vocabulary and cadences of her mind.

"Miss Brill" is the loneliest of all of Katherine Mansfield's stories about lonely women. It is sometimes compared with James Joyce's "Clay",[2] but is different in tone, in its ultimate significance, and in its impression of participation in the miseries of the woman's consciousness which is portrayed. Like Joyce's little laundress, so extravagantly willing to be pleased by a world that gives her little but hard knocks, Miss Brill is eager to be part of a scene that ruthlessly excludes her. But whereas in the *Dubliners* story we are asked to pity Maria, and we are not sure of the extent to which she absorbs the humiliation we so painfully see, in "Miss Brill" the reader is more closely implicated, both with the character and with the world, as we are made to watch the character take the full force of the transformation of her consciousness of herself from participant to exile. It is a cruel process, and Katherine Mansfield refuses to temper any detail of its typicality.

Miss Brill lives alone in France, patching together an income from scraps of English teaching and from reading the newspaper to an invalid. She keeps herself going by reining her expectations in tightly with a chirpy, inconsequentiality of mind and with her conformity to a tattered notion of gentility. Her surroundings smack of the deprivation of a lone woman—a dark little room, her meagre treat of a honey-cake which she looks forward to each week as her only self-indulgence. She most significantly identifies herself with her fur-piece, a decayed thing she keeps in a box under her bed, and which represents to her all the luxury and adventure in life that she convinces herself she shares. She values, too, the sensuality and flirtatiousness of the fur, itself an emblem of the traditional man-fascinating ways out of poverty for a woman that she still obliquely believes apply to herself. But the fur, her only friend, is not what it used to be; even Miss Brill can see that.

> Dear little thing! It was nice to feel it again. She had taken it out of its box that afternoon, shaken out the moth powder, given it a good brush, and rubbed the life back into the dim little eyes ... But the nose, which was of some black composition, wasn't really at all firm ... Little rogue! Yes, she really felt like that about it. Little rogue biting its tail just by her left ear. (page 264)

The lonely woman feels herself as roguish as her fur as she slips out to the public concert which is her Sunday entertainment. For her, the afternoon in the park is concert and theatre combined, for she feels herself part of a complex drama as she watches the other concert-goers from her bench. She prides herself on her understanding of life and her ability to interpret strangers' affairs from a distance. But her keenest pleasure is in eavesdropping, and at first she is disappointed, as a woman starved for words, with the silent old couple sharing the bench. When a pair of young lovers replace them she is delighted; she loves lovers, they are an unexpected treat. She sees them as the hero and heroine in a thrilling drama she directs and in which she participates. Smiling, she listens to their conversation:

> "No, not now," said the girl. "Not here, I can't."
> "But why? Because of that stupid old thing at the end there?" asked the boy. "Why does she come here at all—who wants her? Why doesn't she keep her silly old mug at home?"
> "It's her fu-fur which is so funny," giggled the girl. "It's exactly like a fried whiting." (page 268)

Miss Brill drags herself back to "her room like a cupboard" and, without looking, puts the fur into its box. "But when she put the lid on she thought she heard something crying" (page 268). The extraordinary pathos of the story and of Miss Brill herself derives from the depth of the central character's courage and self-control which is nevertheless expended in acquiescence to a view of a woman's function that is bound to abase her. The story portrays a consciousness distancing itself from its own suffering isolation with a tremendous degree of pain and yet with a dignity that is in itself a kind of virtue. Miss Brill is written off as a horror by a code that condemns her on the grounds of sex, age, beauty, poverty and singleness, the same code that Miss Brill herself uses to explain her disappointment with the old couple on the bench and which now comes full circle to indict her as less than human. This is a portrait of a woman caught by the contradictions of social preconceptions that she herself has internalised. What Miss Brill stuffs into the box under the lonely bed of the *femme seule* is, according to the logic of the image, herself.

---

[1] *Letters*, vol. II, p. 89. Letter to Richard Murry dated 17 January 1921. See also Katherine Mansfield's review of Gertrude Stein's *Three Lives* in terms of the musicality of the prose in Katherine Mansfield, *Novels and Novelists* (London: Constable, 1930), pp. 273-4.

[2] See, for example, Berkman, *Katherine Mansfield*, pp. 161-3.

Charlotte Perkins Gilman

Why I Wrote "The Yellow Wall Paper"?

In this brief essay, the author reveals personal circumstances which motivated her to write her story.

Many and many a reader has asked that. When the story first came out, in the *New England Magazine* about 1891, a Boston physician made protest in *The Transcript.* Such a story ought not to be written, he said; it was enough to drive anyone mad to read it.

Another physician, in Kansas I think, wrote to say that it was the best description of incipient insanity he had ever seen, and—begging my pardon—had I been there?

Now the story of the story is this:

For many years I suffered from a severe and continuous nervous breakdown tending to melancholia—and beyond. During about the third year of this trouble I went, in devout faith and some faint stir of hope, to a noted specialist in nervous diseases, the best known in the country. This wise man put me to bed and applied the rest cure, to which a still-good physique responded so promptly that he concluded there was nothing much the matter with me, and sent me home with solemn advice to "live as domestic a life as far as possible," to "have but two hours' intellectual life a day," and "never to touch pen, brush, or pencil again" as long as I lived. This was in 1887.

I went home and obeyed those directions for some three months, and came so near the borderline of utter mental ruin that I could see over.

Then, using the remnants of intelligence that remained, and helped by a wise friend, I cast the noted specialist's advice to the winds and went to work again—work, the normal life of every human being; work, in which is joy and growth and service, without which one is a pauper and a parasite—ultimately recovering some measure of power.

Being naturally moved to rejoicing by this narrow escape, I wrote "The Yellow Wall Paper," with its embellishments and additions, to carry out the ideal (I never had hallucinations or objections to my mural decorations) and sent a copy to the physician who so nearly drove me mad. He never acknowledged it.

The little book is valued by alienists and as a good specimen of one kind of literature. It has, to my knowledge, saved one woman from a similar fate—so terrifying her family that they let her out into normal activity and she recovered.

But the best result is this. Many years later I was told that the great specialist had admitted to friends of his that he had altered his treatment of neurasthenia since reading "The Yellow Wall Paper."

It was not intended to drive people crazy, but to save people from being driven crazy, and it worked.

Timothy Findley

from Inside Memory: March 1990

In a journal entry, the author of "Foxes" recalls a memorable and formative evening with Thornton Wilder, the famous American author of Our Town.

Beyond the windows, the sun was setting beyond the city, way beyond the visible skyline. London was still a mass of chimney pots then, and every chimney gave off smoke. The sunset colours infused this smoke with reds and yellows smudged with grey, and all you could see was colour and light and the gradual coming on of lamps as the darkness increased.

This fading light and growing darkness have remained for me an integral part of Thornton's presence and his words that night. But the darkness was neither threatening nor depressing.

"Be confident," he said, "that whatever I say is said as one writer to another. I do not mince words—but neither do I mince writers. You are a writer, Findley. That's a certainty. What you have written, on the other hand. . . ."

What I had written, on the other hand, was everything I had feared it was and hoped it was not:

an intellectual forum in which your
characters talk their problems to death—
not an active exploration of their lives—
—an arrogant tirade, written from a
position of ignorance, not—as it should
be—an impassioned questioning written

from a position of bafflement—
The characters in a play must never know
what is going to happen next. In a play,
the moment is always now. Do you know what
is going to happen in the next five
minutes, Findley?
No, sir—
Well, then—

On the other hand, he conceded that I could handle dialogue.

—and some of your images are
good. Good enough to suggest that more good
images will be forthcoming—

All the while he spoke, he paced and smoked and drank. His cigarette ashes fell helter-skelter. Drops from his glass were spewed out over the carpet every time he turned his pacing in a new direction. But the words he spoke were spare and well considered.

He was always out of breath. His voice had edge—but the edge kept cracking.

He pulled at his tie. His collar wilted. He forgot—or seemed to have forgotten—where he was. He might have been on a hill in Athens five hundred years before the birth of Christ—he might have been blind, dictating to his daughters—he might have been sitting in an eighteenth century drawing-room, wrapped in flesh and warts—he might have been musing out loud on the fate of roses in a Paris garden, circa 1910. He was all great teachers in one. The only assumptions he made were that knowledge was important and that I cared.

"Pay attention, Findley. Pay attention. That is all you have to do. Never, for an instant, leave off paying attention."

So it was. That evening, my attentions garnered the following:

I could write—but had written a travesty.
Talk is cheap—but you pay a hefty price
for the written word.

> *Come down from all high-minded places—no*
> *one down here can hear you.*
> *A writer—however good he may be*
> *intrinsically—cannot communicate without*
> *a sense of craft. In writing—the craft is*
> *all.*

After he had spoken and I had eaten, he gave me back my pages and urged me to put them away in a drawer.

"When you write again, write something new," he said. "Ordinarily, I say the wastepaper basket is a writer's best friend—but keep these pages as a reminder of how intentions go awry. Otherwise, forget it. Don't even mourn it, Findley. You've more important things to do than that."

He walked me to the elevator.

After I had thanked him, he wanted to know if I was going to go home on the bus or on the tube.

"I'm going to walk," I said.

Which I did.

It took me about two hours. But every step was worth it. All the way home, I smiled.

You only have such an evening once in your life. There isn't room for two.

Glen Kirkland

An Interview with Timothy Findley

In a long-distance phone interview, one of the co-editors of Inside Stories for Senior Students *talks with the author of "Foxes" about the sources, meanings, and techniques of that intriguing story.*

Glen Kirkland [GK]:
The first question that does emerge is about the epigraph: "The face is only the thing to write." Would you like to comment on its function?

Timothy Findley [TF]:
This is a quote that is taken from Roland Barthes' book, *Empire of Signs,* about the iconography that he explored when he was in Japan. It was because of my own interest in Japan and Japanese culture that I got this book. And, as you can see, that plays into the hands of the story itself. There is about Japanese culture a wonderful sense of presentation and ceremony and face, and "The face is only the thing to write" comes from the section in Barthes' book about Japanese theatre. When an actor makes up to play in *kabuki*—and all the young performers in *kabuki* are male—the first thing they do is to completely whiten their face; in other words, they completely remove their own face. Then they write upon that face the mode of expression that is the most telling aspect of the character they're going to play. So they are not just writing but making a statement in a single expression or a single line. And that's what that epigraph is about for me; it's literally the wiping away of self and the placing of the most telling aspect of the character.

GK: It certainly reverberates through the story. Thank you.

That brings up the story's main character, Morris Glendenning. Would you like to comment on what he emerged from in terms of your own experience, in terms of imagination. What brought him to light for you?

TF: Well, let's go to the end of that question. I have argued that you conceive of the character versus the situation. When I'm writing, most of what I write starts with a person. The person always comes first—they and the story attached to them—*by necessity* because my first encounter with characters in my mind as they loom up is that they have something they want to tell me *or* something they don't want to tell me and their silence is so extraordinary that I figure that I gotta get it out of them.

So, it *usually* does start with the person. I want to say that right off the top: that is the normal procedure. But, in this one instance I had been invited to write a story for *Rotunda*. At the Royal Ontario Museum (or ROM, the publisher of *Rotunda*), they said "Is there a story in your mind that might emerge from the museum?" and, of course, I went straight in my mind to Japanese masks. I had already encountered some of these masks at the museum. Morris zapped into my mind on his own and I thought: "My goodness, I do have a story and the story has to do with the masks and this man who encounters them." The character himself has very large elements in him emerging from Marshall McLuhan.

GK: I was wondering about the communications expert.

TF: Yes. The whole impetus in Morris Glendenning to think about how we communicate comes from McLuhan. But the recluse, the genius, the artist aspect comes from Glenn Gould. My encounter with Gould involved his making music for the film based on *The Wars*. I found him a very fascinating and very moving person.

GK: There's so much of the artist in the character. His experiences, I'm sure, reflect some of the writer's, generally speaking. (Yes, absolutely.) Certainly, the tension between the privacy and the need to communicate is there.

TF: And the precision. So it's a kind of blend, I guess.... I can only speak for myself, but I can't believe it would be otherwise for other authors given some conversations I've had with other writers. There is *always* some autobiographical element if in this sense only: it is *you* who's putting it on the page. So, you're drawing not only from a field of imagery and knowledge that you've acquired but also from the stuff of your own daily life, so that the views from the window, the sense of being in that building or walking along Bloor Street are very much reflections of my own presence in those places. But I don't think that there's much of my personal character in Morris; I was really trying much more to capture someone like Gould or McLuhan.

GK: The link to the foxes certainly becomes something of a metaphor for Morris' predicament or the tension I mentioned between his need to avoid contact and his need for communication. I'm curious why perhaps it felt so right to use foxes. Had you considered any other animal?

TF: That idea stemmed from the fact that that sequence of masks tells the story as it's told in Japan. They were created to be used in a play that exists, I think a "Noh" play, about a fox that becomes a priest, which is interesting because priests, too, are aesthetically inclined to view the world from a kind of silence. They are observers in the Buddhist sense of priests and they're very deeply involved with nature.

GK: I was wondering if there was a Japanese cultural view of the fox as a creature that might be part of this as well, or if the concept of the wildness, and the community with nature is the important dimension there.

TF: My own sense is that nature is very much a part of life in Japan as reflected in classical writing, as reflected in all the paintings, as reflected in the necessity of that huge mass of people living in that tiny little place. They can't get away from it. But also I think there's a great respect for animals and animal characteristics that North American culture has ignored. The fox is a greatly respected figure, however, in the culture that produced these masks.

GK: That accounts even more for the link to the priest which would also be a figure of respect.

TF: Yes. I'm fascinated, too, by the whole aspect of opposites in things Japanese, which is a constant reflection that occurs over and over again. The opposite is the opposite is the opposite: black for joy and white for mourning, etc.; and, in this instance, that the fox becomes a man—but, in our culture, the man becomes a fox. You know the British story "The Lady and the Fox" and the whole thing of hunting the fox, the fox as a wily enemy we must outwit. Whereas, in Japan, the fox is a wily *companion* living in nature with us and we must understand it, rather than outwit it.

GK: Certainly the camaraderie Morris feels more when he dons the mask, the sense of peacefulness, as such, is part of what you're saying there. (Yes.)

Now, I'll invite you to comment further on whether there is something further about Timothy Findley's writing that emerges in the experiences of the story "Foxes."

TF: I think so. I very often find that I'm trying to write my way out of despair. And I don't mean that is *why* I write. I'm a writer and that's why I write. My motto is taken from Sam Johnson who wrote just before he died and as he was preparing to die: "Make prayers against despair." Isn't that incredible? (Yes, indeed.) That is my motto. So, the story is yet one more way to find my way past despair; the thoughts that Morris has walking on Bloor Street are very much the same thoughts that I have there.

GK: In a sense I felt the ending of the story moved from despair to the positive or to some strengthening. In the end Morris returns—through his need to communicate—to being with people again.

TF: Absolutely. Because he gets back to where he came from. Because he gets back to looking down through the mask. I found I was moved by this, because that image conjured itself in my own mind as I was writing of this golden circle, the smell of the earth and this circle of beasts which is the circle we have lost. And when he goes out smelling like a dog, he's found it again.

GK: Yes. Indeed. There's a real feeling of affirmation for him that he would carry on and he would get past this depth of despair he was in. (Absolutely. No question.) I found, too, the closing scene suggested to me that inside of him there was an acceptance of the world because of what we have in us; though it may not give him everything, it still is part of him.

TF: Oh, indeed. He cannot utterly walk away from it because that's where we have to do our living—in the real world. That is something that I share as well; that's the way I think.

GK: Thank you.

You've indicated the reason for the setting at the Royal Ontario Museum and I'd like to broaden the question about setting. How does setting work in relation to your story? You mention you begin with character most often. Have you perhaps thought of stories from settings?

TF: Oh, yes. Settings will also trigger. Of course, they trigger people. In and of themselves, yes indeed they do. I went up the road this morning—I walk every morning—and I went up to the graveyard where the man, who in 1840 built this house where I live, is buried. And I had a little chat with him in a totally non-mystical way: I just said "I have come because I want to tell you how glad I am that you made our house" and I wouldn't have got to that if that cemetery hadn't been there and *all* that it implies. The depth of the earth in which he's buried is equal to the depth of time. So you're triggered forward to an encounter with another person.

There's a scene in "Almeyer's Mother"—another story in *Stones,* where you found "Foxes"—where the characters have lunch in the dining room at the ROM and Mrs. Almeyer looks around the room and she draws a terrific kind of security from being in this place that she's known for so long and she knows everyone there and gets that sense of community. Place does that as well so the reader can say "I've sat there. I know the very table she's talking about. I walked through those doors."

There is a marvellous thing, I think, that has happened to Canadian writing over the last twenty-five years or so that didn't really happen much before. We now talk about *here* with total confidence. We don't have to pretend that Toronto is New York or Paris or something. Toronto *is,* significantly, unique.

GK: Certainly a lot of stories are there just as much as anywhere else. We talked before the interview about Canadian writers and I'm curious to know if you would like to comment on being described as a Toronto or even, Canadian, writer *per se.*

TF: I always have an answer which you may already have heard: I'm not a Canadian writer; I'm a Canadian who writes. Although, for instance in *Stones,* virtually every story is connected in one way or another to the Queen Street

Mental Health Centre. They are all set, in other words, with a line that pulls them toward a landmark that is unquestionably one of the major landmarks of my life and my childhood as a visible place and institution. And there's no question that the fact of that place and the fact of that city and the fact of everything that the word "Canada" implies informs every word I write. My sense is that the "Canadianness" in me is basically that I get to see the whole world from here and this is where I'm looking from and *that's* what is important about place. I love where I am. I wouldn't leave it for all the world.

GK: That's very good to hear. I'd like to shift over to style of the story "Foxes" with the general question. I was intrigued by the way in which the story moved and I'd like to invite you to comment if this story emerged as naturally and fluidly. (Laughter.) Would you like to comment on some of the decisions you made about the technique of the story or how it worked for you as you were writing it?

TF: There's not a lot I can say about that, because all I'm aware of doing is sitting at my desk and attempting to get this thing to be right. The best example, and an anecdote you probably know, is about the artist who has made an astonishing sculpture of an elephant in marble and it *is* elephant—it rings with elephant. And a fellow artist comes into the studio and says "My God! I don't understand. I've tried to do that for … I couldn't accomplish anything like that … How did you do that?" And the artist says "Well, I had this block of marble and I simply cut away everything that didn't look like an elephant." (Laughter.) When I'm at the desk, what I'm trying to do is to cut away everything that doesn't look like the story. So lots of stuff crowds on to the page that I then have to pull away and fight my way through to the one little bit I've left on the page that *is* this story. There is a *tremendous* amount of cutting that I do, searching for the precise words.

GK: That brings me to my following question. "Foxes" is a "large" story in some ways in that there are many dimensions to it. When we speak of the masks of Morris', perhaps, near obsession or madness or despair, so much is going on in the story. The richness is all centred around Morris' own consciousness and the tension I've referred to earlier between his need to avoid and his need to communicate. Morris' is a positive story in spite of that and I'd like to leave it open for any kind of comment. You mentioned that the character is the heart of the story, and character is that which tells you what doesn't belong in the story and what does belong.

TF: Yes, absolutely. But I think that there's one more step to go with that in reference to this question, and that is: because Morris *is* Morris, that's one thing, and that generates certain elements; but because Morris *as* Morris is at this moment looking from a *particular* perspective in terms of his own moment of crisis, what he is *looking* at is form and face and mask. That was for me the joy in making this story: that *that* matched the thing from which it sprung, which was the mask itself. And that means looking at the faces and the encounter with the mask. Morris and his boyhood friend don't speak but then go away and each one says, "I saw old so and so out on Bloor Street today...." Everything is an encounter that is struck through the appearance of the mask worn by the person on the street.

GK: This in itself is a story as opposed to a novel because it explores *this* particular moment in Morris' life where he seems to move forward and know himself better. Would a character like Morris or a concern like Morris' emerge again in a different work or in a different way in a later work?

TF: Oh, absolutely. People turn up again either as themselves or as larger explorations of that *kind* of person in *that* situation.

He, I think, in fact, or someone very like him is about to turn up in my writing now which is a novel but he would be one of many characters. This—what Morris is about—is what is going on in this book.

GK: This brings up the question of your feelings about this particular story, whether it may be one of your favorites, or what you think it might touch in those who read it. I know in past interviews you've commented about readers' participation in the story....

TF: You have to leave room for the reader; that's terribly important. That's a large part of theatre too; you have leave room for the audience. The actor cannot do everything ... and nor can the writer. You're there to provoke.

I don't have favourites; they line up, probably, in different ways. Your own sense of success or failure has to do with saying "Does this say what I wanted it to say?" And in that sense then you say "Yes, I can let that go out as it is because it does what I want it to do." My only regret about this story is that, because where it was originally published there was a word count involved, I had to keep it to a certain length and I suspect that if I hadn't been bound in by the fact of that given length that I might have done a bit more. But, basically, who cares? The fact is "Foxes" is "Foxes" as it is.

GK: Would you like to say something directly to students who wish to become story writers and, in the context of that, anything about your own development or recognition of self as a writer?

TF: Very early on, I did a fair amount of writing which was done for the sheer entertainment of having something to do. I was unlucky enough, and lucky enough in a sense, to have a long bout of illness which kept me out of school for quite a long time—about a year and a half—and in that time one of the things I did was write. But I wrote *then* as a means of escape from that bed. It was a form of making a world out there and bringing it inside my room. So, that is one way that writing is valuable, but it isn't really the best, ultimately, for writing because it's necessarily selfish. The point about writing is the person at the other end of the writing. You're writing *to* someone. What you want to do is to *tell* something—the impulse to *tell* something, explain something.

The very first story I wrote in my adult life I wrote for that very reason. I'd had an argument with a famous actress, Ruth Gordon, and she had said something to me which provoked the *need* in me to respond and the only way I could respond was by writing a story. I had to *tell her a story.* I couldn't sit down and sit across the table from her because then she could interrupt me (laughter) and make it go awry and when you sit down by yourself and couch what you have to say in a story form *you* get to do all the talking (laughter) and to really have a chance to tell it as you believe it to be. That's a very good reason for writing—because you have *not* something *to say,* in the pompous sense, but something *to tell.* There's a huge difference.

GK: In terms of the developing writer, what will you tell us about the craft of storywriting?

TF: You need to get yourself out of it as much as you can because there are little teeny tiny private opinions or moments of revenge or little moments that are there for other reasons than for telling this one story. Take them out at once. William Faulkner said this extraordinary thing: he said the last thing you had to do after you had finished a book was to go back inside and kill all your "darlings." (Laughter.) Isn't that marvellous? Cut all the lovely writing. What's lovely writing? Nothing, if it doesn't serve the story. Trash it.

GK: … leaving, as you alluded to earlier, leaving the story itself (Yes.) and removing all that isn't in the story (That's right.) or isn't that particular story.

TF: … everything but the elephant. That's a wonderful image. I've always loved that image: "I just took away everything that didn't look like an elephant." (Laughter.)

GK: Well, I'd like to thank you very much.

TF: You're very welcome.

Timothy Findley

from Inside Memory: February 1989

Timothy Findley remembers the late classical pianist, Glenn Gould, one of the eccentric models for the protagonist in "Foxes."

Someone once described the phenomenon of genius as "a rarified spirit's search for embodiment." Over time, given the fact my life has largely been lived in the worlds of theatre and books, I have had occasional glimpses of that rarified spirit's embodiment during encounters with Tyrone Guthrie, Edith Evans, Thornton Wilder, Margaret Laurence and a very few others. Always, whatever form the genius takes, there are signals given: qualities that let you know at once with whom you're dealing. Some of these can be off-putting at first. For instance, a sense of inviolate aloofness (think of Baryshnikov); a private, often eccentric vocabulary (think of Marshall McLuhan); coolness (think of Meryl Streep).

One of the most alarming of these signal qualities is a certain testiness that emerges, probably unbidden, from these men and women—creatures not of habit, but of concentrated energies. On the way to making their unique discoveries, interruption is the worst of their enemies. It is anathema. *DON'T INTERRUPT!* they will yell at you. *LEAVE ME ALONE!* ...

Glenn Gould had a way with words, when he chose the destructive mode, that was almost appallingly cruel. Cruel, but not sadistic. Cruel because he could write people off—dismiss them, life and limb and heart and soul, with a judgement call that wrote them out of history entirely. *So-and-so,* he would say—naming some name, the voice coming brittle, disparaging, amused down the wire the way it did: *it's too bad. It's too sad. He can't make anything happen—and he's taking up all that room!* His behaviour, afterward, to whatever person had been named would reflect this judgement; the person would become invisible—ceasing, somehow, through lack of communication, to exist.

Why? It wasn't, in retrospect, something Gould did to other people—it was something he did to himself. He cut himself off. Over and over—both in my own small experience of Gould and in the larger, wider experience of him afforded all of us in Otto Friedrich's evocation of his life [in the biography *A Life and Variations*]—Gould puts the world of other people aside and locks himself in his room. Even as I wrote that sentence, I was thinking—hoping—I meant it theoretically—rhetorically. But, of course, his apartness was all too real. It became, over time, his whole way of life. His trademark.

Gould had more than one way of creating apartness. Gould made the discovery at an early age that he could push the immediate world away by means of sound. Once, while young Glenn was attempting to master a difficult passage of music and getting nowhere, the maid turned on the vacuum cleaner and, in his urgent need for silence, the boy took advantage of the dreadful whining and made of the noise a kind of wall—or barrier. Inside the "wall," he found he could work in perfect seclusion, safe as houses sitting in a desert.

Later in his life, when he lacked the patience to drag out the vacuum cleaner, or even to *own* a vacuum cleaner, he developed the sure-fire technique of setting two radios—one on either side of the piano—turning them up full blast and settling into his work at the keyboard happily walled in his private cell. The thing he needed most was to be alone with the music—all of the music, even the parts he wasn't playing.

8
Stories for Further Reading

Tobias Wolff

The Liar

Often my lies came back to her in embarrassing ways ...

My mother read everything except books. Advertisements on buses, entire menus as we ate, billboards; if it had no cover it interested her. So when she found a letter in my drawer that was not addressed to her she read it. "What difference does it make if James has nothing to hide?"—that was her thought. She stuffed the letter in the drawer when she finished it and walked from room to room in the big empty house, talking to herself. She took the letter out and read it again to get the facts straight. Then, without putting on her coat or locking the door, she went down the steps and headed for the church at the end of the street. No matter how angry or confused Mother might be, she always went to four o'clock Mass and now it was four o'clock.

It was a fine day, blue and cold and still, but Mother walked as though into a strong wind, bent forward at the waist with her feet hurrying behind in short busy steps. My brother and sisters and I considered this walk of hers funny, and smirked at one another when she crossed in front of us to stir the fire or water a plant. We didn't let her catch us at it. It would have puzzled Mother to think that there might be anything amusing about her. Her one concession to the fact of humor was an insincere, startling laugh. Strangers often stared at her.

While Mother waited for the priest, who was late, she prayed. She prayed in a familiar, orderly, firm way: first for her late husband, my father, then for her parents—also dead. She said a quick prayer for my father's parents (just touching base—she had disliked them) and finally for her children in order of their ages, ending with me. Mother did not consider originality a virtue, and until my name came up her prayers were exactly the same as on any other day.

But when she came to me she spoke up boldly. "I thought he wasn't going to do it anymore. Murphy said he was cured. What am I supposed to do now?" There was reproach in her tone. Mother put great hope in her notion that I was cured. She regarded my cure as an answer to her prayers and by way of thanksgiving sent a lot of money to the Thomasite Indian Mission, money she had been saving for a trip to Rome. She felt cheated and she let her feelings be known. When the priest came in Mother slid back on the seat and followed the Mass with concentration. After Communion she began to worry again and went straight home without stopping to talk to Frances, the woman who always cornered Mother after Mass to tell about the awful things done to her by communists, devil-worshippers, and Rosicrucians. Frances watched her go with narrowed eyes.

Once in the house, Mother took the letter from my drawer and brought it into the kitchen. She held it over the stove with her fingernails, looking away so that she would not be drawn into it again, and set it on fire. When it began to burn her fingers, she dropped it in the sink and watched it blacken and flutter and close upon itself like a fist. Then she washed it down the drain and called Doctor Murphy.

The letter was to my friend Ralphy in Arizona. He used to live across the street from us but he had moved. Most of the letter was about a tour of Alcatraz we, the junior class, had taken. That was all right. What got Mother was the last paragraph, where I said that she had been coughing up blood and the doctors weren't sure what was wrong with her, but that we were hoping for the best.

This wasn't true. Mother took pride in her physical condition, considered herself a horse. "I'm a regular horse," she would reply when people asked about her health. For several years now I had been saying unpleasant things that weren't true, and this habit of mine irked Mother greatly, enough to persuade her to send me to Doctor Murphy, in whose office I was sitting when she burned the letter. Doctor Murphy was our family physician and had no training in psychoanalysis, but he took an interest in "things of the mind," as he put it. He had treated me for appendicitis and tonsillitis and Mother thought that he could put the truth into me as easily as he took things out of me, a hope Doctor Murphy did not share. He was basically interested in getting me to understand what I did, and lately he had been moving toward the conclusion that I understood what I did as well as I ever would.

Doctor Murphy listened to Mother's account of the letter and what she had done with it. He was curious about the wording I had used and became irritated when Mother told him she had burned it. "The point is," she said, "he was supposed to be cured and he's not."

"Margaret, I never said he was cured."

"You certainly did. Why else would I have sent over a thousand dollars to the Thomasite mission?"

"I said that he was responsible. That means that James knows what he's doing, not that he's going to stop doing it."

"I'm sure you said he was cured."

"Never. To say that someone is cured, you have to know what health is. With this kind of thing that's impossible. What do you mean by curing James, anyway?"

"You know."

"Tell me anyway."

"Getting him back to reality, what else?"

"Whose reality? Mine or yours?"

"Murphy, what are you talking about? James isn't crazy, he's a liar."

"Well, you have a point there."

"What am I going to do with him?"

"I don't think there's much you can do. Be patient."

"I've been patient."

"If I were you, Margaret, I wouldn't make too much of this. James doesn't steal, does he?"

"Of course not."

"Or beat people up or talk back."

"No."

"Then you have a lot to be thankful for."

"I don't think I can take any more of it. That business about leukemia last summer. And now this."

"Eventually he'll outgrow it, I think."

"Murphy, he's sixteen years old. What if he doesn't outgrow it? What if he just gets better at it?"

Finally Mother saw that she wasn't going to get any satisfaction from Doctor Murphy, who kept reminding her of her blessings. She said something cutting to him and he said something pompous back and she hung up. Doctor Murphy stared at the receiver. "Hello," he said, then replaced it on the cradle. He ran his hand over his head, a habit remaining from a time when he had hair. To show that he was a good sport, he often joked about his baldness, but I had the feeling that he regretted it deeply. Looking at me across the desk, he must have wished that he hadn't taken me on. Treating a friend's child was like investing a friend's money.

"I don't have to tell you who that was."

I nodded.

Doctor Murphy pushed his chair back and swiveled it around so he could look out the window behind him, which took up most of the wall. There were still a few sailboats out on the Bay, but they were all making for shore. A woolly gray fog had covered the bridge and was moving in fast. The water seemed calm from this far up, but when I looked closely I could see white flecks everywhere.

"I'm surprised at you," he said. "Leaving something like that lying around for her to find. If you really have to do these things, you could at least be kind and do them discreetly. It's not easy for your mother, what with your father dead and all the others somewhere else."

"I know. I didn't mean for her to find it."

"Well." He tapped his pencil against his teeth. He was not convinced professionally, but personally he may have been. "I think you ought to go home now and straighten things out."

"I guess I'd better."

"Tell your mother I might stop by, either tonight or tomorrow. And James—don't underestimate her."

While my father was alive we usually went to Yosemite for three or four days during the summer. My mother would drive and Father would point out places of interest, meadows where boomtowns once stood, hanging trees, rivers that were said to flow upstream at certain times. Or he read to us; he had the grown-ups' idea that children love Dickens and Sir Walter Scott. The four of us sat in the back seat with our faces composed, attentive, while our hands and feet pushed, pinched, stomped, goosed, prodded, dug, and kicked.

One night a bear came into our camp just after dinner. Mother had made a tuna casserole and it must have smelled to him like something worth dying for. He came into the camp while we were sitting around the fire and stood swaying back and forth. My brother, Michael, saw him first and elbowed me, then my sisters saw him and screamed. Mother and Father had their backs to him but Mother must have guessed what it was because she immediately said: "Don't scream like that. You might frighten him and there's no telling what he'll do. We'll just sing and he'll go away."

We sang "Row Row Row Your Boat," but the bear stayed. He circled us several times, rearing up now and then on his hind legs to stick his nose into the air. By the light of the fire I could see his doglike face and watch the muscles roll under his loose skin like rocks in a sack. We sang harder as he circled us, coming closer and closer. "All right," said Mother, "enough's enough." She stood abruptly. The bear stopped moving and watched her. "Beat it," said Mother. The bear sat down and looked from side to side. "Beat it," she said again, and leaned over and picked up a rock.

"Margaret, don't," said my father.

She threw the rock hard and hit the bear in the stomach. Even in the dim light I could see the dust rising from his fur. He grunted and stood to his full height. "See that?" Mother shouted. "He's filthy. Filthy!" One of my sisters giggled. Mother picked up another rock. "Please, Margaret," said my father. Just then the bear turned and shambled away. Mother pitched the rock after him. For the rest of the night he loitered around the camp until he found the tree where we had hung our food. He ate it all. The next day we drove back to the city. We could have bought more supplies in the valley, but Father wanted to go and would not give in to any argument. On the way home he tried to jolly everyone up by making jokes, but Michael and my sisters ignored him and looked stonily out the windows.

Things were never easy between my mother and me, but I didn't underestimate her. She underestimated me. When I was little she suspected me of delicacy, because I didn't like being thrown up into the air, and because when I saw her and the others working themselves up for a roughhouse, I found somewhere else to be. When they did drag me in I got hurt, a knee in the lip, a bent finger, a bloody nose, and this too Mother seemed to hold against me, as if I arranged my hurts to get out of playing.

Even things I did well got on her nerves. We all loved puns except Mother, who didn't get them, and next to my father I was the best in the family. My specialty was the Swifty— " 'You can bring the prisoner down,' said Tom condescendingly." Father encouraged me to perform at dinner, which must have been a trial for outsiders. Mother wasn't sure what was going on, but she didn't like it.

She suspected me in other ways. I couldn't go to the movies without her examining my pockets to make sure I had enough money to pay for the ticket. When I went away to camp she tore my pack apart in front of all the boys who were waiting in the bus outside the house. I would rather have gone without my sleeping bag and a few changes of underwear, which I had forgotten, than be made such a fool of. Her distrust was the thing that made me forgetful.

And she thought I was coldhearted because of what happened the day my father died and later at his funeral. I didn't cry at my father's funeral, and showed signs of boredom during the eulogy, fiddling around with the hymnals. Mother put my hands into my lap and I left them there without moving them as though they were things I was holding for someone else. The effect was ironical and she resented it. We had a sort of reconciliation a few days later after I closed my eyes at school and refused to open them. When several teachers and then the principal failed to persuade me to look at them, or at some reward they claimed to be holding, I was handed over to the school nurse, who tried to pry the lids open and scratched one of them badly. My eye swelled up and I went rigid. The principal panicked and called Mother, who fetched me home. I wouldn't talk to her, or open my eyes, or bend, and they had to lay me on the back seat and when we reached the house Mother had to lift me up the steps one at a time. Then she put me on the couch and played the piano to me all afternoon. Finally I opened my eyes. We hugged each other and I wept. Mother did not really believe in my tears, but she was willing to accept them because I had staged them for her benefit.

My lying separated us too, and the fact that my promises not to lie anymore seemed to mean nothing to me. Often my lies came back to her in embarrassing ways, people stopping her in the street and saying how sorry they were to hear that ———. No one in the neighborhood enjoyed embarrassing Mother, and these situations stopped occurring once everybody got wise to me. There was no saving her from strangers, though. The summer after Father died I visited my uncle in Redding and when I got back I found to my surprise that Mother had come to meet my bus. I tried to slip away from the gentleman who had sat next to me but I couldn't shake him. When he saw Mother embrace me he came up and presented her with a card and told her to get in touch with him if things got any worse. She gave him his card back and told him to mind his own business. Later, on the way home, she made me repeat what I had said to the man. She shook her head. "It's not fair to people," she said, "telling them things like that. It confuses them." It seemed to me that Mother had confused the man, not I, but I didn't say so. I agreed with her that I shouldn't say such things and promised not to do it again, a promise I broke three hours later in conversation with a woman in the park.

It wasn't only the lies that disturbed Mother, it was their morbidity. This was the real issue between us, as it had been between her and my father. Mother did volunteer work at Children's Hospital and St. Anthony's Dining Hall, collected things for the St. Vincent de Paul Society. She was a lighter of candles. My brother and sisters took after her in this way. My father was a curser of the dark. And he loved to curse the dark. He was never more alive than when he was indignant about something. For this reason the most important act of the day for him was the reading of the evening paper.

Ours was a terrible paper, indifferent to the city that bought it, indifferent to medical discoveries—except for new kinds of gases that made your hands fall off when you sneezed—and indifferent to politics and art. Its business was outrage, horror, gruesome coincidence. When my father sat down in the living room with the paper, Mother stayed in the kitchen and kept the children busy, all except me, because I was quiet and could be trusted to amuse myself. I amused myself by watching my father.

He sat with his knees spread, leaning forward, his eyes only inches from the print. As he read he nodded to himself. Sometimes he swore and threw the paper down and paced the room, then picked it up and began again. Over a period of time he developed the habit of reading aloud to me. He always started with the society section, which he called the parasite page. This column began to take on the character of a comic strip or a serial, with the same people showing up from one day to the next, blinking in chiffon, awkwardly holding their drinks for the sake of Peninsula orphans, grinning under sunglasses on the deck of a ski hut in the Sierras. The skiers really got his goat, probably because he couldn't understand them. The activity itself was inconceivable to him. When my sisters went to Lake Tahoe one winter weekend with some friends and came back excited about the beauty of the place, Father calmed them right down. "Snow," he said, "is overrated."

Then the news, or what passed in the paper for news: bodies unearthed in Scotland, former Nazis winning elections, rare animals slaughtered, misers expiring naked in freezing houses upon mattresses stuffed with thousands, millions of dollars, marrying priests, divorcing actresses, high-rolling oilmen building fantastic mausoleums in honor of a favorite horse, cannibalism. Through all this my father waded with a fixed and weary smile.

Mother encouraged him to take up causes, to join groups, but he would not. He was uncomfortable with people outside the family. He and my mother rarely went out, and rarely had people in, except on feast days and national holidays. Their guests were always the same, Doctor Murphy and his wife and several others whom they had known since childhood. Most of these people never saw each other outside our house and they didn't have much fun together. Father discharged his obligations as host by teasing everyone about stupid things they had said or done in the past and forcing them to laugh at themselves.

Though Father did not drink, he insisted on mixing cocktails for the guests. He would not serve straight drinks such as rum and Coke, or even scotch on the rocks, only drinks of his own devising. He gave them lawyerly names such as "The Advocate,"

"The Hanging Judge," "The Ambulance Chaser," "The Mouthpiece," and described their concoction in detail. He told long, complicated stories in a near-whisper, making everyone lean in his direction, and repeated important lines; he also repeated the important lines in the stories my mother told, and corrected her when she got something wrong. When the guests came to the ends of their own stories he would point out the morals.

Doctor Murphy had several theories about Father, which he used to test on me in the course of our meetings. Doctor Murphy had by this time given up his glasses for contact lenses, and had lost weight in the course of fasts which he undertook regularly. Even with his baldness, he looked years younger than when he had come to the parties at our house. Certainly he did not look like my father's contemporary, which he was.

One of Doctor Murphy's theories was that Father had exhibited a classic trait of people who had been gifted children, by taking an undemanding position in an uninteresting firm. "He was afraid of finding his limits," Doctor Murphy told me. "As long as he kept stamping papers and making out wills, he could go on believing that he didn't *have* limits." Doctor Murphy's fascination with Father made me uneasy, and I felt traitorous listening to him. While he lived, my father would never have submitted to analysis; it seemed a betrayal to put him on the couch now that he was dead.

I did enjoy Doctor Murphy's recollections of Father when they were both in the Boy Scouts. Their troop had been on a long hike and Father had fallen behind. Doctor Murphy and the others decided to ambush him as he came down the trail. They hid in the woods on each side and waited. But when Father walked into the trap none of them moved or made a sound and he strolled on without even knowing they were there. "He had the sweetest look on his face," said Doctor Murphy, "listening to the birds, smelling the flowers, just like Ferdinand the Bull." He also told me that my father's drinks tasted like medicine.

While I rode my bicycle from Doctor Murphy's office, Mother fretted. She felt terribly alone but she didn't call anyone because she also felt like a failure. My lying had that effect on her. She took it personally. At such times she did not think of my sisters, one happily married, the other doing brilliantly at Fordham. She did not think of my brother, Michael, who had given up college to work with runaway children in Los Angeles. She thought of me. She thought that she had made a mess of her family.

Actually she managed the family well. While my father was dying upstairs she pulled us together. She made lists of chores and gave each of us a fair allowance. Bedtimes were adjusted and she stuck by them. She set regular hours for homework. Each child was made responsible for the next eldest; and I was given a dog. She told us frequently, predictably, that she loved us. At dinner we were each expected to contribute something, and after dinner she played the piano and tried to teach us to sing in harmony, which I could not do. Mother, who was an admirer of the Trapp family, considered this a character defect.

Our life together was more orderly, healthy, while Father was dying than it had been before. He had set us rules to follow, not much different from the ones Mother gave us after he got sick, but he had administered them in a fickle way. Though we were supposed to get an allowance, we always had to ask him for it, and then he would give us too much because he enjoyed seeming magnanimous. Sometimes he punished us for no reason, because he was in a bad mood. He was likely to decide, as one of my sisters was going out to a dance, that she had better stay home and do something to improve herself. Or he would sweep us all up on a Wednesday night and take us ice-skating.

He changed after he learned about the cancer, and became more calm as the disease spread. He relaxed his teasing way with us, and from time to time it was possible to have a conversation with him which was not about the last thing that had made him angry. He stopped reading the paper and spent time at the window.

He and I became close. He taught me to play poker and sometimes helped me with my homework. But it wasn't his illness that drew us together. The reserve between us had begun to break down after the incident with the bear, during the drive home. Michael and my sisters were furious with him for making us leave early and wouldn't talk to him or look at him. He joked: though it had been a grisly experience we should grin and bear it, and so on. His joking seemed perverse to the others, but not to me. I had seen how terrified he was when the bear came into the camp. He had held himself so still that he had begun to tremble. When Mother started pitching rocks, I thought he was going to bolt, really. I understood—I had been frightened too. The others took it as a lark after they got used to having the bear around, but for me and Father it got worse through the night. I was glad to be out of there, grateful to Father for getting me out. I saw that his jokes were the way he held himself together. So I reached out to him with a joke: " 'There's a bear outside,' said Tom intently." The others turned cold looks on me. They thought I was sucking up. But Father smiled.

When I thought of other boys being close to their fathers, I thought of them hunting together, tossing a ball back and forth, making birdhouses in the basement, and having long talks about girls, war, careers. Maybe the reason it took us so long to get close was that I had this idea. It kept getting in the way of what we really had, which was a shared fear.

Anyway, we never had long talks, and when we were alone we didn't joke much. That was our way of keeping in touch when others were around. We played cards, seriously, to win. Toward the end he slept most of the time and I watched him. From below, sometimes, faintly, I heard Mother playing the piano. Occasionally he nodded off in his chair while I was reading to him; his bathrobe would fall open then, and I would see the long new scar on his stomach, red as blood against his white skin. His ribs all showed and his legs were like cables.

I once read in a biography of a great man that he "died well." I assume the writer meant that he kept his pain to himself, did not set off false alarms, and did not inconvenience too much those who were to stay behind. My father died well. His irritability gave way to something else, something like serenity. In the last days he went tender. It was as though he had been rehearsing the scene, as though the anger of his life had been a kind of stage fright. He managed his audience—us—with an old trouper's sense of when to clown and when to stand on his dignity. We were all moved, and admired his courage, as he intended we should. He died downstairs in a shaft of late afternoon sunlight on New Year's Day, while I was reading to him. I was alone in the house and didn't know what to do. His body did not frighten me but immediately and sharply I missed my father. It seemed wrong to leave him sitting up and I tried to carry him upstairs to the bedroom but it was too hard, alone. So I called up my friend Ralphy across the street. When he came over and saw what I wanted him for, he started crying, but I made him help me anyway. A couple of hours later Mother got home and when I told her that Father was dead she ran upstairs, calling his name. A few minutes later she came back down. "Thank God," she said, "at least he died in bed." This seemed important to her and I didn't tell her otherwise. But that night Ralphy's parents called. They were, they said, shocked at what I had done, and so was Mother when she heard the story, shocked and furious. Why? Because I had not told her the truth? Or because she had learned the truth, and could not go on believing that Father had died in bed? I really don't know.

"Mother," I said, coming into the living room, "I'm sorry about the letter. I really am."

She was arranging wood in the fireplace and did not look at me or speak for a moment. Finally she finished, straightened up and brushed her hands. She stepped back and looked at the fire she had laid. "That's all right," she said. "Not bad for a consumptive."

"Mother, I'm sorry."

"Sorry? Sorry you wrote it or sorry I found it?"

"I wasn't going to mail it. It was a sort of joke.""

"Ha ha." She took up the whisk broom and swept bits of bark into the fireplace, then closed the drapes and settled on the couch. "Sit down," she said. She crossed her legs. "Listen, do I give you advice all the time?"

"Yes."

"I do?"

I nodded.

"Well, that doesn't make any difference, I'm supposed to. I'm your mother. I'm going to give you some more advice, for your own good. You don't have to make all these things up, James. They'll happen anyway." She picked at the hem of her skirt. "Do you understand what I'm saying?"

"I think so."

"You're cheating yourself, that's what I'm trying to tell you. When you get to be my age, you won't know anything at all about life. All you'll know is what you've made up."

I thought about that. It seemed logical.

She went on. "I think maybe you need to get out of yourself more. Think more about other people."

The doorbell rang.

"Go see who it is," said Mother. "We'll talk about this later."

It was Doctor Murphy. He and Mother made their apologies and she insisted that he stay for dinner. I went to the kitchen to fetch ice for their drinks, and when I returned they were talking about me. I sat on the sofa and listened. Doctor Murphy was telling Mother not to worry. "James is a good boy," he said. "I've been thinking about my oldest, Terry. He's not really dishonest, you know, but he's not really honest either. I can't seem to reach him. At least James isn't furtive."

"No," said Mother, "he's never been furtive."

Doctor Murphy clasped his hands between his knees and stared at them. "Well, that's Terry. Furtive."

Before we sat down to dinner Mother said grace; Doctor Murphy bowed his head and closed his eyes and crossed himself at the end, though he had lost his faith in college. When he told me that during one of our meetings, in just those words, I had the picture of a raincoat hanging by itself outside a dining hall. He drank a good deal of wine and persistently turned the conversation to the subject of his relationship with Terry. He admitted that he had come to dislike the boy. Then he mentioned several patients of his by name, some of them known to Mother and me, and said that he disliked them, too. He used the word "dislike" with relish, like someone on a diet permitting himself a single potato chip. "I don't know what I've done wrong," he said abruptly, and with reference to no particular thing. "Then again maybe I haven't done anything wrong. I don't know what to think anymore. Nobody does."

"I know what to think," said Mother.

"So does the solipsist. How can you prove to a solipsist that he's not creating the rest of us?"

This was one of Doctor Murphy's favorite riddles, and almost any pretext was sufficient for him to trot it out. He was a child with a card trick.

"Send him to bed without dinner," said Mother. "Let him create that."

Doctor Murphy suddenly turned to me. "Why do you do it?" he asked. It was a pure question, it had no object beyond the satisfaction of his curiosity. Mother looked at me and there was the same curiosity in her face.

"I don't know," I said, and that was the truth.

Doctor Murphy nodded, not because he had anticipated my answer but because he accepted it. "Is it fun?"

"No, it's not fun. I can't explain."

"Why is it all so sad?" asked Mother. "Why all the diseases?"

"Maybe," said Doctor Murphy, "sad things are more interesting."

"Not to me," said Mother.

"Not to me, either," I said. "It just comes out that way."

After dinner Doctor Murphy asked Mother to play the piano. He particularly wanted to sing "Come Home, Abbie, the Light's on the Stair."

"That old thing," said Mother. She stood and folded her napkin deliberately and we followed her into the living room. Doctor Murphy stood behind her as she warmed up. Then they sang "Come Home, Abbie, the Light's on the Stair," and I watched him stare down at Mother intently, as if he were trying to remember something. Her own eyes were closed. After that they sang "Oh Magnum Mysterium." They sang it in parts and I regretted that I had no voice, it sounded so good.

"Come on, James," said Doctor Murphy as Mother played the last chords. "These old tunes not good enough for you?"

"He just can't sing," said Mother.

When Doctor Murphy left, Mother lit the fire and made more coffee. She slouched down in the big chair, sticking her legs straight out and moving her feet back and forth. "That was fun," she said.

"Did you and Father ever do things like that?"

"A few times, when we were first going out. I don't think he really enjoyed it. He was like you."

I wondered if Mother and Father had had a good marriage. He admired her and liked to look at her; every night at dinner he had us move the candlesticks slightly to right and left of center so he could see her down the length of the table. And every evening when she set the table she put them in the center again. She didn't seem to miss him very much. But I wouldn't really have known if she did, and anyway I didn't miss him all that much myself, not the way I had. I thought about other things now, a lot of the time.

"James?"

I waited.

"I've been thinking that you might like to go down and stay with Michael for a couple of weeks or so."

"What about school?"

"I'll talk to Father McSorley. He won't mind. Maybe this problem will take care of itself if you start thinking about other people."

"I do."

"I mean helping them, like Michael does. You don't have to go if you don't want to."

"It's fine with me. Really. I'd like to see Michael."

"I'm not trying to get rid of you."

"I know."

Mother stretched, then tucked her feet under her. She sipped noisily at her coffee. "What did the word mean that Murphy used? You know the one?"

I thought. "Paranoid? That's where somebody thinks everyone is out to get him. Like that woman who always grabs you after Mass—Frances."

"Not paranoid. Everyone knows what that means. *Sol*—something."

"Oh. Solipsist. A solipsist is someone who thinks he creates everything around him."

Mother nodded and blew on her coffee, then put it down without drinking from it. "I'd rather be paranoid. Do you really think Frances is?"

"Of course. No question about it."

"I mean really *sick*?"

"That's what paranoid *is*, is being sick. What do you think, Mother?"

"What are you so angry about?"

"I'm not angry." I lowered my voice. "I'm not angry. But you don't believe those stories of hers, do you?"

"Well, no, not exactly. I don't think she knows what she's saying, she just wants someone to listen. She probably lives all by herself in some little room. So she's paranoid. Think of that. And I had no idea. James, we should pray for her. Will you remember to do that?"

I nodded. I thought of Mother singing "O Magnum Mysterium," saying grace, praying with easy confidence, and it came to me that her imagination was superior to mine. She could imagine things as coming together, not falling apart. She looked at me and I shrank; I knew exactly what she was going to say. "Son," she said, "do you know how much I love you?"

The next afternoon I took the bus to Los Angeles. I looked forward to the trip, to the monotony of the road and the empty fields by the roadside. Mother walked with me down the long concourse. The station was crowded and oppressive. "Are you sure this is the right bus?" she asked at the loading platform.

"Yes."

"It looks so old."

"Mother—"

"All right." She pulled me against her and kissed me, then held me an extra second to show that her embrace was sincere, not just like everyone else's, never having realized that everyone else does the same thing. I boarded the bus and we waved at each other until it became embarrassing. Then Mother began checking through her handbag for something. When she had finished I stood and adjusted the luggage over my seat. I sat and we smiled at each other, waved when the driver gunned the engine, shrugged when he got up suddenly to count the passengers, waved again when he resumed his seat. As the bus pulled out my mother and I were looking at each other with plain relief.

I had boarded the wrong bus. This one was bound for Los Angeles but not by the express route. We stopped in San Mateo, Palo Alto, San Jose, Castroville. When we left Castroville it began to rain, hard; my window would not close all the way, and a thin stream of water ran down the wall onto my seat. To keep dry I had to stay away from the wall and lean forward. The rain fell harder. The engine of the bus sounded as though it were coming apart.

In Salinas the man sleeping beside me jumped up but before I had a chance to change seats his place was taken by an enormous woman in a print dress, carrying a shopping bag. She took possession of her seat and spilled over onto half of mine, backing me up to the wall. "That's a storm," she said loudly, then turned and looked at me. "Hungry?" Without waiting for an answer she dipped into her bag and pulled out a piece of chicken and thrust it at me. "Hey, by God," she hooted, "look at him go to town on that drumstick!" A few people turned and smiled. I smiled back around the bone and kept at it. I finished that piece and she handed me another, and then another. Then she started handing out chicken to the people in the seats near us.

Outside of San Luis Obispo the noise from the engine grew suddenly louder and just as suddenly there was no noise at all. The driver pulled off to the side of the road and got out, then got on again dripping wet. A few moments later he announced that the bus had broken down and that they were sending another to pick us up. Someone asked how long that might take and the driver said he had no idea. "Keep your pants on!" shouted the woman next to me. "Anybody in a hurry to get to L. A. ought to have his head examined."

The wind was blowing hard around the bus, driving sheets of rain against the windows on both sides. The bus swayed gently. Outside the light was brown and thick. The woman next to me pumped all the people around us for their itineraries and said whether or not she had ever been where they were from or where they were going. "How about you?" She slapped my knee. "Parents own a chicken ranch? I hope so!" She laughed. I told her I was from San Francisco. "San Francisco, that's where my husband was stationed." She asked me what I did there and I told her I worked with refugees from Tibet.

"Is that right? What do you do with a bunch of Tibetans?"

"Seems like there's plenty of other places they could've gone," said a man in front of us. "Coming across the border like that. We don't go there."

"What do you do with a bunch of Tibetans?" the woman repeated.

"Try to find them jobs, locate housing, listen to their problems."

"You understand that kind of talk?"

"Yes."

"Speak it?"

"Pretty well. I was born and raised in Tibet. My parents were missionaries over there."

Everyone waited.

"They were killed when the communists took over." The big woman patted my arm. "It's all right," I said.

"Why don't you say some of that Tibetan?"

"What would you like to hear?"

"Say 'The cow jumped over the moon.' " She watched me, smiling, and when I finished she looked at the others and shook her head. "That was pretty. Like music. Say some more."

"What?"

"Anything."

They bent toward me. The windows suddenly went blind with rain. The bus driver had fallen asleep and was snoring softly to the swaying of the bus. Outside the muddy light flickered to pale yellow, and far off there was thunder. The woman next to me leaned back and closed her eyes and then so did the others as I sang to them in what was surely an ancient and holy tongue.

Brian Fawcett

Mules

The cute little car was parked in the back yard, but as I trudged down the stairs from the house it took on a definite air of menace.

The day I turned sixteen my father poked me awake at eight o'clock in the morning.

"Get up," he said. "We've got work to do."

I was still too sleepy to think straight, but the first thing that woke up was my sense of injustice. It was too early in the morning. He made matters worse by jerking all the covers off the bed. It was bad enough that my birthday wasn't celebrated as a national holiday. Now I was being forced to work. But as I awakened a little more, I noticed that my father was grinning instead of snarling, which was what he usually did if he found me lying around and he had work for me to do. I was about to tell him why I shouldn't have to do any work when he took my excuse away from me.

"It's your birthday. You're going to learn how to drive today."

Most kids think driving a car is one of the very best games, but I didn't think about driving at all, and when I did, it didn't come up as a game or as fun. Learning to drive meant having to go to work, and the only reason my father was teaching me was so I could drive his trucks and make all the weekend deliveries no one else wanted to do.

Until that morning, I hadn't spent more than about five minutes in my whole life thinking about learning to drive. The last time I'd practiced driving was on a business trip with my father when I was five or six years old and he had an old Pontiac with an insignia on the dashboard which I used as an imaginary steering wheel.

Cars didn't interest me, and neither did anything else mechanical. Even when my parents had brought a Volkswagen back from a trip in Europe a few months before, I hadn't thought about driving it. I thought it was cute, and I liked to ride around in it, but that was about all. And now I was going to have to learn to drive *that* car, and *all* my father's trucks, and practically every automobile in the world. Some birthday present.

I stalled my way through breakfast, and my father began to glower openly. I stalled openly, but finally I realized that I had the rest of my life in front of me, and I couldn't hold out for another fifteen minutes before my father created an uproar that might be even more frightening than having to learn how to drive.

The cute little car was parked in the back yard, but as I trudged down the stairs from the house it took on a definite air of menace. I walked over to the passenger side of the car and got yelled at, so I walked around the car as slowly as I could, checking all the fenders and the bumpers with exaggerated care. I got into the car, and my father wedged himself in on the other side.

"Now what?" I said, fingering the steering wheel and staring through the window at the once-friendly alley.

"What do you mean, now what?" my father hooted.

He'd been lecturing me for fifteen minutes on the fine points of driving and I hadn't heard a word. "You turn the key on, stupid!"

"Which direction?" I asked, staring at him.

He reached over without saying anything and turned the key, holding it on until even I knew he should stop. I continued to stare at him. I don't think he'd realized I knew nothing about driving until that moment.

"Put your stupid foot on the clutch," he said.

I did, but I didn't press it in.

"Push it down."

I did.

"Put it into gear."

"What gear?" I said, gazing through the window.

"FIRST GEAR, YOU NUMBSKULL!" he roared.

He was really getting mad, so I decided I'd better pretend I knew what was going on.

"I guess I let the clutch out now, right?" I said, and let it out without waiting for an answer.

We lurched forward about ten feet before it stalled.

"You have to give it some gas when you let out the clutch," my father said in a choked voice that also said he was about to strangle me.

"Oh. Right." I restarted the car, let the clutch out the right way, and we made it out of the driveway.

"Shift it!" my father roared.

"Shift what?" I hollered back at him, and whammed the shift lever back without depressing the clutch. Luckily the car stalled before the transmission exploded.

We tried it again, and again. About half an hour later we made it out of the alley. My father's troubles were just beginning, and I think he knew it. There was a wealth of things he assumed everyone knew about the mechanical universe, and I didn't know any of them. Just because I was supposed to push the clutch pedal down when I shifted from first to second didn't mean, as far as I could figure, that I had to do the same between all the other gears. So I didn't, and ground more gears, and got yelled at some more. Finally, he told me to stop the car, and he started from the beginning. After about four sentences, my head was reeling.

"So then after the horsepower and torque go through the transmission they're connected to the rear wheels through the universal joint. . . ."

I tried to listen, but it was hopeless.

"Start the car again," he said when he was finished. "Do you understand how it works now?"

"Sure," I lied, and turned the key.

This time it went better. I lurched the car down the alley and steered it onto the gravel street without slowing down. I got yelled at for that. There were no cars coming so I couldn't see what I'd done wrong.

"You've got to stop at corners," he said.

"Why?" I asked. "You don't."

"I don't because I *know* how to drive," he snapped.

That didn't make a lot of sense, but I didn't say anything because I was busy stopping at the next corner.

"Why are you stopping here?" he asked.

"You told me to stop at corners."

"You don't have to stop unless there's a stop sign. You just slow down to make sure there isn't anybody coming."

"How about after I learn to drive?" I asked, trying to show how well I was listening. "I can drive straight through like you do, right?"

He glared at me and didn't answer. I had enough to think about to keep me going for several days, but I couldn't tell him that because we were headed up the street and the motor was making a lot of noise.

"Shift it!" he hollered.

"Oh, yeah. Sorry," I said, shifting it into fourth gear without a hitch.

He didn't seem to think that was very smart, so I shifted it back to what I thought was first and ended up in third. He appeared to approve, so I left it there.

We drove the car around the block about four times, and I was beginning to think it was pretty easy. My father was beginning to relax a little. I think he relaxed a little too much because he told me to pull into the alley when we were already past it. I did as I'd been ordered, and drove into a neighbour's front yard. My father started screeching again, so I somehow found reverse and pulled back onto the street. I thought I'd executed the entire manoeuvre pretty well, but my father was shaking his head. He gestured toward the alley, and I drove into it.

It wasn't the end of the alley we'd come out of, and it was much narrower than it was supposed to be. What was worse, it made a complicated turn, and on the inside of the turn a malicious neighbour had sunk an enormous post to keep people from driving into the corner of his garage. For about a year, every time we'd driven into the alley my father had cursed the neighbour and his post, threatening to bring one of his trucks up and pull it out. But for some reason its presence must have slipped his mind, although I certainly was painfully aware of it. My father became aware of it again too when I cut the corner sharply and scraped the side of the Volkswagen along it.

"Stop the car," he screamed.

He got out to survey the damage. The running board was badly dented, and so were the front and back fenders. The back bumper had hooked itself on the post and it was pulled back about six inches from where it should have been. My father was frothing at the mouth.

Luckily for me he was undecided as to whether I was a complete moron for hitting the post or whether the neighbour was a complete moron for putting it there. By the time he'd decided, after some noisy debate with himself, that we were both morons, he'd cooled down a little, and ordered me in a tight voice to drive back to the house.

"I don't want to drive," I whined, going back to my basic stance on the entire matter.

"I don't care what you want," he shouted, his anger suddenly focused. "You're going to learn how to drive, even if it kills you, you bloody mule. And that's that!"

But that wasn't that, not by a long shot. I prepared myself to die, because I wasn't going to learn to drive. It wasn't worth it. It was already changing my life. I dreamed about driving—and about driving into things—and I thought about how driving was going to take away my freedom.

I'd discovered fairly early on in life that if I wanted to be left alone by all the things and people who had organized a conspiracy to get me to be like them, I had to find ways to make myself useless to them. As I grew older it became the one political understanding I'd gathered from the world around me that made sense: freedom means not having to work.

Up to this point, I'd been fairly successful at making myself useless and therefore free, but this looked like the end of all that. I was now going to be of use to my father.

It was a gloomy future. I liked being a kid, and every adult in the world seemed like a jerk. They'd built a jerky world and now they were going to force me to drive cars and trucks in it, and soon I would begin to act and feel like a jerk and one morning I would wake up and that would be it—no more fun, no fooling around, nothing but work and coming home and eating my jerky dinner with my jerky wife and jerky kids and talking about jerky things like money or how jerky my friends all were and then one day they'd drop their jerky bombs and blow us all to smithereens. It really was the end of the world.

The end came three days later. My father sent one of the drivers he knew I really liked to pick me up after school. Bud, the driver, spotted me coming out of the building, and beeped the horn of his empty truck. I ambled over without the slightest suspicion that it was a trap. I often went with him to make deliveries after school, and being picked up wasn't all that unusual. My father was prepared to go to any length to get me to work, and this truck was one of the ones I didn't mind. Actually, it was pretty cool getting picked up this way. Even better, Bud knew the words to what seemed like a million dirty songs. He even knew all the words to the dirty version of "Dangerous Dan McGrew," and that impressed me to no end. I walked up to the truck and asked him what was up.

"Get in," he grinned.

I headed around the truck.

"This side!" he yelled. "You're driving."

"No, I'm not," I said, and stopped where I was. "I don't know how to drive."

"You're sixteen now, aren't you?"

"Yeah," I admitted.

"Then you've gotta learn to drive. Get in."

I started for the passenger door.

"This side," he hollered.

I stopped again. "Why?" I asked, still stubborn.

"Because that's how things are."

"Just because things are the way they are doesn't mean that's the way they have to be, does it? Things are jerky."

"GET IN."

Bud didn't seem any more impressed by my logic than my father had been, so I reluctantly got in behind the wheel.

"Now what?" I asked.

He reached over and twisted the key to shut the motor off. "We're going to talk," he said.

"Sure," I said. "What's up?"

It was one thing not to listen to your father, and quite another not to listen to someone real, like Bud.

"Your dad says he doesn't understand you," Bud began.

"So what?" I asked.

It had never occurred to me that he wanted to understand me, or that he was supposed to. I began to coil defensively around the thought, but Bud saw it.

"No!" he said irritably. "Listen for once. You're just like a mule. As a matter of fact, that's what he said you were. You think whatever he says you should do is the opposite of what you're supposed to do."

I shrugged. I couldn't see anything wrong with being a mule. I liked mules. Francis the Talking Mule was one of my heroes. Mules were smarter than horses or donkeys, and when they could talk, they were smarter than people. The more I thought about being a mule, the more I liked it.

"So what?" I said. "What's wrong with being a mule?"

"Only one thing's wrong with being a mule."

"Oh yeah? What?" I imagined that I was flattening my ears against the side of my head and bridling back against the rope that held me.

"A mule isn't anything," he said, searching for some way to break through my resistance. "It isn't a horse and it isn't a donkey. It's a big nothing. All it can do is be ornery and fight back at everything."

"Yeah?" I said, caught halfway between pride and truculence.

"Yeah. And mules have to work just as hard as horses and donkeys anyway. Probably harder, because that's all they're good for."

"What's all that got to do with me learning how to drive?" Bud had succeeded in making me feel uncomfortable, and I was changing the subject.

"Driving is fun," he said. "You can go wherever you want once you learn. You can buy a car and do whatever you want. You're free."

"I don't want to do any of that junk," I replied, without feeling very confident about it any longer.

Bud was a person, and he was telling me the opposite of what I knew was true. He was right, but it was suspicious stuff he was saying.

"Besides," I quibbled, "I don't have any money."

"Save some. Go to work for your dad."

I'd heard that before and it didn't convince me any more now than it had in the past. Bud was just trying to get me to do work for my father.

"If I learn to drive, will you lend me your car?" I asked, grinning at my own sneakiness.

Bud hesitated. "Sure," he said. "If you learn how to drive properly."

I thought about that for a minute. Some of my friends already had their driver's licences, and one or two of them had bought old cars. Mainly, the cars gave all of us someplace to be on Friday night. I felt a heavier rope inching across my ears and I shrugged unconsciously. I would, I decided, go to work for my father exactly as often as I needed to in order to afford gas for Bud's car. Maybe, I thought, since we would all have to learn to drive, and we were all mules, or at least my best friends were, there was nothing to worry about. My dream would somehow remain safe from the wily schemes of ordinary men. I reached for the ignition key, twisted it, and the truck's motor started.

"Okay," I said. "What do I do?"

I did what Bud told me to, and twenty minutes later I knew I could drive. The next day I took my driving test with the same truck, and soon I was doing exactly what I'd most feared I would end up doing: all the weekend deliveries no one else wanted to do.

It was fun. Donnie and Artie often came along with me, and that made it even more fun. I started going to work every day, and I opened up a savings account so I could buy a car. I even began to get along with my father. He began to try to have conversations with me, and I would catch him looking at me speculatively, as if he were seeing the possibility of something unexpected and useful beneath the furry snout and long ears.

I wasn't very good at driving, and I demonstrated that in a series of hilarious car accidents during the next several months. I put the Volkswagen through the front window of a supermarket one afternoon after I'd impressed one of my friends with a thrilling zip-zap through the parking lot. I mistook the gas pedal for the brake pedal at the climax of this operation and almost zapped the manager of the store, who was one of my father's more important customers and knew exactly who I was. Two or three days later I ran over someone else's Volkswagen with one of my father's trucks as I rounded the corner of the town's busiest intersection. I'd seen someone I knew standing across the street and I'd stopped driving to wave at him.

My older brother, who was anything but a mule, was naturally skilled at every terror my father served up for him, and wouldn't let me near his new Chev convertible. He took it upon himself to give me a lecture about driving.

"Look, idiot," he said. "You've got to stop wrecking vehicles." He imitated my father's habit of never calling anything by its simple name. "These conveyances cost a lot of money."

"I'm not trying to," I pointed out. "Driving is hard."

He didn't think anything was hard, and he conceded my difficulty with a sniff of contempt.

"You'd better spend a couple of nights talking to the mechanic," he said, making it plain that the sessions weren't optional. "Maybe he can teach you what it's about."

The mechanic was a middle-aged man who treated my father's trucks as if they were his personal harem of exotic beauties. He wasn't enamoured of my gear-grinding antics, nor with me, but he obviously saw the opportunity to save his beauties from me, and spent several evenings showing me exactly the right way to treat a truck. He was showing me what *he* thought was perfection, but I gathered precisely three things from it all: when to shift up, when to shift down, and the idea that I was supposed to keep my foot pressed firmly on the gas pedal as long as those shifting points were not upon me. The accidents stopped, but the wreckage didn't cease. It merely took the form of destroyed transmissions and clutches, and worn out brakes.

Bud lent me his car right after the mechanic told him I knew all about how to drive. Later that night the police stopped me with eleven of my friends in the car. They'd clocked me at fifty-five miles an hour, and I didn't have the car lights on. I told the officer I hadn't been able to find the light switch, and then handed him a two dollar bill out of my wallet instead of my driver's licence, explaining that I'd just gotten it a few weeks before. He started to laugh, and had to let me go, but he phoned my parents about it.

Thankfully, he got my mother on the phone, and she took me aside the next day.

"Just what is it you think you're doing?" she asked.

It was a genuine question; not, as expected, the opening salvo of a lecture on my irresponsible behaviour. She'd maintained an amused silence throughout the previous weeks, and had even smiled while I was explaining to my father how it was that I'd come to make my unusual entry into the supermarket. I looked at her carefully, and flattened my ears slightly anyway.

"Driving Bud's car," I said, noncommittally.

"Well, you know, cars aren't everything in life," she said, almost as if she were discussing the matter with one of her friends.

"They aren't?" I was confused. I'd more or less decided that cars were everything in life. "What do you mean?"

She stared at me for a moment as if she were sizing me up for something, trying to decide who or what I really was, and whether or not it was worth imparting to me what she knew. Her amused silence over the previous weeks suddenly became a mystery to me. I prodded her impatiently.

"Tell me what you mean."

"You don't really want a car," she said.

"I don't?" This truly was mysterious. Everybody wanted a car, and here was my own mother telling me that I didn't want one.

"No," she said firmly, "it'd be much better not to have one. If you need a car you can use mine."

She was deeply enveloped in her mystery, and was gazing at the top of my head as if she could see the mule ears, or maybe she was looking beyond all that to some imaginary future she alone knew about. I interrupted her reverie. The rope was around my neck and I'd begun to like it.

"Why shouldn't I have my own car?"

She shrugged, and a more familiar vagueness appeared in her reply.

"Oh, well," she said. "They cost a lot of money. You save your money for something else."

I shook the rope and snorted, but she continued before I could think of anything to say.

"There's lots of things you can do," she said. "Don't get tied down with a car."

She reached across the table and, so help me, scratched me behind the ear and patted my neck. As she removed her hand, the rope went with it, and I glimpsed a kind of field in her eyes.

There was nothing there that I could see clearly. Some grass, maybe, and some blurry shapes in the distance. Certainly not what she imagined. I stood there for a moment looking, shook my mane a little, and asked her when I could borrow the car.

Ernest Buckler

The Harness

I kept calling him all the way along the road.

There are times when you can only look at your son and say his name over and over in your mind.

I would say, "David, David ..." nights when he was asleep—the involuntary way you pass your hand across your eyes when your head aches, though there is no way for your hand to get inside. It seemed as if it must all have been my fault.

I suppose any seven-year-old has a look of accusing innocence when he is asleep, an assaulting grudgelessness. But it seemed to me that he had it especially. It seemed incredible that when I'd told him to undress he'd said, "You make me!" his eyes dark and stormy. It seemed incredible that those same legs and hands, absolutely pliant now, would ever be party to that isolating violence of his again.

His visible flesh was still; yet he was always moving in a dream. Maybe he'd cry, "Wait.... Wait up, Art." Where was I going in the dream, what was I doing, that even as I held him in my arms he was falling behind?

He called me "Art," not "Dad." The idea was: we were pals.

I had never whipped him. The thought of my wife—who died when David was born—had something to do with that, I guess. And a curious suggestion of vulnerability about his wire-thin body, his perceptive face, so contrasted with its actual belligerence that the thought of laying a hand on him—well, I just couldn't do it. We were supposed to *reason* things out.

Sometimes that worked. Sometimes it didn't.

He *could* reason, as well as I. His body would seem to vibrate with obedience. His friendship would be absolutely unwithholding. "You stepped on my hand," he'd say, laughing, though his face was pinched with the pain of it, "but that doesn't matter, does it, Art? Sometimes you can't see people's hands when they stick them in the way." Or if we were fishing, he'd say, "You tell me when to pull on the line, won't you, Art ... just right *when*."

Then, without any warning whatever, he'd become possessed by this automatic inaccessible mutiny.

I'd get the awful feeling then that we were both lost. That whatever I'd done wrong had not only failed, but that he'd never know I'd been *trying* to do it right for him. Worse still, that his mind was rocked by some blind contradiction he'd never understand himself.

Maybe I'd be helping him with a reading lesson. I tried to make a game of it, totalling the words he named right against words he named wrong. He'd look at me, squinting up his face into a contortion of deliberate ingratiation. He'd say "Seventeen right and only one wrong ... wouldn't that make you *laugh*, Art?" Then maybe the very next word I'd ask him, he'd slump against the table in a pretended indolence, or flop the book shut while the smile was still on my face.

Or maybe we'd be playing with his new baseball bat and catcher's mitt.

His hands were too small to grasp the bat properly and his fingers were lost in the mitt. But he couldn't have seemed more obliteratingly happy when he did connect with the ball. ("Boy, that was a solid hit, wasn't it, Art? You throw them to me *just* right, Art, just *right*.") He'd improvise rules of his own for the game. His face would twist with the delight of communicating them to me.

Then, suddenly, when he'd throw the ball, he'd throw it so hard that the physical smart of it on my bare fingers would sting me to exasperation.

"All right," I'd say coolly, "if you don't want to play, I'll go hoe the garden."

I'd go over to the garden, watching him out of the corner of my eye. He'd wander forlornly about the yard. Then I'd see him coming slowly toward the garden (where his tracks still showed along the top of a row of carrots he'd raced through yesterday). He'd come up behind me and say, "I have to walk right between the rows, don't I? Gardens are hard *work*, aren't they, Art ... you don't want anyone stepping on the rows."

David, David....

The strange part, it wasn't that discipline had no effect because it made no impression.

One evening he said out of a blue sky, "*You're* so smart, Art ... I haven't got a brain in my head, not one. You've got so many *brains*, Art, *brains....*" I was completely puzzled.

Then I remembered: I had countered with complete silence when he'd called me "dumb" that morning. I'd forgotten the incident entirely. But he hadn't. Though he'd been less rather than more tractable since then, he'd been carrying the snub around with him all day.

Or take the afternoon there was only one nickel in his small black purse. I saw him take it out and put it back again several times before he came and asked me for another. He never asked me for money unless he wanted it terribly. I gave him another nickel. He went to the store and came back with two Cokes. For some reason he had to treat me.

My face must have shown my gratification. He said, with his devastating candour, "You look happier with me than you did this morning, don't you, Art?"

I couldn't even recall the offence that time. *He* had felt my displeasure, though on my part it must have been quite unconscious.

What had I done wrong? I didn't know.

Unless it was that, when he was small, I'd kept a harness on him in the yard. He rebelled, instinctively, at any kind of bond. But what else could I do? Our house was on a blind corner. What else could I do, when I had the picture of the strength of his slight headlong body falling against the impersonal strength of a truck, or the depth of a well?

David, David....

I said, "David, David ..." out loud, that particular afternoon he lay so still on the ground; because this is the way it had happened.

I had taken him fencing with me that morning. It was one of those perfect spring mornings when even the woods seem to breathe out a clean water-smell. He was very excited. He'd never been to the back of the pasture before.

I carried the axe and the mall. He carried the staple-box and the two hammers. Sometimes he walked beside me, sometimes ahead.

There was something about him that always affected me when I watched him moving *back to*. I'd made him wear his rubber boots because there was a swamp to cross. Now the sun was getting hot. I wished I'd let him wear his sneakers and carried him across the swamp. There was something about the heavy boots *not* slowing up his eager movement and the thought that they must be tiring him without his consciousness of it.

I asked him if his legs weren't tired. "Noooooo," he scoffed. As if that were the kind of absurd question people kid each other with to clinch the absolute perfection of the day. Then he added, "If your legs do get a little tired when you're going some place, that doesn't hurt, does it, Art?"

His unpredictable twist of comment made him good company, in an adult way. Yet there was no unnatural shadow of precocity about him. His face had a kind of feature-smalling brightness that gave him a peaked look when he was tired or disappointed, and when his face was washed and the water on his hair, for town, a kind of shining. But it was as childlike and unwithholding as the clasp of his hand. (Or maybe he didn't look much different from any other child. Maybe I couldn't see him straight because I loved him.)

This was one of his days of intense, jubilant, communicativeness. One of his "How come?" days. As if by his questions and my answers we (and we alone) could find out about everything.

If I said anything mildly funny he worked himself up into quite a glee. I knew his laughter was a little louder than natural. His face would twitch a little, renewing it, each time I glanced at him. But that didn't mean that his amusement was false. I knew that his intense willingness to think anything funny I said was as funny as anything could possibly be, tickled him more than the joke itself. "You always say such funny things, Art!"

We came to the place where I had buried the horse. Dogs had dug away the earth. The brackets of its ribs and the chalky grimace of its jaws stared whitely in the bright sun.

He looked at it with a sudden quietness beyond mere attention; as if something invisible were threatening to come too close. I thought he was a little pale. He had never seen a skeleton before.

"Those bones can't move, *can* they, Art?" he said.

"No," I said.

"How can bones move?"

"Oh, they have to have flesh on them, and muscles, and...."

"Well, could he move when he was just dead? I mean right then, when he was right just dead?"

"No."

"How come?"

I was searching for a reply when he moved very close to me. "Could *you* carry the hammers, Art, please?" he said.

I put the hammers in my back overalls pocket.

"Could you carry an axe and a mall both in one hand?" he said.

I took the axe in my left hand, with the mall, so that now we each had a hand free. He took my hand and tugged me along the road.

He was quiet for a few minutes, then he said, "Art? What goes away out of your muscles when you're dead?"

He was a good boy all morning. He was really a help. If you fence alone you can't carry the tools through the brush at once. You have to replace a stretch of rotted posts with the axe and mall; then return to where you've left the staple-box and hammers and go over the same ground again, tightening the wire.

He carried the staple-box and hammers and we could complete the operation as we went. He held the wire taut while I drove the staples. He'd get his voice down very low. "The way you do it, Art, see, you get the claw of your hammer right behind a barb so it won't slip ... so it won't *slip*, Art, see?" As if he'd discovered some trick that would now be a conspiratorial secret between just us two. The obbligato of manual labour was like a quiet stitching together of our presences.

We started at the far end of the pasture and worked toward home. It was five minutes past eleven when we came within sight of the skeleton again. The spot where my section of the fence ended. That was fine. We could finish the job before noon and not have to walk all the way back again after dinner. It was aggravating when I struck three rotten posts in a row; but we could still finish, if we hurried. I thought David looked a little pale again.

"You take off those heavy boots and rest, while I go down to the intervale and cut some posts," I said. There were no trees growing near the fence.

"All right, Art." He was very quiet. There was that look of suspension in his flesh he'd get sometimes when his mind was working on something it couldn't quite manoeuvre.

It took me no more than twenty minutes to cut the posts, but when I carried them back to the fence he wasn't there.

"Bring the staples, chum," I shouted. He didn't pop out from behind any bush.

"David! David!" I called, louder. There was only that hollow stillness of the wind rustling the leaves when you call to someone in the woods and there is no answer. He had completely disappeared.

I felt a sudden irritation. Of all the damn times to beat it home without telling me!

I started to stretch the wire alone. But an uneasiness began to insinuate itself. Anyone could follow that wide road home. But what if ... I didn't know just what ... but what if something ...? Oh dammit, I'd have to go find him.

I kept calling him all the way along the road. There was no answer. How could he get out of sound so quickly, unless he ran? He must have run all the way. But why? I began to run, myself.

My first reaction when I saw him standing by the house, looking toward the pasture, was intense relief. Then, suddenly my irritation was compounded.

He seemed to sense my annoyance, even from a distance. He began to wave, as if in propitiation. He had a funny way of waving, holding his arm out still and moving his hand up and down very slowly. I didn't wave back. When I came close enough that he could see my face he stopped waving.

"I thought you'd come home without me, Art," he said.

"Why should you think that?" I said, very calmly.

He wasn't defiant as I'd expected him to be. He looked as if he were relieved to see me; but as if at the sight of me coming from that direction he knew he'd done something wrong. Now he was trying to pass the thing off as an amusing quirk in the way things had turned out. Though half-suspecting that this wouldn't go over. His tentative over-smiling brushed at my irritation, but didn't dislodge it.

"I called to you, Art," he said.

I just looked at him, as much as to say, do you think I'm deaf?

"Yes, I called. I thought you'd come home some other way."

"Now I've got to traipse all the way back there this afternoon to finish one rod of fence," I said.

"I thought you'd gone and left me," he said.

I ignored him, and walked past him into the house.

He didn't eat much dinner, but he wasn't defiant about that, either, as he was, sometimes, when he refused to eat. And after dinner he went out and sat down on the banking, by himself. He didn't know that his hair was sticking up through the heart-shaped holes in the skullcap with all the buttons pinned on it.

When it was time to go back to the woods again he hung around me with his new bat and ball. Tossing the ball up himself and trying to hit out flies.

"Boy, you picked out the very best bat there was, didn't you, Art?" he said. I knew he thought I'd toss him a few. I didn't pay any attention to what he was doing.

When I started across the yard, he said, "Do you want me to carry the axe this afternoon? That makes it *easier* for you, doesn't it, Art?"

"I'll be back in an hour or so," I said. "You play with Max."

He went as far as the gate with me. Then he stopped. I didn't turn around. It sounds foolish, but everything between us was on such an adult basis that it wasn't until I bent over to crawl through the barbed wire fence that I stole a glance at him, covertly. He was tossing the ball up again and trying to hit it. It always fell to the ground, because the bat was so unwieldy and because he had one eye on me.

I noticed he still had on his hot rubber boots. I had intended to change them for his sneakers. He was the sort of child who seems unconsciously to invest his clothes with his own mood. The thought of his clothes, when he was forlorn, struck me as hard as the thought of his face.

Do you know the kind of thoughts you have when you go back alone to a job which you have been working at happily with another? When that work together has ended in a quarrel … with your accusations unprotested, and, after that, your rejection of his overtures unprotested too?

I picked up my tools and began to work. But I couldn't seem to work quickly.

I'd catch myself, with the hammer slack in my hands, thinking about crazy things like his secret pride in the new tie (which he left outside his pullover until he saw that the other children had theirs inside) singling him so abatedly from the town children, the Saturday I took him to the matinee, that I felt an unreasonable rush of protectiveness toward him.... Of him laughing dutifully at the violence in the comedy, but crouching a little toward me, while the other children, who were not nearly so violent as he, shrieked together in a seizure of delight.

I thought of his scribblers, with the fixity there of the letters which his small hand had formed earnestly, but awry.

I thought of those times when the freak would come upon him to recount all his transgressions of the day, insisting on his guilt with phrases of my own I had never expected him to remember.

I thought of him playing ball with the other children.

At first they'd go along with the outlandish variations he'd introduce into the game, because it was his equipment. Then, somehow, *they'd* be playing with the bat and glove and he'd be out of it, watching.

I thought now of him standing there, saying, "Boy, I hope my friends come to play with me *early* tomorrow, early, Art" —though I knew that if they came at all their first question would be, "Can we use your bat and glove?"

I thought of him asleep. I thought, if anything should ever happen to him that's the way he would look.

I laughed; to kid myself for being such a soft and sentimental fool. But it was no use. The feeling came over me, immediate as the sound of a voice, that something *was* happening to him right now.

It was coincidence, of course, but I don't believe that ... because I had started to run even before I came over the crest of the knoll by the barn. Before I saw the cluster of excited children by the horse stable.

I couldn't see David among them, but I saw the ladder against the roof. I saw Max running toward the stable, with my neighbour running behind him. I knew, by the way the children looked at me—with that half-discomfited awe that was always in their faces whenever any recklessness of David's was involved—what had happened.

"He fell off the roof," one of them said.

I held him, and I said, "David, David...."

He stirred. "Wait," he said drowsily, "Wait up, Art...."

I suppose it's foolish to think that if I hadn't been right there, right then, to call his name, he would never have come back. Because he was only stunned. The doctor could scarcely find a bruise on him. (I don't know just why my eyes stung when the doctor patted his head in admiration of his patience, when the exhaustive examination was over. He was always so darned quiet and brave at the doctor's and dentist's.)

I read to him the rest of the afternoon. He'd sit quiet all day, with the erasure on his face as smooth as the erasure of sleep, if you read to him.

After supper, I decided to finish the fence. It was the season of long days.

"Do you want to help me finish the fence?" I said. I thought he'd be delighted.

"No," he said. "You go on. I'll wait right here. Right here, Art."

"Who's going to help me stretch the wire?" I said.

"All right," he said.

He scarcely spoke until we got almost back to the spot where the skeleton was. Then he stopped and said, "We better go back, Art. It's going to be dark."

"G'way with ya," I said. "It won't be dark for hours." It wouldn't be although the light *was* an eerie after-supper light.

"I'm going home," he said. His voice and his face were suddenly defiant.

"You're not going home," I said sharply. "Now come on, hurry up."

I was carrying an extra pound of staples I had picked up in town that afternoon. He snatched the package from my hand. Before I could stop him he broke the string and strewed them far and wide.

I suppose I was keyed up after the day, for I did then what I had never done before. I took him and held him and I put it onto him, hard and thoroughly.

He didn't try to escape. For the first few seconds he didn't make a sound. The only retraction of his defiance was a kind of crouching in his eyes when he first realized what I was going to do. Then he began to cry. He cried and cried.

"You're *going* home," I said, "and you're going right to *bed*."

I could see the marks of my fingers on his bare legs, when I undressed him. He went to sleep almost immediately. But though it was perfectly quiet downstairs for reading, the words of my book might have been any others.

When I got him up to the toilet, he had something to say, as usual. But this time he was wide awake. I sat down on the side of his bed for a minute.

"Bones make you feel funny, don't they, Art?" was what he said.

I remembered then.

I remembered that the skeleton was opposite the place where he sat down to rest. I remembered how he had shrunk from it on the way back. I remembered then that the wind had been blowing *away* from me, when I was cutting the posts. That's why I hadn't heard him call. I thought of him calling, and then running along the road alone, in the heavy, hot, rubber boots.

David, David, I thought, do I always fail you like that? ... the awful misinterpretation a child has to endure! I couldn't answer him.

"I thought you'd gone home, Art," he said.

"I'm sorry," I said. I couldn't seem to find any words to go on with.

"I'm sorry too I threw the staples," he said eagerly.

"I'm sorry I spanked you."

"No, no," he said. "You spank me every time I do that, won't you, Dad? ... *spank* me, Dad."

His night-face seemed happier than I had ever seen it. As if the trigger-spring of his driving restlessness had been finally cut.

I won't say it came in a flash. It wasn't such a simple thing as that. But could that be what I had done wrong?

He had called me "Dad." Could it be that a child would rather have a father than a pal? ("Wait.... Wait up, Art.") By spanking him I had abrogated the adult partnership between us and set him free. He could cry. His guilt could be paid for all at once and absolved.

It wasn't the spanking that had been cruel. What had been cruel were all the times I had snubbed him as you might an adult—with implication of shame. There was no way he could get over that. The unexpiable residue of blame piled up in him. Shutting him out, spreading (who can tell what unlikely symptoms a child's mind will translate it into?), blocking his access to me, to other children, even to himself. His reaction was violence, deviation. Any guilt a sensitive child can't be absolved of at once he blindly adds to, whenever he thinks of it, in a kind of desperation.

I had worried about failing him. That hadn't bothered him. What had bothered him was an adult shame I had taught him, I saw now, for failing *me*.

I kissed him good-night. "Okay, son," I said, "I'll spank you sometimes."

He nodded, smiling. "Dad," he said then, "how come you knew I jumped off the roof?"

That should have brought me up short—how much farther apart we must be than I'd imagined if he was driven to jump off a roof to shock me back into contact. "Jumped," he said, not "fell."

But somehow it didn't. It gave me the most liberating kind of hope. Because it hadn't been a question, really. It had been a statement. "How come you *knew* … ?" He hadn't the slightest doubt that no matter what he did, wherever I was I would know it, and that wherever I was I would come.

Anyhow, it is a fine day today, and we have just finished the fence. He is playing ball with the other children as I put this down. Their way.

Helen Potrebenko

Diary of a Temp

There is something intricately evil about a company where people can type policies for four years or five and a half years.

April

Although I tell them irritably I know everything there is to know about policies, I have never actually typed them before. Until now, no matter what else happened, I had been successful in avoiding that lowest of the low. It was even my one example of why it was all right for computers to replace people because typing policies is a job no human being should have to do.

So how do I feel about myself now that I'm typing policies? I'm doing it for you, I tell my dearly beloved solemnly. He does not take me seriously. The very volubility of my complaints leads him to believe I'm not serious. If I was in as great a state of despair as I maintain, would I be so glibly descriptive of it?

A policy is a printed form with a large number of carbon copies. You put the whole thing in the typewriter, line up the boxes one at a time from the top down and either type something in each box (insured's name and address, agent's name and number, mortgage holder if there is one, various business locations, description of property, etc.) or type an X in the appropriate box for new or renewal, for each kind of coverage, amount of coverage, and so on.

Then you take the forms out of the typewriter, tear off the top strip and while doing so, pull away all the carbon paper, throw that in the garbage and then assemble the copies with any relevant attachments for mailing to the agent. I never did get the hang of snapping out all the carbons at once. Georgia Malinowski showed me how to fold over the top strip and how, with a sharp snap, to remove all the carbon paper in one movement. Not me, I tear off the top strip but only a few of the carbons come out; the rest

I have to remove one at a time and in the process, the carbon smudges on my fingers and therefore on subsequent policies.

This necessitates many trips to the washroom to wash off the carbon. Of course, I have to make frequent trips to the washroom anyway to smoke, the washroom being the designated smoking area in this workplace.

In the washroom, I meet only one other red-eyed desperate puffer; I do not identify with her. She is overly skinny and winks at me all the time; possibly this is due to a nervous twitch. A few puffs and winks and it's back to typing policies.

You put the form in the typewriter, turn to the right line, space over to the box, type, space over, type, turn, space, type. The regular policy typists have a quota and must type a specified number of policies each day (fifty, I think) in order to keep their job.

Then suppose you've done the typing and the assembly and Georgia Malinowski finds that an X is missing from a certain box. You disassemble the forms back into their original order, put carbon paper back between the pages, straighten the whole thing out very carefully by tapping the sides and top against something. There is no room on the desk, there is only the typewriter to tap against. Shuffle, shuffle, shuffle, tap, tap, turn, tap, tap, tap. Then carefully put the whole shebang in the typewriter. Almost always this moves at least one of the copies and they all have to be dead straight otherwise the boxes won't line up. So then you pull the release lever and, grasping the offending paper, try to move it without disarranging the others. Finally it is more or less straight. You space down, space across to the box and, whang, you hit the X key. That's it. All the shuffling and tapping and adjusting just for one whang.

I tell myself I shall learn humility at this job but all that I am learning is resentment.

Georgia Malinowski has been working here five and a half years and Marion Singh, four years. If I am going to resent me typing policies, I have to resent for them too.

But how can I resent for them when they don't take me to coffee? Only the second day, under close questioning, does Georgia reveal that there is a coffee break at all. Ten twenty she tells me. I wait until ten twenty-five; Georgia does not call me. I go alone and find

her and Marion ensconced at a large table at which there is not room for me. They do not look at me.

I plot ways to get even. I observe that Marion's desk blotter is covered with pictures of children. Without being too obvious about gawking, I observe that they are probably pictures of the same two children but at different ages. If I was nice, I would ask her if those were her children. Her face would light up, she would tell me about the children, the husband, the mother-in-law or aunt who looks after them during the day, the house they live in, the school they go to, what classes or sports they excel in, and for whatever length of time that took, she would lose the dazed, glazed look of a policy typist.

It's probable she would be lying anyway. All those happy families. All those kind mothers-in-law. I think it was Tolstoy who said all happy families are the same; I imagine all families who lie about being happy are also all the same. But maybe they really are happy? Who knows? Since Marion does not invite me along for coffee, I cannot ask her.

Georgia Malinowski does not have pictures. She has even more makeup on than Marion or Emily or Charlene. Her face and eyes and lips are thickly covered with goop. Even though I am much older and arthritic, I feel disgustingly healthy beside such a gooped-up person. Apart from the makeup, what is remarkable about Georgia Malinowski is that she is unable to say I have done something wrong. When she brings back a pile of typed policies, she says happily: Oh, this is very good, this is all correct, you are very good. And I smile, thinking, of course I am.

But as I sit there beaming in self-congratulation, Georgia tells me that this form I will have to put back in the typewriter and add this and that, and this one, I will take out such and such and on most of them, I have forgotten to type 838 where it says other forms which apply. And it finally dawns on me that she is returning about a third of the policies for correction.

I exclaim how awful it is that I made all those errors. Georgia says, no, no, I didn't make any errors, I am very good. But if I refuse to correct the things which are not errors, she gets very distressed and finally has to say in no uncertain terms, the terrible, the unspeakable. She rubs her eyes whenever she is forced to say someone has made an error. How can she rub her eyes when there is so much makeup on them? She rubs them carefully, with the back of a smooth, manicured hand.

After the second day, she does not talk to me about errors any more. When I return from the washroom or the coffee room, there is a neat pile of files on my desk with little notes attached. "Correction to be made," the notes are headed, leaving a space in which Georgia Malinowski has written various things like the address of the insured is this instead of that, and so on. I do wish she invited me along for coffee.

Georgia Malinowski has been typing policies for five and a half years. There is no way she can invite a temp for coffee; her own position is too precarious for such generosity. Only the secure can afford to be generous. If Georgia came into the coffee room and the big table was full, they would not shift around and make room for her, no one would get a chair, no one would say: We'll make room for you, Georgia Malinowski.

And as far as the inability to tell me I have made an error goes, maybe that's from insecurity also or maybe it's a cultural thing. Maybe in Georgia it simply isn't done to tell someone in cold blood they goofed. But then maybe she isn't from Georgia. In another office, I would have said: Are you from Georgia, Georgia? But here I do not.

There is something intricately evil about a company where people can type policies for four years or five and a half years. At my previous assignment (a soothing one), everyone had been there many years but they always had a long list of jobs they had done within the company in those years. Here they do the same job.

It's not like they can quit and go elsewhere. It's been some years since there has been any elsewhere to go. These women have jobs, they are the envy of the unemployed, while they themselves envy those without a vocation. But it is only the invisible unemployed they envy, not the visible beggars crowding the streets.

When I worked at the Harbour Centre where the liquor store was moved to, there were many beggars and people said it was because it was a bad part of town. So I am considerably agitated when I go out for lunch and find there are beggars on Robson Street too. All those jazzy clothes in store windows, all that expensive jewellery displayed just out of reach, all those exotic restaurants, and there are beggars. How can I go and eat lunch if they can't?

Somebody has to pay for circuses and superhighways. I do not identify with the beggars nor fear them because the assignments are coming close together. The beggars only remind me that there are many ways to lower wages. One way is to withhold more money for income tax. Another way is to withhold the same tax money but not provide any social services with it so that workers have to pay taxes and give money to beggars.

I will tell the temp agency I will never work here again. I'll phone and say: Ginny, never for this company again, okay? And she'll say "why" and I'll say: Well, there's twenty-six floors in the building. So when you stand there waiting for the elevator, and other people are waiting for the elevator, they all smile at each other. Then when people get on the elevator, they all smile at the people already on the elevator and the people already on the elevator smile at the people getting on at each floor. All the time.

Oh, Ginny will say. I completely understand. And she will never send me here again.

Then they'll never know. Nobody really looks at temps. Arthritic temp, run, run, running through uptown, downtown. Liniment and aspirin and a smoke in the washroom.

I had hoped to discover humility at this job; I have not apprehended even one single solitary insight. But it will soon be over and there is no other building in all of the lower mainland where the people getting on the elevator smile at everyone already on the elevator and the people already on the elevator smile at all the people getting on the elevator.

May

One day I worked at UBC and found there are now beggars at the University Village. Somebody has to pay for circuses and superhighways.

For a few days, I typed for some hip mining promoters in Gastown. They had the windows boarded up so they wouldn't have to look at the regular inhabitants of the area. Every once in a while, one of the bosses would run out to swear at some poor old guy who had taken the opportunity to sit in a sunny doorway for a few minutes.

June

I got trained on a number of machines at the bank and immediately fell in love with the Swift Interbank Telex. There is also a Nanotec for transmission to places other than banks or banks not on the Swift system and there are a number of other machines into which I input various kinds of data when there isn't any telexing to do.

It was not until the second week when in a gush of insight, I rushed down to the smoking room to phone my dearly beloved: Do you know what these things are??? They are VDTs!!!

So then I recall what all I have read and written about VDTs and think about being more cautious. I know I should raise my eyes to look at distance regularly and take frequent breaks. But this is difficult because there are only blank walls and no distance to look at around the machines and I get kind of hypnotized and continue punching stuff in until I am dizzy from not smoking and with vision so blurred I can barely find my way to the smoking room.

The machine makes soft little clicks, not at all like the way a typewriter whangs and clatters, just nice soft little clicks. The first couple of weeks I was sick and found the sound immeasurably comforting. Even though I was nauseated and in pain (stomach ulcer from the aspirin for arthritis), I could hardly wait to get to work in the morning and be comforted by the sound of the keyboard.

Even sick, I have had no trouble learning the Swift (although the Nanotec will be the death of me yet) so nobody knows. Arthritic temp, run, run, running uptown, downtown.

Besides the machines, I have learned how the layoffs were done. I know all about layoffs.

At union places, layoffs are done by seniority and the laid off ones are on a recall list. In the old days, this meant they had a good chance of being called back to work and in the meantime, they had an enforced holiday on UIC. There has been a lot of debate over the years about seniority as the criterion and the only thing that can be said in its favour is that it works. So at F———, for one example, when the number of workers to be laid off was decided on, the seniority list was posted on all the bulletin boards with a red line drawn on it. Everyone above the red line stayed; everyone below the red line was laid off. There was despair but no demoralization.

In non-union places, there is no recognition of seniority and therefore no orderly system for layoffs. At R———, each department manager was given a figure for the number of people to be got rid of in his department and he decided on the basis of favouritism alone who should go. This meant that sucking up to the manager and backstabbing one's fellow workers was a useful thing to do. As the branch shrank in size, the wicked and the sycophants were all that was left, save for the occasional accidentally essential job or someone being away on maternity leave at exactly the right time. Eventually, of course, even these people went. But in the two or three years before the branch closed, the recurring layoffs turned people into monsters.

I was forewarned of my layoff so I didn't cry. Every other laid off one cried. There were hundreds of them and they all cried. They'd come to work in the morning and they were people with a job and a pay cheque and just before noon, they were unemployed. I got one week's severance pay.

At M——— they got more severance pay. The floor Margaret worked on had thirty-three desks in an open space. The only closed office was the manager's. Every Thursday morning for four weeks, the manager would phone one of the supervisors. The supervisor's phone would ring, she would pick it up, talk briefly, then walk over to the desk of one of the workers. She would guide that worker to the manager's office. In the office, the manager would read a prepared letter telling the employee she no longer worked there and then escort her to her desk to pick up her personal belongings. Still under guard by the manager, she was then taken to the elevator and down to Personnel. At Personnel, the ex-employee would be given her cheque and a letter. And that was it. No more job.

The manager would then go back upstairs, pick up his phone and call another supervisor, give her another name and the procedure would continue, like something out of a horror movie.

The laid off employees were given books to instruct them on how to write a resume and how to look for work. They were allowed to come in and use a telephone and a typewriter in an office for that purpose on a different floor nowhere near M——— offices. Margaret never used the office but she did read the books and followed all the instructions but she never got a job. More than two years later, she got a part-time job through friends.

At the Bank of———, there was also no forewarning. Branches were closing but if the staff in the head offices thought about the possibility of layoff at all, they thought maybe a number proportional to the closed branches would be laid off. They never considered that half of them would go.

Again, the criteria had to do with straight favouritism. People chosen for layoff were called into the department manager's office one at a time, told they were gone, and told they were forbidden from discussing it with anyone else. They picked up their personal belongings and left. I don't know if they cried. I do know that they did not talk to the ones remaining and these were called in later to be told the others were never coming back.

I asked a smoking buddy how the no talking rule had been enforced. What would they do—fire them? I see what you mean, she said, as if she had never thought of it before.

I asked my supervisor why a temp was called in rather than one of the laid off ones being recalled. They can't come back, she told me nervously. They're on severance pay, it would be illegal. Come on! I said irritably. I don't know why then, I just know they will never be called back. Never. Non-union, that's why.

I asked the temp agency about the phenomenon of layoffs and then temps being called in. Ginny gave me a rap in that language I can understand but can't speak about how it was more cost effective to reduce the total staff complement.

What she really means is that there is a massive speed-up campaign going on. The point is not so much to lay people off as to make the remaining ones do twice as much work. They've got children, some have husbands and mortgages, and they all have to eat. They have seen their sisters driven out. So they work. Boy, do they work! They burn out fast, and get sick a lot, but in the short term, they work. They spend a lot of time envying the ones who were laid off, which is not surprising even while it is disgusting.

We got a bulletin from the President and Chief Executive Officer that said in part: While an organization will always continue to evolve we do not foresee further personnel adjustments due to downsizing. Evil men hide behind a screen of words as if they believed that if what they do is not named, they will not be punished for it. The same President and Chief Executive Officer apparently would walk through offices once in a while to make sure none of the workers were wearing sundresses and that all of the workers were wearing pantyhose. He probably got paid more than $100,000 a year and couldn't think of any better way to spend his time.

I couldn't tell at first. At first I thought, boy, what a great place, lots of desk space for a change. Only after I had already phoned my dearly beloved that those machines I loved were really VDTs, did I phone to say there was so much desk space because half the staff were gone. I still love the machines though.

The other day, Ginny delivered to me at work a basket with two apples in it and a balloon tied on with a ribbon, in honour of National Temporaries week. Ageing temp, run, run, running, all for $7.45 an hour and two apples.

July

In every office I have ever worked, people deem their elevators to be impossibly slow. Compared to what? Presumably there exists somewhere the Platonic Ideal of an Elevator to which all these other elevators are compared and found wanting.

The other characteristic of office workers in these demoralized times is that "we," whoever that may be at any given time, find "them" to be incredibly stupid. For example, we in Foreign Exchange talk among ourselves about the stupidity of them in Letters of Credit, who are at the other end of the room. However, our whole room finds endless fault with Loans, who are down the hall. And, our whole floor has nothing but scorn for the stupid ones in the branches.

I always think if they are so stupid, it must be that we are so smart but whenever I join these conversations by proclaiming our superiority rather than declaiming their inferiority, a terrible pall is cast on the conversation. It is not done to blow one's own horn so we have no compensating joy or pride in ourselves and our work and the incompetence of the rest of the world is unrelieved by the slightest bit of smartness here.

Still, they are always nice to me. There are an incredible number of nice people in the world. Ageing temp, run, run, running, uptown, downtown for $7.45 an hour, two apples and a little warmth.

August

What luxury! I'm in the Mortgage Department of another bank and it has two coffee breaks! The only problem is that I'm typing the same hate letter over and over again to people who are late with their mortgage payments. There are actually several variations of the letter which are sent out at suitable intervals. The first one says pay up; the second one says pay up or else; the third one gets much more serious and declares that foreclosure proceedings are about to begin. There are a lot of people late with mortgage payments. What would happen to a temp who started identifying with the recipients of these letters?

September

You didn't close the door of the supply cupboard, the supervisor says.

Oh, sorry. I get up and close the door.

I always close the supply cupboard door, the supervisor says. Don't you, Roberta?

Yes, Roberta proclaims virtuously. I always close the doors of my closets at home too.

Me, too, the supervisor says. I can't sleep if my bedroom closet is open.

I refuse to take this seriously. One person's neatness is another person's obsession, I remark, expecting that to be the end of the conversation. But it isn't.

I always think, the supervisor goes on, that people who don't close doors don't do proper work.

You don't buy an expensive bedroom suite and expensive drapes and then leave the closet door open, Roberta says.

I should think not, the supervisor says. It's like putting on a nice outfit and having one item not matching.

Roberta shudders with horror. Then they catch sight of my shoes. They look at each other in complete shock and then stare at my shoes. They are unable to look away.

I think there is a difference now between the clothes of the full-time senior staff and the rest of us who are casual or part-time. Most of the temps are recognizable as such even though all the agencies have dress codes.

At lunch the other day, a woman said she had read in a women's magazine that if you couldn't afford nice clothes, you should buy a really good handbag and then you would look well dressed even without the dressy clothes. She thought this was an excellent idea until she priced handbags. If you can't afford the clothes, you can't afford the handbag either.

Generally, the rules at workplaces seem to be far more rigid. It is rare to be allowed to talk except, of course, to the supervisor. Smoking is almost never allowed. They say it's for health reasons but the actual effect is just more rigidity. If they were really worried about our health, there would be more opportunity for moving around instead of jobs being refined down to one type of thing repeated over and over again. You sit in one place, don't get up, don't talk and work like crazy. There are rarely any windows for office workers to look out of; the offices with windows are for male management. Similarly, the smoking rules do not apply to management; they are for workers on the shop floor only.

It has always been difficult to correct the grammar and spelling of something you're typing; I used to do it anyway. I don't any more. It is less important that a thing be correct than that the workers be obedient. A typist who corrects an incoherent sentence is warped, dangerous and disrespectful.

I don't know what the long term effects of the long hours and incredible speed that full-time workers are subjected to are because I am never in one place long enough. All I see is the immediate effect which is irritability. I notice a lot of people's hands shake. It is rare to see anyone's eyes because they are always bent over their work.

At one of the places I get sent to at irregular intervals, the full-time employees routinely work long hours without a break. Twelve hours is common and even sixteen hours is not unknown. They never know when they come to work in the morning what time they are going to get home. They are young and still healthy but remarkably irritable.

One day last week they went to the boss's office all together to complain about the long hours. They wanted to be allowed to eat; they even wanted to have dates. Later in the week they discovered there was an ad in the paper for all their jobs. At least five hundred people phoned in. That'll teach them.

February

I have started to have nightmares. Some are about never getting another job. Some are about getting another job. I don't know which are worse.

March to June

Usually the first letter I type preparatory to the firing says something like: you have called in sick twice in two weeks, or: you have been off sick almost a day every month, and then asks the offending employee to bring a letter from a doctor certifying that that employee is healthy enough to fulfill the requirements of the job description. The later letters I type get gradually altered to say the employee is unreliable due to absenteeism with the final separation slip usually stating that the employee is terminated due to unreliability.

I am astounded but not greatly upset by this since I am not an employee of this workplace but of the agency. What does bother me is working without proper breaks. I get a half hour for lunch and that's it. For people who don't eat much or who don't smoke, this might be enough and for a few days at a time this might be enough but after some months I start losing weight.

All the regular staff get coffee breaks and they don't care that I don't. Nobody knows my name. I get to know names from typing lists, typing the aforementioned letters, giving out resident trust money but to the end, few among the staff and none of the residents knew my name. Office workers are a function, not a person.

One day some people in the lunch room were talking about buying lottery tickets and daydreaming about winning five million dollars.

I daydream about coffee breaks, I said, gulping my food and talking with my mouth full. (I hate people who talk with their mouth full.) I daydream of fifteen minutes a day in the middle of the working day away from the phone, the reception desk, the typing. I would sit and stare into space and put my head back in gear.

They gaped at me with great interest and then went back to talking about five million dollars.

Ageing temp, run, run, running, uptown, downtown, all for $7.45 an hour and a few daydreams.

July

At the bank, there were two coffee breaks a day and an hour for lunch. While the work was boring, there was a whole group of us to do it so we talked and talked while typing addresses on about 9,000 letters and 9,000 envelopes in record time.

Slowing down temp, still run, run, running uptown, downtown, all for $7.45 an hour and a friendly chat.

August

I had two of the most incredibly wonderful jobs finally, one right after the other. One job finally acknowledged typing properly by displaying it on the wall. It involved typing labels for prints in various art shows. I did 600 labels in eight hours listing the name of the painting, the name of the artist and the price of the print both framed and unframed. The pictures are boring but the typing is wonderful.

Another high was a boss who hovered over me telling me to type slowly and take many breaks! Gee, it was nice.

This latter employer kept calling and asking for me but I went on to bigger and better things after that and was unable to go back. Gee, it was nice.

Even before the temping ended, I was nostalgic for it. I was good at it. Ageing temp, run, run, running through offices and jobs and hard times and worry. Even though I acquired arthritis instead of money or knowledge, I knew it was there, somewhere, in one of those offices, in one of those buildings, known by some of those people, it was there.

Lyudmila Petrushevskaya

Through the Fields

But we laughed terribly as we rocked on those waves of earth ...

I never met him again; once and only once we traveled together to someone's distant dacha, in a workers' village. We had to walk about four kilometers through a forest and then through a bare field, which may, in fact, have been pretty at any time of year, but on that day was awful. We stood at the edge of the forest and couldn't bring ourselves to go out into the open space, there was such a thunderstorm. Lightning struck the clay earth of the path, and the field was strangely bare. I remember those mounds of clay, the bare, absolutely bare, broken earth, the cloudburst, and the lightning. Perhaps something had been planted in this field, but at that moment nothing was growing, and our feet slid every which way, buckled, and twisted in this exposed bare field, because we had decided to take the shortest route and go straight across. The way led steeply upward, and hunching over for some reason, we laughed wildly. He was a very taciturn person, from what I remembered of him on previous group outings of this kind—birthdays, trips, and the like. At the time I still did not know the value of silence, didn't appreciate silence, and tried my best to get Vovik to open up, all the more so because we had an hour-and-a-half train ride, just the two of us, alone among strangers, and it was uncomfortable and somehow embarrassing to remain silent. Looking at me with his kind little eyes, he grinned and said almost nothing. But that was all right; it could have been endured were it not for the cloudburst that greeted us at the station. My head, my freshly washed and curled hair, my made-up eyelashes—everything was ruined, everything, my light dress and my bag, which later shriveled and faded—in short, everything. Smiling foolishly, Vovik hunched his head into his shoulders and raised the collar of his white shirt. A drop immediately formed on the tip of his thin nose, but there was nothing that could be done. For some reason we began to wander in the rain through the clay; he knew the way—I didn't. He said that the straight route was closer, so we started across that cursed field through which the lightning gamboled, leaping now close to us, now farther away, and we jumped over the waves of clay earth. We didn't remove our shoes; evidently we were embarrassed in front of each other. I don't know. At that time any manifestations of my natural state embarrassed me and most of all my bare feet, which seemed to me the incarnation of unsightliness on earth. Later on I met women who felt the same way and never went barefoot, especially in the presence of the men they loved. One even went to such extremes to hide her feet that when she got married she deserved her husband's remark "What ugly feet you have!" But others were not concerned in the least by crooked or hairy or long or hairless feet—not in the least. And they turned out to be right, but then, on that day, we walked on the cursed soles of our shoes, slipping and sliding, a hairbreadth from death, and had a wonderful time. We were both twenty years old. Glancing around shyly, good-naturedly, he walked at a distance of about one and a half meters from me; later I found out that lightning can kill two people if they are walking side by side. It was not shyness, however, that kept him from offering me his hand; on that day his fiancée was waiting for him at the dacha, so he didn't offer me his hand out of youthful zeal to serve his love and her alone. But we laughed terribly as we rocked on those waves of earth, and covered all over with clay, we hit it off somehow. Those four kilometers through the clay in the rain dragged on for a remarkably long time: There are times in life that are very difficult to live through and drag on endlessly—hard labor, for example, or sudden solitude or a marathon. We endured those four kilometers together. At the end, when we reached the porch, he even helped me climb up the steps, and accompanied by the astonished laughter of the assembled group and the constrained exclamation of his fiancée, we entered the warm home, still cackling. Everything had gone to hell—his and my clothing, our shoes, our hair; a drop still hung from his nose, but there was not a single person dearer to me than he. I vaguely surmised that I had been lucky to meet in the course of my life a very good and faithful man; the treasures of his soul together with the drop hanging from his nose touched me to the point of tears. I was distraught and didn't know what to do. They showed us to different rooms in this empty, dusty summer house, still not inhabited by summer guests. They changed my clothes and his, too, led us back, and gave both of us half a glass of vodka—how marvelous! At the table he glanced in my direction now and then, smiling foolishly, sniffling, and warmed his hands on a mug of tea. I knew that none of this was mine and never would be mine, this miracle of kindness, purity, and what have you—even beauty. His friend took charge of him; they settled down to a game of chess—even his fiancée was waiting for him. I was not waiting, however, for I was warming my soul after the long and difficult path of my life, realizing that tomorrow and even today I would be torn away from the warmth and the light and thrust out again to walk alone through the clay field in the rain. And that's how life is and one must become stronger, everyone has to—not just me, but Vovik, and even Vovik's poor fiancée, because a person shines for only one person once in his life and that is all.

translated by Stefani Hoffman

Sinclair Ross

The Painted Door

Even the distant farmsteads she could see served only to intensify a sense of isolation.

Straight across the hills it was five miles from John's farm to his father's. But in winter, with the roads impassable, a team had to make a wide detour and skirt the hills, so that from five the distance was more than trebled to seventeen.

"I think I'll walk," John said at breakfast to his wife. "The drifts in the hills wouldn't hold a horse, but they'll carry me all right. If I leave early I can spend a few hours helping him with his chores, and still be back by suppertime."

Moodily she went to the window, and thawing a clear place in the frost with her breath, stood looking across the snowswept farmyard to the huddle of stables and sheds. "There was a double wheel around the moon last night," she countered presently. "You said yourself we could expect a storm. It isn't right to leave me here alone. Surely I'm as important as your father."

He glanced up uneasily, then drinking off his coffee tried to reassure her. "But there's nothing to be afraid of—even if it does start to storm. You won't need to go near the stable. Everything's fed and watered now to last till night. I'll be back at the latest by seven or eight."

She went on blowing against the frosted pane, carefully elongating the clear place until it was oval-shaped and symmetrical. He watched her a moment or two longer, then more insistently repeated, "I say you won't need to go near the stable. Everything's fed and watered, and I'll see that there's plenty of wood in. That will be all right, won't it?"

"Yes—of course—I heard you—" It was a curiously cold voice now, as if the words were chilled by their contact with the frosted pane. "Plenty to eat—plenty of wood to keep me warm—what more could a woman ask for?"

"But he's an old man—living there all alone. What is it, Ann? You're not like yourself this morning."

She shook her head without turning. "Pay no attention to me. Seven years a farmer's wife—it's time I was used to staying alone."

Slowly the clear place on the glass enlarged: oval, then round, then oval again. The sun was risen above the frost mists now, so keen and hard a glitter on the snow that instead of warmth its rays seemed shedding cold. One of the two-year-old colts that had cantered away when John turned the horses out for water stood covered with rime at the stable door again, head down and body hunched, each breath a little plume of steam against the frosty air. She shivered, but did not turn. In the clear, bitter light the long white miles of prairie landscape seemed a region strangely alien to life. Even the distant farmsteads she could see served only to intensify a sense of isolation. Scattered across the face of so vast and bleak a wilderness it was difficult to conceive them as a testimony of human hardihood and endurance. Rather they seemed futile, lost. Rather they seemed to cower before the implacability of snow-swept earth and clear pale sun-chilled sky.

And when at last she turned from the window there was a brooding stillness in her face as if she had recognized this mastery of snow and cold. It troubled John. "If you're really afraid," he yielded, "I won't go today. Lately it's been so cold, that's all. I just wanted to make sure he's all right in case we do have a storm."

"I know—I'm not really afraid." She was putting in a fire now, and he could no longer see her face. "Pay no attention to me. It's ten miles there and back, so you'd better get started."

"You ought to know by now I wouldn't stay away," he tried to brighten her. "No matter how it stormed. Twice a week before we were married I never missed—and there were bad blizzards that winter too."

He was a slow, unambitious man, content with his farm and cattle, naïvely proud of Ann. He had been bewildered by it once, her caring for a dull-witted fellow like him; then assured at last of her affection he had relaxed against it gratefully, unsuspecting it might ever be less constant than his own. Even now, listening to the restless brooding in her voice, he felt only a quick, unformulated kind of pride that after seven years his absence for a day should still concern her. While she, his trust and earnestness controlling her again:

"I know. It's just that sometimes when you're away I get lonely.... There's a long cold tramp in front of you. You'll let me fix a scarf around your face."

He nodded. "And on my way I'll drop in at Steven's place. Maybe he'll come over tonight for a game of cards. You haven't seen anybody but me for the last two weeks."

She glanced up sharply, then busied herself clearing the table. "It will mean another two miles if you do. You're going to be cold and tired enough as it is. When you're gone I think I'll paint the kitchen woodwork. White this time—you remember we got the paint last fall. It's going to make the room a lot lighter. I'll be too busy to find the day long."

"I will though," he insisted, "and if a storm gets up you'll feel safer, knowing that he's coming. That's what you need, Ann—someone to talk to besides me."

She stood at the stove motionless a moment, then turned to him uneasily. "Will you shave then, John—now—before you go?"

He glanced at her questioningly, and avoiding his eyes she tried to explain, "I mean—he may be here before you're back—and you won't have a chance then."

"But it's only Steven—he's seen me like this—"

"He'll be shaved, though—that's what I mean—and I'd like you too to spend a little time on yourself."

He stood up, stroking the heavy stubble on his chin. "Maybe I should all right, but it makes the skin too tender. Especially when I've got to face the wind."

She nodded and began to help him dress, bringing heavy socks and a big woollen sweater from the bedroom, wrapping a scarf around his face and forehead. "I'll tell Steven to come early," he said, as he went out. "In time for supper. Likely there'll be chores for me to do, so if I'm not back by six don't wait."

From the bedroom window she watched him nearly a mile along the road. The fire had gone down when at last she turned away, and already through the house there was an encroaching chill. A blaze sprang up again when the drafts were opened, but as she went on clearing the table her movements were furtive and constrained. It was the silence weighing upon her—the frozen silence of the bitter fields and sun-chilled sky—lurking outside as if alive, relentlessly in wait, mile-deep between her now and John. She listened to it, suddenly tense, motionless. The fire crackled and the clock ticked. Always it was there. "I'm a fool," she whispered hoarsely, rattling the dishes in defiance, going back to the stove to put in another fire. "Warm and safe—I'm a fool. It's a good chance when he's away to paint. The day will go quickly. I won't have time to brood."

Since November now the paint had been waiting warmer weather. The frost in the walls on a day like this would crack and peel it as it dried, but she needed something to keep her hands occupied, something to stave off the gathering cold and loneliness. "First of all," she said aloud, opening the paint and mixing it with a little turpentine, "I must get the house warmer. Fill up the stove and open the oven door so that all the heat comes out. Wad something along the window sills to keep out the drafts. Then I'll feel brighter. It's the cold that depresses."

She moved briskly, performing each little task with careful and exaggerated absorption, binding her thoughts to it, making it a screen between herself and the surrounding snow and silence. But when the stove was filled and the windows sealed it was more difficult again. Above the quiet, steady swishing of her brush against the bedroom door the clock began to tick. Suddenly her movements became precise, deliberate, her posture self-conscious, as if someone had entered the room and were watching her. It was the silence again, aggressive, hovering. The fire spit and crackled at it. Still it was there. "I'm a fool," she repeated. "All farmers' wives have to stay alone. I mustn't give in this way. I mustn't brood. A few hours now and they'll be here."

The sound of her voice reassured her. She went on: "I'll get them a good supper—and for coffee tonight after cards bake some of the little cakes with raisins that he likes.... Just three of us, so I'll watch, and let John play. It's better with four, but at least we can talk. That's all I need—someone to talk to. John never talks. He's stronger—he doesn't understand. But he likes Steven—no matter what the neighbours say. Maybe he'll have him come again, and some other young people too. It's what we need, both of us, to help keep young ourselves.... And then before we know it we'll be into March. It's cold still in March sometimes, but you never mind the same. At least you're beginning to think about spring."

She began to think about it now. Thoughts that outstripped her words, that left her alone again with herself and the ever-lurking silence. Eager and hopeful first; then clenched, rebellious, lonely. Windows open, sun and thawing earth again, the urge of growing, living things. Then the days that began in the morning at half-past four and lasted till ten at night; the meals at which John gulped his food and scarcely spoke a word; the brute-tired stupid eyes he turned on her if ever she mentioned town or visiting.

For spring was drudgery again. John never hired a man to help him. He wanted a mortgage-free farm; then a new house and pretty clothes for her. Sometimes, because with the best of crops it was going to take so long to pay off anyway, she wondered whether they mightn't better let the mortgage wait a little. Before they were worn out, before their best years were gone. It was something of life she wanted, not just a house and furniture; something of John, not pretty clothes when she would be too old to wear them. But John of course couldn't understand. To him it seemed only right that she should have the clothes—only right that he, fit for nothing else, should slave away fifteen hours a day to give them to her. There was in his devotion a baffling, insurmountable humility that made him feel the need of sacrifice. And when his muscles ached, when his feet dragged stolidly with weariness, then it seemed that in some measure at least he was making amends for his big hulking body and simple mind. That by his sacrifice he succeeded only in the extinction of his personality never occurred to him. Year after year their lives went on in the same little groove. He drove his horses in the field; she milked the cow and hoed potatoes. By dint of his drudgery he saved a few months' wages, added a few dollars more each fall to his payments on the mortgage; but the only real difference that it all made was to deprive her of his companionship, to make him a little duller, older, uglier than he might otherwise have been. He never saw their lives objectively. To him it was not what he actually accomplished by means of the sacrifice that mattered, but the sacrifice itself, the gesture—something done for her sake.

And she, understanding, kept her silence. In such a gesture, however futile, there was a graciousness not to be shattered lightly. "John" she would begin sometimes, "you're doing too much. Get a man to help you—just for a month—" but smiling down at her he would answer simply, "I don't mind. Look at the hands on me. They're made for work." While in his voice there would be a stalwart ring to tell her that by her thoughtfulness she had made him only the more resolved to serve her, to prove his devotion and fidelity.

They were useless such thoughts. She knew. It was his very devotion that made them useless, that forbade her to rebel. Yet over and over, sometimes hunched still before their bleakness, sometimes her brush making swift sharp strokes to pace the chafe and rancour that they brought, she persisted in them.

This now, the winter, was their slack season. She could sleep sometimes till eight, and John till seven. They could linger over their meals a little, read, play cards, go visiting the neighbours. It was the time to relax, to indulge and enjoy themselves; but instead, fretful and impatient, they kept on waiting for the spring. They were compelled now, not by labour, but by the spirit of labour. A spirit that pervaded their lives and brought with idleness a sense of guilt. Sometimes they did sleep late, sometimes they did play cards, but always uneasily, always reproached by the thought of more important things that might be done. When John got up at five to attend to the fire he wanted to stay up and go out to the stable. When he sat down to a meal he hurried his food and pushed his chair away again, from habit, from sheer work-instinct, even though it was only to put more wood in the stove, or go down cellar to cut up beets and turnips for the cows.

And anyway, sometimes she asked herself, why sit trying to talk with a man who never talked? Why talk when there was nothing to talk about but crops and cattle, the weather and the neighbours? The neighbours, too—why go visiting them when still it was the same—crops and cattle, the weather and the other neighbours?

Why go to the dances in the schoolhouse to sit among the older women, one of them now, married seven years, or to waltz with the work-bent tired old farmers to a squeaky fiddle tune? Once she had danced with Steven six or seven times in the evening, and they had talked about it for as many months. It was easier to stay at home. John never danced or enjoyed himself. He was always uncomfortable in his good suit and shoes. He didn't like shaving in the cold weather oftener than once or twice a week. It was easier to stay at home, to stand at the window staring out across the bitter fields, to count the days and look forward to another spring.

But now, alone with herself in the winter silence, she saw the spring for what it really was. This spring—next spring—all the springs and summers still to come. While they grew old, while their bodies warped, while their minds kept shrivelling dry and empty like their lives. "I mustn't," she said aloud again. "I married him—and he's a good man. I mustn't keep on this way. It will be noon before long, and then time to think about supper.... Maybe he'll come early—and as soon as John is finished at the stable we can all play cards."

It was getting cold again, and she left her painting to put in more wood. But this time the warmth spread slowly. She pushed a mat up to the outside door, and went back to the window to pat down the woollen shirt that was wadded along the sill. Then she paced a few times round the room, then poked the fire and rattled the stove lids, then paced again. The fire crackled, the clock ticked. The silence now seemed more intense than ever, seemed to have reached a pitch where it faintly moaned. She began to pace on tiptoe, listening, her shoulders drawn together, not realizing for a while that it was the wind she heard, thin-strained and whimpering through the eaves.

Then she wheeled to the window, and with quick short breaths thawed the frost to see again. The glitter was gone. Across the drifts sped swift and snakelike little tongues of snow. She could not follow them, where they sprang from, or where they disappeared. It was as if all across the yard the snow were shivering awake—roused by the warnings of the wind to hold itself in readiness for the impending storm. The sky had become a sombre, whitish grey. It, too, as if in readiness, had shifted and lay close to earth. Before her as she watched a mane of powdery snow reared up breast-high against the darker background of the stable, tossed for a moment angrily, and then subsided again as if whipped down to obedience and restraint. But another followed, more reckless and impatient than the first. Another reeled and dashed itself against the window where she watched. Then ominously for a while there were only the angry little snakes of snow. The wind rose, creaking the troughs that were wired beneath the eaves. In the distance, sky and prairie now were merged into one another linelessly. All round her it was gathering; already in its press and whimpering there strummed a boding of eventual fury. Again she saw a mane of snow spring up, so dense and high this time that all the sheds and stables were obscured. Then others followed, whirling fiercely out of hand; and, when at last they cleared, the stables seemed in dimmer outline than before. It was the snow beginning, long lancet shafts of it, straight from the north, borne almost level by the straining wind. "He'll be there soon," she whispered, "and coming home it will be in his back. He'll leave again right away. He saw the double wheel—he knows the kind of storm there'll be."

She went back to her painting. For a while it was easier, all her thoughts half-anxious ones of John in the blizzard, struggling his way across the hills; but petulantly again she soon began, "I knew we were going to have a storm—I told him so—but it doesn't matter what I say. Big stubborn fool—he goes his own way anyway. It doesn't matter what becomes of me. In a storm like this he'll never get home. He won't even try. And while he sits keeping his father company I can look after his stable for him, go ploughing through snowdrifts up to my knees—nearly frozen—"

Not that she meant or believed her words. It was just an effort to convince herself that she did have a grievance, to justify her rebellious thoughts, to prove John responsible for her unhappiness. She was young still, eager for excitement and distractions; and John's steadfastness rebuked her vanity, made her complaints seem weak and trivial. Fretfully she went on, "If he'd listen to me sometimes and not be so stubborn we wouldn't be living still in a house like this. Seven years in two rooms—seven years and never a new stick of furniture.... There—as if another coat of paint could make it different anyway."

She cleaned her brush, filled up the stove again, and went back to the window. There was a void white moment that she thought must be frost formed on the window pane; then, like a fitful shadow through the whirling snow, she recognized the stable roof. It was incredible. The sudden, maniac raging of the storm struck from her face all its pettishness. Her eyes glazed with fear a little; her lips blanched. "If he starts for home now," she whispered silently— "But he won't—he knows I'm safe—he knows Steven's coming. Across the hills he would never dare."

She turned to the stove, holding out her hands to the warmth. Around her now there seemed a constant sway and tremor, as if the air were vibrating with the violent shudderings of the walls. She stood quite still, listening. Sometimes the wind struck with sharp, savage blows. Sometimes it bore down in a sustained, minute-long blast, silent with effort and intensity, then with a foiled shriek of threat wheeled away to gather and assault again. Always the eaves-troughs creaked and sawed. She started towards the window again, then detecting the morbid trend of her thoughts, prepared fresh coffee and forced herself to drink a few mouthfuls. "He would never dare," she whispered again. "He wouldn't leave the old man anyway in such a storm. Safe in here—there's nothing for me to keep worrying about. It's after one already. I'll do my baking now, and then it will be time to get supper ready for Steven."

Soon, however, she began to doubt whether Steven would come. In such a storm even a mile was enough to make a man hesitate. Especially Steven, who, for all his attractive qualities, was hardly the one to face a blizzard for the sake of someone else's chores. He had a stable of his own to look after anyway. It would be only natural for him to think that when the storm rose John had turned again for home. Another man would have—would have put his wife first.

But she felt little dread or uneasiness at the prospect of spending the night alone. It was the first time she had been left like this on her own resources, and her reaction, now that she could face and appraise her situation calmly, was gradually to feel it a kind of adventure and responsibility. It stimulated her. Before nightfall she must go to the stable and feed everything. Wrap up in some of John's clothes—take a ball of string in her hand, one end tied to the door, so that no matter how blinding the storm she could at least find her way back to the house. She had heard of people having to do that. It appealed to her now because suddenly it made life dramatic. She had not felt the storm yet, only watched it for a minute through the window.

It took nearly an hour to find enough string, to choose the right socks and sweaters. Long before it was time to start out she tried on John's clothes, changing and rechanging, striding around the room to make sure there would be play enough for pitching hay and struggling over snowdrifts; then she took them off again, and for a while busied herself baking the little cakes with raisins that he liked.

Night came early. Just for a moment on the doorstep she shrank back, uncertain. The slow dimming of the light clutched her with an illogical sense of abandonment. It was like the covert withdrawal of an ally, leaving the alien miles unleashed and unrestrained. Watching the hurricane of writhing snow rage past the little house she forced herself, "They'll never stand the night unless I get them fed. It's nearly dark already, and I've work to last an hour."

Timidly, unwinding a little of the string, she crept out from the shelter of the doorway. A gust of wind spun her forward a few yards, then plunged her headlong against a drift that in the dense white whirl lay invisible across her path. For nearly a minute she huddled still, breathless and dazed. The snow was in her mouth and nostrils, inside her scarf and up her sleeves. As she tried to straighten a smothering scud flung itself against her face, cutting off her breath a second time. The wind struck from all sides, blustering and furious. It was as if the storm had discovered her, as if all its forces were concentrated upon her extinction. Seized with panic suddenly she threshed out a moment with her arms, then stumbled back and sprawled her length across the drift.

But this time she regained her feet quickly, roused by the whip and batter of the storm to retaliative anger. For a moment her impulse was to face the wind and strike back blow for blow; then, as suddenly as it had come, her frantic strength gave way to limpness and exhaustion. Suddenly, a comprehension so clear and terrifying that it struck all thought of the stable from her mind, she realized in such a storm her puny insignificance. And the realization gave her new strength, stilled this time to a desperate persistence. Just for a moment the wind held her, numb and swaying in its vise; then slowly, buckled far forward, she groped her way again towards the house.

Inside, leaning against the door, she stood tense and still a while. It was almost dark now. The top of the stove glowed a deep, dull red. Heedless of the storm, self-absorbed and self-satisfied, the clock ticked on like a glib little idiot. "He shouldn't have gone," she whispered silently. "He saw the double wheel—he knew. He shouldn't have left me here alone."

For so fierce now, so insane and dominant did the blizzard seem, that she could not credit the safety of the house. The warmth and lull around her was not real yet, not to be relied upon. She was still at the mercy of the storm. Only her body pressing hard like this against the door was staving it off. She didn't dare move. She didn't dare ease the ache and strain. "He shouldn't have gone," she repeated, thinking of the stable again, reproached by her helplessness. "They'll freeze in their stalls—and I can't reach them. He'll say it's all my fault. He won't believe I tried."

Then Steven came. Quickly, startled to quietness and control, she let him in and lit the lamp. He stared at her a moment, then flinging off his cap crossed to where she stood by the table and seized her arms. "You're so white—what's wrong? Look at me—" It was like him in such little situations to be masterful. "You should have known better than to go out on a day like this. For a while I thought I wasn't going to make it here myself—"

"I was afraid you wouldn't come—John left early, and there was the stable—"

But the storm had unnerved her, and suddenly at the assurance of his touch and voice the fear that had been gripping her gave way to an hysteria of relief. Scarcely aware of herself she seized his arm and sobbed against it. He remained still a moment, unyielding, then slipped his other arm around her shoulder. It was comforting and she relaxed against it, hushed by a sudden sense of lull and safety. Her shoulders trembled with the easing of the strain, then fell limp and still. "You're shivering," —he drew her gently towards the stove. "There's nothing to be afraid of now, though. I'm going to do the chores for you."

It was a quiet, sympathetic voice, yet with an undertone of

insolence, a kind of mockery even, that made her draw away quickly and busy herself putting in a fire. With his lips drawn in a little smile he watched her till she looked at him again. The smile too was insolent, but at the same time companionable; Steven's smile, and therefore difficult to reprove. It lit up his lean, still-boyish face with a peculiar kind of arrogance: features and smile that were different from John's, from other men's—wilful and derisive, yet naïvely so—as if it were less the difference itself he was conscious of, than the long-accustomed privilege that thereby fell his due. He was erect, tall, square-shouldered. His hair was dark and trim, his young lips curved soft and full. While John, she made the comparison swiftly, was thickset, heavy-jowled, and stooped. He always stood before her helpless, a kind of humility and wonderment in his attitude. And Steven now smiled on her appraisingly with the worldly-wise assurance of one for whom a woman holds neither mystery nor illusion.

"It was good of you to come, Steven," she responded, the words running into a sudden, empty laugh. "Such a storm to face—I suppose I should feel flattered."

For his presumption, his misunderstanding of what had been only a momentary weakness, instead of angering quickened her, roused from latency and long disuse all the instincts and resources of her femininity. She felt eager, challenged. Something was at hand that hitherto had always eluded her, even in the early days with John, something vital, beckoning, meaningful. She didn't understand, but she knew. The texture of the moment was satisfyingly dreamlike: an incredibility perceived as such, yet acquiesced in. She was John's wife—she knew—but also she knew that Steven standing here was different from John. There was no thought or motive, no understanding of herself as the knowledge persisted. Wary and poised round a sudden little core of blind excitement she evaded him, "But it's nearly dark—hadn't you better hurry if you're going to do the chores? Don't trouble—I can get them off myself—"

An hour later when he returned from the stable she was in another dress, hair rearranged, a little flush of colour in her face. Pouring warm water for him from the kettle into the basin she said evenly, "By the time you're washed supper will be ready. John said we weren't to wait for him."

He looked at her a moment, "But in a storm like this you're not expecting John?"

"Of course." As she spoke she could feel the colour deepening in her face. "We're going to play cards. He was the one that suggested it."

He went on washing, and then as they took their places at the table, resumed, "So John's coming. When are you expecting him?"

"He said it might be seven o'clock—or a little later." Conversation with Steven at other times had always been brisk and natural, but now suddenly she found it strained. "He may have work to do for his father. That's what he said when he left. Why do you ask, Steven?"

"I was just wondering—it's a rough night."

"He always comes. There couldn't be a storm bad enough. It's easier to do the chores in daylight, and I knew he'd be tired—that's why I started out for the stable."

She glanced up again and he was smiling at her. The same insolence, the same little twist of mockery and appraisal. It made her flinch suddenly, and ask herself why she was pretending to expect John—why there should be this instinct of defence to force her. This time, instead of poise and excitement, it brought a reminder that she had changed her dress and rearranged her hair. It crushed in a sudden silence, through which she heard the whistling wind again, and the creaking saw of the eaves. Neither spoke now. There was something strange, almost terrifying, about this Steven and his quiet, unrelenting smile; but strangest of all was the familiarity: the Steven she had never seen or encountered, and yet had always known, always expected, always waited for. It was less Steven him-self that she felt than his inevitability. Just as she had felt the snow, the silence and the storm. She kept her eyes lowered, on the window past his shoulder, on the stove, but his smile now seemed to exist apart from him, to merge and hover with the silence. She clinked a cup—listened to the whistle of the storm—always it was there. He began to speak, but her mind missed the meaning of his words. Swiftly she was making comparisons again; his face so different to John's, so handsome and young and clean-shaven. Swiftly, helplessly, feeling the imperceptible and relentless ascendancy that thereby he was gaining over her, sensing sudden menace in this new, more vital life, even as she felt drawn towards it.

The lamp between them flickered as an onslaught of the storm sent shudderings through the room. She rose to build up the fire again and he followed her. For a long time they stood close to the stove, their arms almost touching. Once as the blizzard creaked the house she spun around sharply, fancying it was John at the door; but quietly he intercepted her. "Not tonight—you might as well make up your mind to it. Across the hills in a storm like this—it would be suicide to try."

Her lips trembled suddenly in an effort to answer, to parry the certainty in his voice, then set thin and bloodless. She was afraid now. Afraid of his face so different from John's—of his smile, of her own helplessness to rebuke it. Afraid of the storm, isolating her here alone with him in its impenetrable fastness. They tried to play cards, but she kept starting up at every creak and shiver of the walls. "It's too rough a night," he repeated. "Even for John. Just relax a few minutes—stop worrying and pay a little attention to me."

But in his tone there was a contradiction to his words. For it implied that she was not worrying—that her only concern was lest it really might be John at the door.

And the implication persisted. He filled up the stove for her, shuffled the cards—won—shuffled—still it was there. She tried to respond to his conversation, to think of the game, but helplessly into her cards instead she began to ask, Was he right? Was that why he smiled? Why he seemed to wait, expectant and assured?

The clock ticked, the fire crackled. Always it was there. Furtively for a moment she watched him as he deliberated over his hand. John, even in the days before they were married, had never looked like that. Only this morning she had asked him to shave. Because Steven was coming—because she had been afraid to see them side by side—because deep within herself she had known even then. The same knowledge, furtive and forbidden, that was flaunted now in Steven's smile. "You look cold," he said at last, dropping his cards and rising from the table. "We're not playing, anyway. Come over to the stove for a few minutes and get warm."

"But first I think we'll hang blankets over the door. When there's a blizzard like this we always do." It seemed that in sane, commonplace activity there might be release, a moment or two in which to recover herself. "John has nails in to put them on. They keep out a little of the draft."

He stood on a chair for her, and hung the blankets that she carried from the bedroom. Then for a moment they stood silent, watching the blankets sway and tremble before the blade of wind that spurted around the jamb. "I forgot," she said at last, "that I painted the bedroom door. At the top there, see—I've smeared the blankets coming through."

He glanced at her curiously, and went back to the stove. She followed him, trying to imagine the hills in such a storm, wondering whether John would come. "A man couldn't live in it," suddenly he answered her thoughts, lowering the oven door and drawing up their chairs one on each side of it. "He knows you're safe. It isn't likely that he'd leave his father, anyway."

"The wind will be in his back," she persisted. "The winter before we were married—all the blizzards that we had that year—and he never missed—"

"Blizzards like this one? Up in the hills he wouldn't be able to keep his direction for a hundred yards. Listen to it a minute and ask yourself."

His voice seemed softer, kindlier now. She met his smile a moment, its assured little twist of appraisal, then for a long time sat silent, tense, careful again to avoid his eyes.

Everything now seemed to depend on this. It was the same as a few hours ago when she braced the door against the storm. He was watching her, smiling. She dared not move, unclench her hands, or raise her eyes. The flames crackled, the clock ticked. The storm wrenched the walls as if to make them buckle in. So rigid and desperate were all her muscles set, withstanding, that the room around her seemed to swim and reel. So rigid and strained that for relief at last, despite herself, she raised her head and met his eyes again.

Intending that it should be for only an instant, just to breathe again, to ease the tension that had grown unbearable—but in his smile now, instead of the insolent appraisal that she feared, there seemed a kind of warmth and sympathy. An understanding that quickened and encouraged her—that made her wonder why but a moment ago she had been afraid. It was as if the storm had lulled, as if she had suddenly found calm and shelter.

Or perhaps, the thought seized her, perhaps instead of his smile it was she that had changed. She who, in the long, wind-creaked silence, had emerged from the increment of codes and loyalties to her real, unfettered self. She who now felt suddenly an air of appraisal as nothing more than an understanding of the unfulfilled woman that until this moment had lain within her brooding and unadmitted, reproved out of consciousness by the insistence of an outgrown, routine fidelity.

For there had always been Steven. She understood now. Seven years—almost as long as John—ever since the night they first danced together.

The lamp was burning dry, and through the dimming light, isolated in the fastness of silence and storm, they watched each other. Her face was white and struggling still. His was handsome, clean-shaven, young. Her eyes were fanatic, believing desperately, fixed upon him as if to exclude all else, as if to find justification. His were cool, bland, drooped a little with expectancy. The light kept dimming, gathering the shadows round them, hushed, conspiratorial. He was smiling still. Her hands again were clenched up white and hard.

"But he always came," she persisted. "The wildest, coldest nights—even such a night as this. There was never a storm—"

"Never a storm like this one." There was a quietness in his smile now, a kind of simplicity almost, as if to reassure her. "You were out in it yourself for a few minutes. He would have five miles, across the hills.... I'd think twice myself, on such a night, before risking even one."

Long after he was asleep she lay listening to the storm. As a check on the draft up the chimney they had left one of the stovelids partly off, and through the open bedroom door she could see the flickerings of flame and shadow on the kitchen wall. They leaped and sank fantastically. The longer she watched the more alive they seemed to be. There was one great shadow that struggled towards her threateningly, massive and black and engulfing all the room. Again and again it advanced, about to spring, but each time a little whip of light subdued it to its place among the others on the wall.

Yet though it never reached her still she cowered, feeling that gathered there was all the frozen wilderness, its heart of terror and invincibility.

Then she dozed a while, and the shadow was John. Interminably he advanced. The whips of light still flicked and coiled, but now suddenly they were the swift little snakes that this afternoon she had watched twist and shiver across the snow. And they too were advancing. They writhed and vanished and came again. She lay still, paralysed. He was over her now, so close that she could have touched him. Already it seemed that a deadly tightening hand was on her throat. She tried to scream but her lips were locked. Steven beside her slept on heedlessly.

Until suddenly as she lay staring up at him a gleam of light revealed his face. And in it was not a trace of threat or anger—only calm, and stonelike hopelessness.

That was like John. He began to withdraw, and frantically she tried to call him back. "It isn't true—not really true—listen, John—" but the words clung frozen to her lips. Already there was only the shriek of wind again, the sawing eaves, the leap and twist of shadow on the wall.

She sat up, startled now and awake. And so real had he seemed there, standing close to her, so vivid the sudden age and sorrow in his face, that at first she could not make herself understand she had been only dreaming. Against the conviction of his presence in the room it was necessary to insist over and over that he must still be with his father on the other side of the hills. Watching the shadows she had fallen asleep. It was only her mind, her imagination, distorted to a nightmare by the illogical and unadmitted dread of his return. But he wouldn't come. Steven was right. In such a storm he would never try. They were safe, alone. No one would ever know. It was only fear, morbid and irrational; only the sense of guilt that even her new-found and challenged womanhood could not entirely quell.

She knew now. She had not let herself understand or acknowledge it as guilt before, but gradually through the wind-torn silence of the night his face compelled her. The face that had watched her from the darkness with its stonelike sorrow—the face that was really John—John more than his features of mere flesh and bone could ever be.

She wept silently. The fitful gleam of light began to sink. On the ceiling and wall at last there was only a faint dull flickering glow. The little house shuddered and quailed, and a chill crept in again. Without wakening Steven she slipped out to build up the fire. It was burned to a few spent embers now, and the wood she put on seemed a long time catching light. The wind swirled through the blankets they had hung around the door, and struck her flesh like laps of molten ice. Then hollow and moaning it roared up the chimney again, as if against its will drawn back to serve still longer with the onrush of the storm.

For a long time she crouched over the stove, listening. Earlier in the evening, with the lamp lit and the fire crackling, the house had seemed a stand against the wilderness, against its frozen, blizzard-breathed implacability, a refuge of feeble walls wherein persisted the elements of human meaning and survival. Now, in the cold, creaking darkness, it was strangely extinct, looted by the storm and abandoned again. She lifted the stove lid and fanned the embers till at last a swift little tongue of flame began to lick around the wood. Then she replaced the lid, extended her hands, and as if frozen in that attitude stood waiting.

It was not long now. After a few minutes she closed the drafts, and as the flames whirled back upon each other, beating against the top of the stove and sending out flickers of light again, a warmth surged up to relax her stiffened limbs. But shivering and numb it had been easier. The bodily well-being that the warmth induced gave play again to an ever more insistent mental suffering. She remembered the shadow that was John. She saw him bent towards her, then retreating, his features pale and overcast with unaccusing grief. She re-lived their seven years together and, in retrospect, found them to be years of worth and dignity. Until crushed by it all at last, seized by a sudden need to suffer and atone, she crossed to where the draft was bitter, and for a long time stood unflinching on the icy floor.

The storm was close here. Even through the blankets she could feel a sift of snow against her face. The eaves sawed, the walls creaked. Above it all, like a wolf in howling flight, the wind shrilled lone and desolate.

And yet, suddenly she asked herself, hadn't there been other storms, other blizzards? And through the worst of them hadn't he always reached her?

Clutched by the thought she stood rooted a minute. It was hard now to understand how she could have so deceived herself—how a moment of passion could have quieted within her not only conscience, but reason and discretion too. John always came. There could never be a storm to stop him. He was strong, inured to the cold. He had crossed the hills since his boyhood, knew every creek-bed and gully. It was madness to go on like this—to wait. While there was still time she must waken Steven, and hurry him away.

But in the bedroom again, standing at Steven's side, she hesitated. In his detachment from it all, in his quiet, even breathing, there was such sanity, such realism. For him nothing had happened; nothing would. If she wakened him he would only laugh and tell her to listen to the storm. Already it was long past midnight, either John had lost his way or not set out at all. And she knew that in his devotion there was nothing foolhardy. He would never risk a storm beyond his endurance, never permit himself a sacrifice likely to endanger her lot or future. They were both safe. No one would ever know. She must control herself—be sane like Steven.

For comfort she let her hand rest a while on Steven's shoulder. It would be easier were he awake now, with her, sharing her guilt; but gradually as she watched his handsome face in the glimmering light she came to understand that for him no guilt existed. Just as there had been no passion, no conflict. Nothing but the sane appraisal of their situation, nothing but the expectant little smile, and the arrogance of features that were different from John's. She winced deeply, remembering how she had fixed her eyes on those features, how she had tried to believe that so handsome and young, so different from John's, they must in themselves be her justification.

In the flickering light they were still young, still handsome. No longer her justification—she knew now—John was the man—but wistfully still, wondering sharply at their power and tyranny, she touched them a moment with her fingertips again.

She could not blame him. There had been no passion, no guilt; therefore there could be no responsibility. Suddenly looking down at him as he slept, half-smiling still, his lips relaxed in the conscienceless complacency of his achievement, she understood that thus he was revealed in his entirety—all there ever was or ever could be. John was the man. With him lay all the future. For tonight, slowly and contritely through the day and years to come, she would try to make amends.

Then she stole back to the kitchen, and without thought, impelled by overwhelming need again, returned to the door where the draft was bitter still. Gradually towards morning the storm began to spend itself. Its terror blast became a feeble, wornout moan. The leap of light and shadow sank, and a chill crept in again. Always the eaves creaked, tortured with wordless prophecy. Heedless of it all the clock ticked on in idiot content.

They found him the next day, less than a mile from home. Drifting with the storm he had run against his own pasture fence and overcome had frozen there, erect still, both hands clasping fast the wire.

"He was south of here," they said wonderingly when she told them how he had come across the hills. "Straight south—you'd wonder how he could have missed the buildings. It was the wind last night, coming every way at once. He shouldn't have tried. There was a double wheel around the moon."

She looked past them a moment, then as if to herself said simply, "If you knew him, though—John would try."

It was later, when they had left her a while to be alone with him, that she knelt and touched his hand. Her eyes dimmed, still it was such a strong and patient hand; then, transfixed, they suddenly grew wide and clear. On the palm, white even against its frozen whiteness, was a little smear of paint.

Thomas King

Totem

"We need the space for our other shows, and we can't have it singing all the time, either."

Beebe Hill stood at the reception desk of the Southwest Alberta Art Gallery and Prairie Museum and drummed her fingers on the counter until Walter Hooton came out of the director's office. She was annoyed, she told Walter, and she thought other people were annoyed, too, but were too polite to complain about the noises the totem pole in the far corner of the room was making.

"It sounds like gargling."

Walter assured her that there wasn't a totem pole in the entire place including the basement and the storage room. The current show, he explained, featured contemporary Canadian art from the Atlantic provinces.

"It's called 'Seaviews'," Walter said, smiling with all his teeth showing. There had been, he admitted, a show on Northwest Coast carving at the gallery some nine years back, and, as he recalled, there might have been a totem pole in that exhibit.

Mrs. Hill, who was fifty-eight and quite used to men who smiled with all their teeth showing, took his hand and walked him to the back of the gallery. "Gargling," said Beebe. "It sounds like gargling."

Mrs. Hill and Mr. Hooton stood and looked at the corner for a very long time. "Well," said the director finally, "it certainly *looks* like a totem pole. But it doesn't sound at all like gargling. It sounds more like chuckling."

Mrs. Hill snorted and tossed her head over her shoulder. And what, she wanted to know, would a totem pole have to chuckle about. "In any case," said Mrs. Hill, "it is quite annoying, and I think the museum should do something about the problem." It would be a fine world, she pointed out, if paintings or photographs or abstract sculptures began carrying on like that.

Walter Hooton spent much of the afternoon going over the museum's records in an attempt to find out who owned the totem pole or where it had come from. At four o'clock, he gave up and called Larue Denny in the storeroom and asked him to grab Jimmy and a hand cart and meet him in the gallery.

"The problem," Walter explained to the two men, "is that this totem pole is not part of the show, and we need to move it someplace else."

"Where do you want us to take it," Larue wanted to know. "Storeroom is full."

"Find some temporary place, I suppose. I'm sure it's all a mistake, and when the secretary comes back on Monday, we'll have the whole thing straightened out."

"What's that sound?" asked Larue.

"We're not sure," said the director.

"Kinda loud," said Jimmy.

"Yes, it was bothering some of the patrons."

"Sort of like laughing," said Larue. "What do you think, Jimmy?"

Jimmy put his ear against the totem pole and listened. "It's sort of like a chant. Maybe it's Druidic."

"Druidic!"

"There was this movie about Druids on a flight from England to New York ... they did a lot of chanting ... the Druids ..."

Larue told Jimmy to tip the totem pole back so they could get the dolly under the base. But the totem pole didn't move. "Hey," he said, "it's stuck."

Larue pushed on the front, and Jimmy pulled on the top, and nothing happened. "It's really stuck."

Walter got on his hands and knees and looked at the bottom. Then he took his glasses out of their case and put them on. "It appears," he said, "that it goes right through the floor."

Both Larue and Jimmy got down with the director. Larue shook his head. "It doesn't make any sense," he said, "because the floor's concrete. I was here when they built this building, and I don't remember them pouring the floor around a totem pole."

"We could get the chainsaw and cut it off close to the floor," Jimmy volunteered.

"Well, we can't have it making noises in the middle of a show on seascapes," said Walter. "Do what you have to do, but do it quietly."

After the gallery closed for the evening, Larue and Jimmy took the chainsaw out of its case and put on their safety goggles. Larue held the totem pole and Jimmy cut through the base, the chain screaming, the wood chips flying all around the gallery. Some of the larger chips bounced off the paintings and left small dents in the swirling waves and the glistening rocks and the seabirds floating on the wind. Then they loaded the totem pole on a dolly and put it in the basement near the boiler.

"Listen to that," said Jimmy, knocking the sawdust off his pants. "It's still making that noise."

When Walter arrived at the gallery on Monday morning, the secretary was waiting for him. "We have a problem, Mr. Hooton," she said. "There is a totem pole in the corner, and it's grunting."

"Damn!" said Hooton, and he called Larue and Jimmy.

"You're right," said Larue, after he and Jimmy had looked at the totem pole. "It does sound like grunting. Doesn't sound a thing like the other one. What do you want us to do with this one?"

"Get rid of it," said Walter. "And watch the paintings this time."

Larue and Jimmy got the chainsaw and the safety goggles and the dolly, and moved the totem pole into the basement alongside the first one.

"That wasn't hard," said the director.

"Those grunts were pretty disgusting," said the secretary.

"Yes, they were," agreed Walter.

After lunch, the totem pole in the corner of the gallery started shouting, loud, explosive shouts that echoed through the collection of sea scenes and made the paintings on the wall tremble ever so slightly. When Walter returned, the secretary was sitting at her desk with her hands over her ears.

"My God!" said Walter. "How did this happen?"

That evening, Walter and Larue and Jimmy sat in Walter's office and talked about the problem. "The trick I think," said Larue, "is to cut the pole down and then cover the stump with pruning paste. That way it won't grow back."

"What about the shouting?"

"Well, you can't hear it much from the basement."

"Alright," said Walter. "We'll give that a try. How many poles are in storage?"

"Three with this one, and we haven't got room for any more."

The next day, the totem pole in the corner was singing. It started with a high, wailing, nasal sound and then fell back into a patient, rhythmic drone that gave Walter a huge headache just above his eyes and made him sweat.

"This is getting to be a real problem," he told Larue and Jimmy. "If we can't solve it, we may have to get some government assistance."

"Provincial?"

"It could be more serious than that," said Walter.

"Maybe we should just leave it," said Jimmy.

"We can't just leave it there," said the director. "We need the space for our other shows, and we can't have it singing all the time, either."

"Maybe if we ignore it, it will stop singing," said Jimmy. "It might even go away or disappear or something. Besides, we don't have any place to put it. Maybe, after a while, you wouldn't even notice it ... like living next to the train tracks or by a highway."

"Sure," said Larue, who was tired of cutting down totem poles and trying to find space for them. "Couldn't hurt to give that a try."

The totem pole stayed in the corner, but Jimmy and Larue were right. After the first week, the singing didn't bother Walter nearly as much, and, by the end of the month, he hardly noticed it at all.

Nonetheless, Walter remained mildly annoyed that the totem pole continued to take up space and inexplicably irritated by the low, measured pulse that rose out of the basement and settled like fine dust on the floor.

Margaret Atwood

Bread

How long does it take to decide?

Imagine a piece of bread. You don't have to imagine it, it's right here in the kitchen, on the bread board, in its plasti bag, lying beside the bread knife. The bread knife is an old one you picked up at an auction; it has the word BREAD carved into the wooden handle. You open the bag, pull back the wrapper, cut yourself a slice. You put butter on it, then peanut butter, then honey, and you fold it over. Some of the honey runs out onto your fingers and you lick it off. It takes you about a minute to eat the bread. This bread happens to be brown, but there is also white bread, in the refrigerator, and a heel of rye you got last week, round as a full stomach then, now going mouldy. Occasionally you make bread. You think of it as something relaxing to do with your hands.

Imagine a famine. Now imagine a piece of bread. Both of these things are real but you happen to be in the same room with only one of them. Put yourself into a different room, that's what the mind is for. You are now lying on a thin mattress in a hot room. The walls are made of dried earth and your sister, who is younger than you are, is in the room with you. She is starving, her belly is bloated, flies land on her eyes; you brush them off with your han You have a cloth too, filthy but damp, and you press it to her lips and forehead. The piece of bread is the bread you've been saving, for days it seems. You are as hungry as she is, but not yet as weak How long does this take? When will someone come with more bread? You think of going out to see if you might find something that could be eaten, but outside the streets are infested with scavengers and the stink of corpses is everywhere.

Should you share the bread or give the whole piece to your sister? Should you eat the piece of bread yourself? After all, you have a better chance of living, you're stronger. How long does it take to decide?

Imagine a prison. There is something you know that you have not yet told. Those in control of the prison know that you know. So do those not in control. If you tell, thirty or forty or a hundred of your friends, your comrades, will be caught and will die. If you refuse to tell, tonight will be like last night. They always choose the night. You don't think about the night however, but about the piece of bread they offered you. How long does it take? The piece of bread was brown and fresh and reminded you of sunlight falling across a wooden floor. It reminded you of a bowl, a yellow bowl that was once in your home. It held apples and pears; it stood on a table you can also remember. It's not the hunger or the pain that is killing you but the absence of the yellow bowl. If you could only hold the bowl in your hands, right here, you could withstand anything, you tell yourself. The bread they offered you is subversive, it's treacherous, it does not mean life.

There were once two sisters. One was rich and had no children, the other had five children and was a widow, so poor that she no longer had any food left. She went to her sister and asked her for a mouthful of bread. "My children are dying," she said. The rich sister said, "I do not have enough for myself," and drove her away from the door. Then the husband of the rich sister came home and wanted to cut himself a piece of bread; but when he made the first cut, out flowed red blood.

Everyone knew what that meant.

This is a traditional German fairy-tale.

The loaf of bread I have conjured for you floats about a foot above your kitchen table. The table is normal, there are no trap doors in it. A blue towel floats beneath the bread, and there are no strings attaching the cloth to the bread or the bread to the ceiling or the table to the cloth, you've proved it by passing your hand above and below. You didn't touch the bread though. What stopped you?

You don't want to know whether the bread is real or whether it's just a hallucination I've somehow duped you into seeing. There's no doubt that you can see the bread, you can even smell it, it smells like yeast, and it looks solid enough, solid as your own arm. But can you trust it? Can you eat it? You don't want to know, imagine that.

Jamaica Kincaid

What I Have Been Doing Lately

I turned around to see what I had left behind me but nothing was familiar.

What I have been doing lately: I was lying in bed and the doorbell rang. I ran downstairs. Quick. I opened the door. There was no one there. I stepped outside. Either it was drizzling or there was a lot of dust in the air and the dust was damp. I stuck out my tongue and the drizzle or the damp dust tasted like government school ink. I looked north. I looked south. I decided to start walking north. While walking north, I noticed that I was barefoot. While walking north, I looked up and saw the planet Venus. I said, "It must be almost morning." I saw a monkey in a tree. The tree had no leaves. I said, "Ah, a monkey. Just look at that. A monkey." I walked for I don't know how long before I came up to a big body of water. I wanted to get across it but I couldn't swim. I wanted to get across it but it would take me years to build a boat. I wanted to get across it but it would take me I didn't know how long to build a bridge. Years passed and then one day, feeling like it, I got into my boat and rowed across. When I got to the other side, it was noon and my shadow was small and fell beneath me. I set out on a path that stretched out straight ahead. I passed a house, and a dog was sitting on the verandah but it looked the other way when it saw me coming. I passed a boy tossing a ball in the air but the boy looked the other way when he saw me coming. I walked and I walked but I couldn't tell if I walked a long time because my feet didn't feel as if they would drop off. I turned around to see what I had left behind me but nothing was familiar. Instead of the straight path, I saw hills. Instead of the boy with his ball, I saw tall flowering trees. I looked up and the sky was without clouds and seemed near, as if it were the ceiling in my house and, if I stood on a chair, I could touch it with the tips of my fingers. I turned around and looked ahead of me again. A deep hole had opened up before me. I looked in. The hole was deep and dark and I couldn't see the bottom. I thought, What's down there?, so on purpose I fell in. I fell and I fell, over and over, as if I were an old suitcase. On the sides of the deep hole I could see things written, but perhaps it was in a foreign language because I couldn't read them. Still I fell, for I don't know how long. As I fell I began to see that I didn't like the way falling made me feel. Falling made me feel sick and I missed all the people I had loved. I said, I don't want to fall anymore, and I reversed myself. I was standing again on the edge of the deep hole. I looked at the deep hole and I said, You can close up now, and it did. I walked some more without knowing distance. I only knew that I passed through days and nights, I only knew that I passed through rain and shine, light and darkness. I was never thirsty and I felt no pain. Looking at the horizon, I made a joke for myself: I said, "The earth has thin lips," and I laughed.

Looking at the horizon again, I saw a lone figure coming toward me, but I wasn't frightened because I was sure it was my mother. As I got closer to the figure, I could see that it wasn't my mother, but still I wasn't frightened because I could see that it was a woman.

When this woman got closer to me, she looked at me hard and then she threw up her hands. She must have seen me somewhere before because she said, "It's you. Just look at that. It's you. And just what have you been doing lately?"

I could have said, "I have been praying not to grow any taller."

I could have said, "I have been listening carefully to my mother's words, so as to make a good imitation of a dutiful daughter."

I could have said, "A pack of dogs, tired from chasing each other all over town, slept in the moonlight."

Instead, I said, What I have been doing lately: I was lying in bed on my back, my hands drawn up, my fingers interlaced lightly at the nape of my neck. Someone rang the doorbell. I went downstairs and opened the door but there was no one there. I stepped outside. Either it was drizzling or there was a lot of dust in the air and the dust was damp. I stuck out my tongue and the drizzle or the damp dust tasted like government school ink. I looked north and I looked south. I started walking north. While walking north, I wanted to move fast, so I removed the shoes from my feet. While walking north, I looked up and saw the planet Venus and I said, "If the sun went out, it would be eight minutes before I would know it." I saw a monkey sitting in a tree that had no leaves and I said, "A monkey. Just look at that. A monkey." I picked up a stone and threw it at the monkey. The monkey, seeing the stone, quickly moved out of its way. Three times I threw a stone at the monkey and three times it moved away. The fourth time I threw the stone, the monkey caught it and threw it back at me. The stone struck me on my forehead over my right eye, making a deep gash. The gash healed immediately but now the skin on my forehead felt false to me. I walked for I don't know how long before I came to a big body of water. I wanted to get across, so when the boat came I paid my fare. When I got to the other side, I saw a lot of people sitting on the beach and they were having a picnic. They were the most beautiful people I had ever seen. Everything about them was black and shiny. Their skin was black and shiny. Their shoes were black and shiny. Their hair was black and shiny. The clothes they wore were black and shiny. I could hear them laughing and chatting and I said, I would like to be with these people, so I started to walk toward them, but when I got up close to them I saw that they weren't at a picnic and they weren't beautiful and they weren't chatting and laughing. All around me was black mud and the people all looked as if they had been made up out of the black mud. I looked up and saw that the sky seemed far away and nothing I could stand on would make me able to touch it with my fingertips. I thought, If only I could get out of this, so I started to walk. I must have walked for a long time because my feet hurt and felt as if they would drop off. I thought, If only just around the bend I would see my house and inside my house I would find my bed, freshly made at that, and in the kitchen I would find my mother or anyone else that I loved making me a custard. I thought, If only it was a Sunday and I was sitting in a church and I had just heard someone sing a psalm. I felt very sad so I sat down. I felt so sad that I rested my head on my own knees and smoothed my own head. I felt so sad I couldn't imagine feeling any other way again. I said, I don't like this. I don't want to do this anymore. And I went back to lying in bed, just before the doorbell rang.

Gangadhar Gadgil

The Dog That Ran in Circles

Mute shapes that paused on the brink of life and meaning! Suddenly they would acquire bold outlines.

I was walking lazily towards the bus-stop. I had to go somewhere, oh—anywhere. I was feeling so restless and so depressed, I knew I had to write a story. So I was walking to enjoy the restful pause at the end of each step. "I want to write a story ... a story ... a s-t-o-r-y...." I was saying to myself mechanically, over and over again. "A story ... a s-t-o-r-y."

The word became bloated and shapeless. It stared at me and drove my consciousness into a stupid daze. Deeper down, in the half asleep wakefulness something was astir. Meandering circles were being traced with a weak insistence. They were dully luminous. Caught in the tangled web of the circles would appear a shape like a mark left by a faded flower in a book. Mute shapes that paused on the brink of life and meaning! Suddenly they would acquire bold outlines. But before they could mean anything to me, they would become spreading blots of ink, shapeless and dead. I stared at them, hoping to see through them. But they gave away nothing....

I was utterly engrossed in this tantalizing search—lost in a dark brown cloud of concentration tinged by fleeting moods and fancies. I wanted to see nothing, hear nothing. I reached the bus-stop and stood there staring blankly at the street.

I was seeing a shape, although I did not in the least want to see it. It was out there in the street. A brownish shape—a dog, faded and limp, lying in the street. I couldn't take my eyes off its starved and heaving belly. It heaved in quick spasms, as if it wanted to get the whole thing over and done with. The dog lay still in the midst of the endless scribble of traffic and movement on the street. Possibly it had bumped against a passing car and had fainted.

A crowd had gathered on the sidewalk. It was swelling and imperceptibly edging forward over the curb into the street. Vagrant boys, hoodlums gambling at the street corner, old women stooping and shrivelled, hawkers and labourers! The white collared gentry stood at the bus-stop, stiff and indifferent, giving the dog now and then an anaesthetized look. They wouldn't stoop to anything as plebian as a mouthful of pity or a squirt of casual curiosity.

The crowd stood there, hesitant and slightly ashamed of its concern over a street-dog. Yet, they all felt relieved as each car swerved to avoid running over the dog. Unwittingly, they started signalling to the cars that came along.

One of the old women started muttering. She looked around to gauge the attitude of the crowd and then raised her voice.

"You there! You brat! Go and get a pot of water. Pour it on the dog's head, will you?" she said, and shoved a boy in the direction of a restaurant.

"Well auntie! That's a good idea. But why don't you do it yourself?" said a man who stood behind her.

Everybody laughed, and the interest in the dog became more lively. A couple of boys ran forward. A thin straggling line of people followed them hesitantly. Soon the whole crowd was standing on the street around the dog.

I couldn't quite see what was happening. The boy whom the old woman had shoved ran to the restaurant and came back with a pot of water. The whole crowd leaned forward. Those at the back stood on their toes. The people watching through their windows leaned out and craned their necks. "Hey!" everybody cheered happily. The crowd made way and the dog emerged, still dazed, but now on its feet. It staggered towards the curb. The crowd followed it.

It was a starving, shrivelled dog. It had a pitifully meek expression—the kind of dog that gets in everybody's way and is always kicked. But for its eyes, I wouldn't have looked at it twice.

The eyes were moist in a queer way. It wasn't the kind of moistness that calls forth pity, but different. The eyes asked for nothing. In fact, nothing had any meaning for them any more. They expressed no hunger, no fear. They had nothing to do any longer with the world of dogs. If they expressed anything at all, it was compassion—the kind one sees in the eyes of a saint. But this of course was my crazy fancy.

The queer moist look in the eyes made me uneasy. I had a feeling that apart from the people, the vehicles and the shops with their gaudy makeup, there was something else present there, something more substantial and compelling. It was right there in front of me, and those eyes were seeing it.

Mechanically, the dog sniffed at the ground and at people's feet. It wagged its tail and licked its nose. It settled down near the curb, resting its head on its paws.

The crowd still stood around and looked at it with pity. People walking along the sidewalk stopped and asked eagerly what the matter was? Most of the time they didn't get any reply, and if they got one it said nothing. Many in the crowd had come there too late to know what had happened, and even those who had seen everything had nothing to tell. Nothing really had happened.

But there was one in the crowd who had seen everything and, whenever asked, he would look straight ahead with a very solemn face and narrate everything in tedious detail. His listeners would look puzzled, for what he said didn't lead to anything at all. They would conclude that it was all a silly fuss about nothing. Some of them walked away. But others stood there because of the crowd, and looked at the dog with an affectation of sickening pity.

I was losing interest in the whole affair. It seemed to be one of those incidents that holds a promise and then hangs in the air inconclusively, like the loose end of a thread. I tried to think of the story I wanted to write.

But, by now, everything was tangled and adrift. I had lost track of everything that had so tantalizingly remained beyond my reach. All I could think of was that silly incident. It had left a scratch across my consciousness—a scratch that hurt but didn't bleed.

"I want to write a story … a story … a s-t-o-r-y.…" I said to myself, and the words soothingly ran over and around the scratch, like a massaging fingertip. Slowly, I got back into that state of daze. Wandering circles began to be traced again—circles potent with the insubstantial presence of a shape, a form. It was there all the time, not caring to be seen.

Wandering circles—dully luminous!

All of a sudden the dog stood up and started running in circles, tottering and slipping all the time. At first it moved in little circles, in a corner of the street. But, gradually, the circles grew bigger and crazier.

There was a stir in the crowd. Everybody perked up and looked intently at the dog. "Ch-ch!" "Sit down in a corner, you crazy dog …!"

The old auntie darted forward and tried to catch hold of the dog. That little push threw the dog off its balance and it yelped.

"There, auntie! Don't you get mixed up with that dog. It seems to be loony. It might bite you."

"Oh woman! Oh!" cried the auntie, and jumped back to the sidewalk with unsuspected agility. She barely missed having a fall and everybody laughed. The crowd decided to stay away from the dog and shuffled back a couple of steps.

The dog ran in crazy circles seeing nothing with its queer moist eyes. It was now right in the centre of the street. Horns were honking, brakes were screeching and cars were turning and swerving madly to avoid running over the dog.

Sometimes the dog ran in big circles, as wide as the street. Then suddenly, it would trace a ridiculously small circle at the edge of the big one, and achieve a precarious and impossible balance between the two. Sometimes its path had a beautiful oblong shape that contrasted oddly with its ridiculous figure. At times the path wobbled like a reflection in the disturbed water of a pool.

"Stop it! Stop it!" "Come here you crazy dog. You will get killed." "I wish it would get run over so everything was finished." The people in the crowd gesticulated and talked wildly.

But the dog saw nothing, heard nothing. It wasn't bothered about getting killed. It was possessed, held in thrall and driven by some mysterious impulse that sought this odd fulfilment.

People at the wheels of cars expected the dog to behave normally and get out of the way, when they honked their horns. But the dog wouldn't budge and the cars veered at crazy angles, barely missing the dog. It almost seemed to have a charmed life.

The crowd watched tensely in terror. They knew the dog would be run over sooner or later and, in a way, they were resigned to it. Yet they were signalling wildly to the cars, and bursting into happy hysterical laughter whenever the dog had a particularly narrow escape. They were somehow deeply involved in the absurd drama of the street.

"Hey there! Somebody buy a biscuit and offer it to the dog. Tie him up with a piece of string!" the old auntie cried, unable to stand the tension any more.

"Very well, auntie! Give me a couple of coins. I will buy a biscuit for the dog," said a man in the crowd, grinning slyly.

Dear old auntie laughed, opening wide her toothless hole of a mouth. It was a cunning laugh, and yet innocent. Everybody laughed. But the strain was getting unbearable. So somebody bought a few biscuits and offered them to the dog. The dog wagged its tail and licked its nose mechanically. But it didn't stop. It was tired and staggering at every step. Yet it went on.

Nothing could be done for that dog. It wanted no kindness and no help. So all we could do was to play the uncomfortable role of spectators. Everybody felt very foolish about it.

"Shoot the bloody dog! Kill it!" screamed a man in English. He had been sucking at his pipe and reading a paper, trying to affect the indifference of an Englishman.

A woman on the upper storey of a house was leaning out of the window and watching. She would press her head in her palms and grimace in pain when the dog seemed to be going under the wheels of a car. When it escaped, she would scream with joy. She was gesticulating wildly and calling everybody in the house to the window to watch the fun. The lipstick on her lips made her look even more queer and frightening.

People in the crowd were all talking at the same time. "The municipal staff must have poisoned the dog," they were saying, which of course was not true. But the crowd wanted to get mad at somebody.

The dog was certainly being protected by some invisible deity. It escaped death for more than ten minutes on that busy street. The absurd drama continued in the midst of a high voltage circuit of tension and jitters.

Then came a double-decker bus—a huge, brash, red box on wheels. The driver was perched high, sealed in a glass cabin. He was sitting very erect, as if he had a steel rod for a spine. He was wearing outsized sun-glasses that covered half his face and made it look like a fiendish mask.

The dog staggered on unconcerned and in a moment was right in front of the bus. The crowd screamed. The driver jammed the brakes on with an awkward jerk. But the bus kept rolling on. I saw the dog going under a wheel. I closed my eyes and waited for an infinitesimal fraction of time to hear the final yelp. It was a very weak yelp, conveying no pain and no reluctance to die. It was just a motor response of the body.

The woman at the window crushed her head in her palms and screamed. She then burst into an idiotic laughter. Because of the lipstick, it looked as if her lips were smeared with blood.

There were screams all around. The huge, red bus hesitated for a moment on its ponderous wheels, and then moved on with a jerk that was very much like an indifferent shrug. It moved on inexorably in a straight line, gathering momentum amidst the rising roar of its engine.

The dog lay on its side with all its legs outstretched. Blood was trickling from a corner of its mouth.

A few people gathered around the corpse. But they had already lost interest. The rest of the crowd walked away in a hurry, brushing the whole incident off their minds with little impatient gestures.

"I want to write a story … a story … a s-t-o-r-y.…" I said stupidly to myself.

Then a bus came in all its mechanical dignity. I had been almost praying all this time that it should come and take me away before the dog met its inevitable end. It swallowed up the waiting queue in which I stood, and then moved on.

translated from Marathi by the author

Glossary

allusion

An allusion is a brief, direct or indirect reference to a person, place, or event from history, literature, or mythology which the author hopes or assumes the reader will recognize. Most allusions expand on or develop a significant idea, impression, or mood in the story.

In "Horses of the Night," the quotation from Ovid at the end of the story not only refers, ironically, to Duchess and Firefly, but also illuminates Chris' romantic and tormented character. The epigraph in "Foxes" ("The face is only the thing to write.") introduces to the reader both the nature of and the solution to Morris Glendenning's conflict. (*See also* page 295 for the author's comments about the allusion.)

antagonist

The antagonist is the major character or force that opposes the protagonist.

In "The Shining Houses," Mary's and Mrs. Fullerton's neighbors are the antagonists who oppose Mrs. Fullerton's presence and "untidiness" in the midst of their new community.

antecedent action

This is the significant action that takes place before the story begins. *See also* rising action.

In "Just Lather, That's All," a rebellion has put the Captain and the barber on opposite sides, while in "The Harness," the death of Art's wife has left Art with the full responsibility for raising their son, David.

anticlimax

An anticlimax is a sudden shift from a relatively serious or elevated mood to one more comic or trivial. *See also* climax.

The anticlimax in "The Destructors" occurs when the lorry driver cannot help laughing about the collapse of Old Misery's house.

antihero

An antihero is a protagonist who has none of the qualities normally expected of a hero. The term also refers to a person who is a humorous take-off of the traditional hero. The characters played by Woody Allen in his films are examples of antiheroes. The reader or viewer usually feels superior to such characters, likable though they may be. *See also* hero.

James in "The Liar" is an antihero as he is a compulsive liar who cannot help telling entertaining stories that draw attention to himself.

atmosphere (or mood)

The atmosphere or mood is the prevailing feeling created by the story. Atmosphere usually sets up expectations in the reader about the outcome of an episode or plot. It is created by descriptive diction, imagery, and sometimes dialogue. Some teachers and critics may distinguish between the two terms by referring to the "atmosphere of a story" and the "mood created in the reader."

In "The Masque of the Red Death," Edgar Allan Poe creates both a bizarre atmosphere and a sense of doom through his use of color symbolism.

character

This term refers to both a fictional person in a story, and the moral, dispositional, and behavioral qualities of that fictional person. The qualities of a character are generally revealed through dialogue, action, and description. Characters themselves may be classified as: flat or round, stereotyped or realistic, static or dynamic. Each classification is described below. *See also* foil.

Classifications of Character

- A limited, usually minor character with only one apparent quality is a **flat character**. A **round character** is a realistic character with several dimensions.

  In "The Jade Peony," Grandmama, the father, and the narrator are all round characters who have plausible motivations for their actions. In contrast, the passengers in "War" are generally flat characters whose reactions are used to illustrate the story's message. In "The Yellow Wall Paper," the narrator's husband and sister-in-law are both flat characters who serve as foils to the round, main character who is attempting to cope with madness.
- Whereas a **realistic character** is multidimensional and recognizable as having complex relationships and motivations, a **stereotyped character** is predictable, unidimensional, and recognizable to the reader as "of a type," e.g., "the jock," "the brain," "the yuppie."

  Both "Identities" and "On the Right Track" play on the reader's recognition of stereotypes, including those of the suburban man (in "Identities") and the young, female, new office worker (in "On the Right Track"); they then attempt to develop the protagonists beyond those stereotypes.
- A **dynamic character**, often the protagonist, is a character who undergoes a significant, lasting change, usually in his or her outlook on life. A **static character**, on the other hand, is one who does not change in the course of the story.

  Whereas, at the end of "Foxes," Morris Glendenning appears to have changed from being alienated and reclusive to being much more accepting of himself and society, Old Man Warner in "The Lottery" appears to be unchanged.

characterization

Characterization is the process through which the author reveals to the reader the qualities of a character. In short stories, the author will either reveal character directly (through author comments) and/or indirectly (through the character's speech, thought, or action).

In "Identities," the protagonist is characterized through direct author description; e.g., "There grows within him, however, a vague unease with symmetry…." In "On the Right Track," the two women are characterized by their dialogue: "… Kim says never mind the subway, walking is good for you."

character sketch

A character sketch is a description of a character's moral, dispositional, and behavioral qualities, including specific examples and quotations from the story. When writing a character sketch, one does not normally describe the character's physical appearance or dress, though these, incidentally, may reflect the character's personality. The following sample sketch is of Mrs. Fullerton in "The Shining Houses."

Mrs. Fullerton is a static, round character with a colorful personality. A chatty person with the wisdom of hindsight, Mrs. Fullerton delights in telling Mary anecdotes. She is both eccentric and optimistic, as suggested by story details such as her pet raccoon, which she fed chewing gum, and her idea that her husband may return.

Mrs. Fullerton is also a strong, independent character, who ekes out a living selling eggs in the neighborhood. Her underlying pride is suggested by her response to babysitting requests: "I tell them I got my own house to sit in and I raised my share of children." She is as set in her ways as is her house: "The place had become fixed, impregnable...." She has no desire to move despite the pressure of her sons and neighbors. It is this resolute independence which finally brings her into conflict with her neighbors from the "shining houses."

climax

The climax is the highest point of emotional intensity in a story. It is the major crisis in the story and usually marks the turning point in the protagonist's fortunes.

The climax of "The Destructors" comes with the collapse of Old Misery's house. The climax of "Just Lather, That's All" occurs when the barber, having debated his options, decides not to kill Torres.

complicating incident (or complication)

The event which initiates a conflict is the complicating incident.

In "Identities," the protagonist's decision to drive into an unfamiliar area of the city leads to the conflict. The complicating incident in "The Dog That Ran in Circles" is the narrator's decision to write a story.

confidant (or confidante)

The confidant(e) is the person with whom a character, usually the protagonist, shares his or her thoughts, feelings, and intentions.

Vanessa is Chris' reluctant confidante in "Horses of the Night." In "The Rocking-Horse Winner," Bassett is both Paul's betting partner and confidant, although Paul never shares entirely the secret of his racing knowledge source.

conflict

This term refers to the struggle between opposing characters or forces, i.e., the protagonist and someone or something else. Additional conflicts, which the protagonist is not involved in, may also be found in a short story. Three common types of conflicts are as following:

- **conflict between a character and his or her environment.** The "environment" may be nature, society, or circumstance.

Civil war forces the family in "The Ultimate Safari" to make its risky journey through the Kruger Park. In "Miss Brill," the protagonist finds herself to be out of touch with, and scorned by, society, as represented by the young couple in the park.

- **conflict between two characters**. This struggle may be physical, emotional, or psychological.
  In "The Destructors," the conflicts between characters are numerous, e.g., Blackie and T., Old Misery and the boys, Old Misery and the lorry driver.
- **conflict within a character**. In this case, the character experiences conflict(s) in emotion and/or thought.
  In "Pelt," the dog, Queenie, is torn between obedience to her master and the temptation to accept the hazy invitation of the tiger-striped creatures. The protagonist in "Invitations" debates with herself the merits of each option available to her.

contrast (and **juxtaposition**)

Contrast refers to a difference, especially a striking difference, between two things being compared. In this context, contrast may involve situations, characters, settings, moods, or points of view. Contrast is used in order to clarify meaning, purpose, or character, or to heighten certain moods (especially humor, horror, and suspense). Juxtapositions are contrasts in which positioning is important; e.g., two contrasting characters are placed side by side in a story.

"The Setting Sun and the Rolling World" contrasts the father's and son's perceptions of their immediate surroundings and the world at large. "Bread" uses both contrast and juxtaposition in its episodes in order to affect an increase in the reader's social consciousness.

crisis

A crisis is a moment of intense conflict. The major crisis of the story is called the climax.

The grandfather's disappearance in Kruger Park is a crisis in "The Ultimate Safari." A crisis in "The Harness" occurs when David is distressed by the skeleton.

dénouement (or **resolution**)

Dénouement (pronounced day-NEW-mahn) is the French word for "unknotting" and refers to the "unknotting" of or resolution to the plot or conflict. The *dénouement* follows the climax, and constitutes part or all of the falling action.

The *dénouement* in "Horses of the Night" occurs when Vanessa cleans out the attic and reminisces with her mother about Chris. The *dénouement* in "The Lottery" occurs when Tessie is stoned by the other villagers.

dialect

Dialect is a manner of speaking or variation on a language peculiar to an individual, a people, a social class, or a geographic region. A dialect differs from the standard language of a country.

Mrs. Fullerton, in "The Shining Houses" uses a dialect distinct from that of her new neighbors. The boys' talk in "The Destructors" demonstrates one dialect of Londoners.

dialogue

Any conversation between two or more characters in a story is dialogue.

diction

Diction is the vocabulary used by a writer. For each story, the writer chooses and arranges words appropriate to his or her purpose, subject, story type, characters, and style.

The sparse, direct, and active diction in "The Ultimate Safari" reflects the characters' need for decisive action in a life-threatening situation. In contrast, the contemplative, detailed, and intensely emotional diction of "The Yellow Wall Paper" echoes the narrator's prescribed inaction, her extreme circumspection, and her struggle with madness.

dilemma

A dilemma is a situation in which a character must make a choice between two disagreeable, undesirable, or unfavorable alternatives. Posing a dilemma is one method an author can use to generate conflict and suspense in a story.

In "The Guest," Daru must choose between two undesirable options—delivering the prisoner to the French colonial authorities as ordered *or* leaving the prisoner's future to the prisoner and his people. Daru's dilemma is not based in his feelings about the crime or the effects of his actions alone, but also (and most importantly) in the philosophical rightness of his actions.

dynamic character *See* character.

epiphany

Epiphany refers to a moment of significant realization and insight experienced by the protagonist, often at the end of a story. As a literary term, "epiphany" originates with James Joyce, who built each short story in *Dubliners* around what he called an epiphany.

The protagonist of "Imagine a Day at the End of Your Life" has an epiphany in the woods in Batesville.

episode

An episode is an incident or event within the main plot of the story. Episodes can be viewed as selected portions or "scenes" developed in detail by the author.

"Holding Things Together" includes the following episodes: the trip to the gas station for the brakes, the second trip to the gas station with Bee, confronting Alfred over his expenses.

escapist fiction

This refers to stories written solely to entertain the reader, thus helping the reader to escape the daily cares and problems of reality. While provoking thought on the part of the reader and providing entertainment for the reader, of course, are not mutually exclusive, the term "escapist fiction" suggests an extreme. Escapist fiction has lively melodramatic plots and stereotyped or flat characters, and it requires limited involvement on the part of the reader. Many mass-marketed science fiction, westerns, thrillers, and romances fall into the category of escapist fiction.

exposition

Exposition is background information provided by the author to further the development of plot, conflict, setting, and characterization.

In "Small Potatoes," the narrator's recollection of her schooldays in Boston (in the second paragraph), her initial feelings about Alaska, and her friend's history (in the second through fifth paragraphs) are exposition.

fantasy

A fantasy is a highly exaggerated or improbable story. As a rule, a fantasy has fantastic events, characters, and/or settings not found in real life.

"Pelt," "The Rocking Horse Winner," "Totem," "What I Have Been Doing Lately," and "The Dog That Ran in Circles" are all fantasies to some extent.

fiction

Fiction is any narrative which is imagined or invented. Fiction may be based on actual happenings, which can, in turn, make fiction seem realistic.

flashback

A flashback is a sudden switch in the plot from the present to the past. This device may be used to illustrate an important point or to aid in characterization.

In "Identities," the protagonist's flashback to childhood car rides in the country establishes his motivation and sets up a contrast with the events to come. "The Liar" flashes back to the camping trip thwarted by a bear.

flat character *See* character.

foil

A foil is a character whose behavior, attitudes, and/or opinions contrast with those of the protagonist. The contrast of the foil helps the reader to understand better the character and motivation of the protagonist.

In "Holding Things Together," both her husband and her friend, Bee, are foils to the narrator.

foreshadowing

This is a device which hints or warns of events to happen later in the story. Foreshadowing prepares the reader for the climax, the *dénouement*, and any changes in the character.

In "The Yellow Wall Paper," the narrator's early mention of her condition and comments about her surroundings foreshadow her eventual obsessions and madness.

form
Form is a general term referring to the way in which a story is put together, its "shape" or structure. Form is sometimes called the "how" of a story and includes both technique and style.

"Rain" sensuously presents the narrator's experience and punctuates it with a refrain of sorts—variations on the reminder, "I was a stranger in that part of the country." The form of "Diary of a Temp" offers a series of "snapshots" of working life. "Bread" assumes an even more experimental form: a series of descriptions and directions.

goal *See* motivation.

hero (or heroine)
This is a protagonist in a story who possesses heroic qualities, such as courage, or virtues, such as honesty. The terms "hero" and "heroine" are not interchangeable with the more general term "protagonist."

humor
Here, humor refers to writing which is intended to amuse the reader or provoke laughter.

In "Mules," both father's and son's stubborn, mulelike behavior is intended to amuse. "Totem" uses humor to point out relationships among North American native and non-native cultures, institutions, and peoples.

images (and imagery)
Images are concrete details and figures of speech that help the reader form vivid impressions of the subject of the writing. Imagery refers to the pattern of images in a single piece of writing.

The first paragraph of "The Pigeons in St. Louis Square" includes the following image of pigeons: "winged citizens, bold enough to venture out into the middle of the street, deaf to abuse and screaming tires." The story's imagery suggests the indifference of nature to the ways of human beings.

indeterminate ending
A story ending in which there is no clear outcome, result, or resolved conflict is called an indeterminate ending.

The ending of "Rain" has a sense of nonfinality about it which seems appropriate to the traveling "stranger"/narrator and his quest for experiences.

in medias res
In medias res (pronounced in MA-deas RAS) is a Latin term which refers to readers joining a story "in the middle of things."

One story joined *in medias res* is "The Setting Sun and the Rolling World" which opens with the son coming to say goodbye to his father.

irony
Irony involves contrast between two elements and, as a literary device, provides depth of meaning and impact. When irony is used, meanings tend to become concealed or contradictory, which we call "ironic." The following are three common types of irony:

- **Verbal irony** occurs when what a character says contrasts with what the character actually means.
  An example of verbal irony can be found in "The Harness": "I asked him if his legs weren't tired. 'Noooooo,' he scoffed. As if that were the kind of absurd question people kid each other with to clinch the absolute perfection of the day."
- **Dramatic irony** occurs when what a character says or believes contrasts with what we know to be true, e.g., from information given to us by the author.
  In "Foxes," Mrs. Elston and Myrna Stovich's comments about Morris and the dog smell are dramatically ironic. In "Invitations," the passers-by are resentful of being caught up in social obligations, while we, and the protagonist, know there are other options. In "Miss Brill," the narrator's romantic notions contrast with those of the young couple.
- **Situational irony** (or **irony of situation**) occurs when what takes place contrasts with what was expected or seems appropriate.
  At the end of "Identities," the protagonist reaches for his wallet, not realizing that he is misunderstood and about to be shot. In "Just Lather, That's All," the barber spares Torres' life, only to find out that Torres was testing him.

juxtaposition *See* contrast.

local color (and regionalism)

Local color refers to the detail in a story that is specific to a geographic region or an environment. Local color develops the setting and atmosphere, increases reader interest, adds to authenticity, and includes descriptions of locale, dress, and customs as well as dialect and ways of thinking and feeling characteristic of people in that setting. Regionalism refers to stories in which setting (developed with local color) is of significance to the text and necessary to the writer's purpose.

Both "Small Potatoes" and "The Ultimate Safari" are examples of regionalism. "Small Potatoes" includes details of the rugged Alaskan setting and the demands it puts on the characters who live there. Local color—e.g., details of village life and the Kruger Park—creates a sense of Mozambique, South Africa, and the struggles of the characters in "The Ultimate Safari."

mood *See* atmosphere.

moral

The stated or implied lesson of a story is called the moral. Viewed in isolation, a moral, *per se*, is a relatively unimportant part of a story and should not be confused with theme, a more significant element of fiction.

"The Shining Houses" offers directly the moral, "There is nothing you can do at present but put your hands in your pockets and keep a disaffected heart." A reading of the "The Guest" can offer the moral that one cannot live in complete isolation from the outside world and the dilemmas that life entails.

motivation (and goal)

Motivation is both what causes a character to do what he or she does *and* the character's aim, or goal, in taking that action. The character's temperament and circumstances determine motivation. The pursuit by the protagonist of his or her goal results in the story's conflict. Characters must have sufficient and plausible motivation in order for a reader to find the story effective.

In "On the Right Track," the protagonist's interests, observations of others, and drive enable her to clarify her own goals and move more toward them.

narrative

Narrative is another word for story. Narratives contain the following elements: plot, conflict, characters, setting, and point of view. Narratives may be fictional or non-fictional, and include novels, autobiographies, and biographies, as well as short stories and anecdotes.

narrator

The narrator is the storyteller. In the case of a story told from the first person perspective, the narrator is one of the characters; in the case of a story told from the objective, omniscient, or limited omniscient points of view, the author assumes the role of narrator.

Whereas the author assumes the role of narrator in "War," Lucy is the narrator in "Holding Things Together."

plot

The storyline or organization of events or episodes within a story is called the plot. The conventional plot has rising action, a climax, and falling action. *See also* subplot.

In "Just Lather, That's All," the rising action includes the episodes in which the barber shaves Torres; the climax is the barber's decision not to kill Torres; the falling action includes Torres' revelation that he was testing the barber.

point of view

The point of view is the perspective from which a story is seen or told. Point of view establishes the relationships among author, reader, and characters. The following are the three most common points of view:

- **First-person narrative** features a character telling the story directly to the reader in the first person (that is, using "I"). This point of view tells us what the character thinks and feels from a vantage point "inside" the story and one character.

  "The Jade Peony," "Holding Things Together," and "Rain" are examples of first-person narratives.
- **Limited omniscient** or **third person narrative** is a story told from "outside" the characters, but from the perspective of one character. In this point of view, the characters are referred in the third person (as "he" or "she") and the narrator is limited to knowing the thoughts and feelings of only that one character.

  "The Shining Houses" and "The Guest" are examples of limited omniscient narratives.

- **Omniscient narrative**, or "all-knowing" narrative tells the story with knowledge of the thoughts and feelings of several or all the characters.
  "War," "The Masque of the Red Death," and "The Setting Sun and the Rolling World" are examples of omniscient narratives.
- In the less common, **objective narrative**, the narrator has no special knowledge and simply observes. The story is presented unemotionally and matter-of-factly.
  "The Lottery" uses the objective point of view in order to create suspense.

predicament

A predicament is a difficult problem or unpleasant situation. Predicament should not be confused with a related term, dilemma.

Mary, in "The Shining Houses," finds herself in the predicament of disagreeing with most of her neighbors over a community issue. In "Pelt," Queenie faces a new and threatening situation and is only dimly aware of some options.

prose

Ordinary language or literary expression not marked by rhythm or rhyme is called prose. This type of language is used in short stories, essays, and modern plays. The text you are now reading is written in prose.

protagonist

The protagonist is the main character of a story. While some protagonists may be heroes or heroines (or anti-heroes or anti-heroines), the term "protagonist" is broader and does not depend on judgments of the character's actions.

Old Musoni is the protagonist in "The Setting Sun and the Rolling World."

purpose

Purpose refers to the main effect the author hopes to achieve, e.g., entertainment, thought, enlightenment, action, demonstrating something about life or human nature. Rarely does a story have only one purpose. Purpose may include theme, but should not simply be equated with the story's main idea.

The purpose of "War" seems twofold: to demonstrate the effects of war beyond the front lines; and to explore how people express, suppress, and cope with emotions. The purposes of "The Dog That Ran in Circles" could include: to demonstrate the nature and scarcity of inspiration; to demonstrate how society can be unsympathetic to an artist's communications; and to show relationship between the artist and the artist's creation.

realism

This term refers to any subject matter or techniques that create a "true-to-life" impression for the reader. Writers of realism present life "as it is" and as though the stories have simply told themselves. In another sense, realism can also refer to stories about simple, everyday people. *See also* fantasy, romance, *and* verisimilitude.

"The Jade Peony" and "On the Right Track" are examples of realism.

realistic character *See* **character.**

regionalism *See* **local color.**

resolution *See* **dénouement.**

rising action

Rising action in a story consists of the incidents that precede the climax. During this stage of the story, background information is given, characters and conflicts are introduced, and suspense is built up. There may even be moments of crisis. Typically, the rising action is often longer than the falling action of a story. *See also* plot.

The rising action of "The Lottery" consists of all events up to Tessie "winning" the lottery.

romance

Entertaining stories which contain one or more of the following characteristics—fantasy, improbability, extravagance, naïveté, love, adventure, and myth—are generally called romances.

"The Rocking-Horse Winner" and "Through the Fields" are both romances.

round character *See* **character.**

satire

Satire is the use of irony to ridicule an idea, a person, or a thing, often to provoke change. Satire usually targets human vices or foibles.

"Totem" is a satire which targets ignorant and/or prejudicial reactions to North American native cultures. "The Dog That Ran in Circles" makes fun of the relationship between the artist and his or her society.

science fiction

Science fiction is writing which speculates about the effects of technology, science, and the future of human beings. While the purpose of some science fiction is purely escapist entertainment, science fiction can be written for a range of purposes.

"Pelt" is an example of science fiction.

setting

The setting is the time and place of a story. While, in some stories, setting may affect minimally the plot, characters, and theme, in others, it can be of great significance.

The setting of "The Destructors" in the rubble of London following World War II, suggests a destructive tendency not only in gangs but also in humanity. In "The Painted Door," the storm and farm create the moods of anxiety and isolation.

short story

A short story is a brief, fictional prose narrative, having one main character, a single plot, limited setting, and one main effect. Edgar Allan Poe, one of the first

significant theorists and practitioners of short story writing, said that short stories:
1) can be read in one sitting, and derive their power from the fact the writer has to select details for economy and emphasis;
2) have a single effect or purpose and are constructed so that every sentence from the first to the last one supports that effect;
3) leave the reader with a feeling of satisfaction and finality, desiring no further completion or alternate ending;
4) have their basis in truth or life-likeness.

static character *See* character.

stereotype

A stereotype is any fixed pattern of plot or character. Stereotyped plots usually fall into the realm of escapist fiction. Stereotyped characters are familiar figures in fiction, such as the "hard-boiled" private investigator, the "absent-minded" professor, the military officer with a "stiff upper lip." *See also* character.

stream-of-consciousness

Stream-of-consciousness refers to a modern narrative technique which attempts to depict the uninterrupted and frequently illogical flow of thoughts and feelings through a character's mind. The author includes details relevant to plot, character, and theme in the apparently natural flow of thoughts and feelings.

Portions of "Pelt" ("Nice voice, she thought, nice thing. It gives and gives.") attempt to represent the thought processes of the dog protagonist.

style

Style is the individual manner in which an author expresses himself or herself. In fiction, style is basically determined by such grammatical and sensory aspects as diction, sentences, and images.

Because of the matter-of-fact description and folksiness, "The Lottery" seems, at first, a simple, sentimental story about a day in the life of a farming community. Jackson's style contributes to the reader's expectations, and the shock of the ending.

subplot

A subplot is a minor storyline, secondary to the main plot. Subplots may be related or unrelated to the main action, but may also be a reflection of, or variation on, the main plot. Compared to novels, short stories tend to have few, brief subplots (or none) because of the brevity and density required of short stories.

In "The Rocking Horse Winner," the various betting episodes form a subplot. The recollections of childhood in "Rain" form a subplot.

surprise ending

The sudden twist in the direction of a story, producing a resolution which surprises the reader and often the story's characters as well, is called a surprise ending.

The surprise ending in "War" occurs when the very philosophical and restrained traveller breaks down and cries over the loss of his son.

suspense

Suspense is the feeling of anxiety and uncertainty experienced by the reader about the outcome of events or the protagonist's destiny.

There is suspense in "The Masque of the Red Death" as Prince Prospero tries to catch the mysterious reveller who has mocked the party-goers.

symbol

A symbol is something that stands for or represents something else. Characters, objects, events, and settings can all be symbolic.

In "Small Potatoes," the potatoes can be seen to represent the life in the Alaskan countryside with which both friends had once been content, but which stopped satisfying the friend who moved to Anchorage. The narrator sees herself as something of a "small potato," having stayed with a life of self-sufficiency rather than pursuing professional achievement, money, and influence.

theme

The theme is the central idea of the story, usually implied rather than directly stated. Theme should not be confused with either the moral or the plot.

For "Invitations," one theme might be stated as follows: If individuals do not question societal expectations when making their own choices, they jeopardize their heartfelt desires and personal integrity.

universality

Universality is the quality of a story which gives it relevance beyond the narrow confines of its particular characters, subject, or setting. Stories which have universality reveal human nature or common truths of experience. Universality is considered by some critics to be the measure of a story's worth or success.

Although set in a suburban Canadian community, "The Shining Houses" explores how humans seem to distrust differences, reject the old for the new, embrace "progress," and disrespect natural or otherwise uncontrolled environments.

verisimilitude

Verisimilitude is a life-like quality possessed by a story as revealed through its plot, setting, conflict, and characterization. *See also* realism.

Verisimilitude is evident in "The Jade Peony" in the family struggles, and in "Foxes" in its details of city street life.

vicarious experience

Vicarious experience refers to the reader sharing imaginatively in a character's feelings and experiences. Vicarious (literally, "acting or done for another") experiences can be had, for example, through reading travel literature.

"The Guest" offers the reader the vicarious experience of a principled French schoolmaster in northern Africa during colonial times. "Pelt" offers the reader the chance to identify with its canine protagonist.

Contents by Country

Stories are organized by author's nationality.
An asterisk (*) indicates authors and stories with dual listings.

Permission Credits

Identities from WHAT CAN'T BE CHANGED SHOULDN'T BE MOURNED by W.D. Valgardson. Reprinted by permission of Douglas & McIntyre. *Small Potatoes* from SURVIVAL by Nancy Lord (Coffee House Press, 1991). Copyright © 1991 by Nancy Lord. Reprinted by permission of the publisher. *The Shining Houses* from DANCE OF THE HAPPY SHADES by Alice Munro. Copyright © 1968 by Alice Munro. Reprinted by permission of Virginia Barber Literary Agency, Inc. All rights reserved. *War* by Luigi Pirandello. Copyright © 1932, 1967 by E.P. Dutton. Reprinted by permission of the Pirandello Estate and Toby Cole, agent. *The Jade Peony* by Wayson Choy. Copyright © 1979 by Wayson Choy. From VANCOUVER SHORT STORIES (University of B.C., 1985). First published by the UBC Alumni Chronicle, 1979. Reprinted by permission of the author. *Imagine a Day at the End of Your Life* from WHAT WAS MINE by Ann Beattie. Copyright © 1991 by Irony & Pity, Inc. Reprinted by permission of Random House, Inc. *Horses of the Night* from A BIRD IN THE HOUSE by Margaret Laurence. Reprinted by permission of the Canadian Publishers, McClelland & Stewart, Toronto. *The Guest* from EXILE AND THE KINGDOM by Albert Camus, translated by Justin O'Brien. Copyright © 1957, 1958 by Alfred A. Knopf, Inc. Reprinted by permission of Alfred A. Knopf, Inc. *Foxes* by Timothy Findley. First published in "Rotunda," Summer 1987; collected in STONES (Viking 1988). Copyright © 1987 by Pebble Productions, Inc. Reprinted by permission of the author. *The Ultimate Safari* from CRIMES OF CONSCIENCE by Nadine Gordimer. Copyright © 1989 by Felix Licensing BV. Reprinted by permission of Russell & Volkening, Inc. as agents. *Pelt* from THE START OF THE END OF IT ALL by Carol Emshwiller. Copyright © 1991 by Carol Emshwiller. Reprinted by permission of Mercury House, San Francisco. *The Lottery* from THE LOTTERY AND OTHER STORIES by Shirley Jackson. Copyright © 1948, 1949 by Shirley Jackson. Copyright renewed © 1976, 1977 by Lawrence Hyman, Barry Hyman, Mrs. Sara Webster and Mrs. Joanne Schurer. Reprinted by permission of Brandt & Brandt Literary Agents, Inc. *The Destructors* from TWENTY ONE STORIES by Graham Greene. Copyright © 1954, Verdant S.A. Reprinted by permission of David Higham Associates. *Invitations* from VARIOUS MIRACLES by Carol Shields. Reprinted by permission of Stoddart Publishing. *The Pigeons in St. Louis Square* by Yvette Naubert, translated by Margaret Rose. Reprinted by permission. *Just Lather, That's All* by Hernando Téllez, translated by Donald Yates. From GREAT SPANISH SHORT STORIES (Dell 1962). Reprinted by permission. *Holding Things Together* by Anne Tyler. Originally appeared in "The New Yorker." Copyright © 1977 by Anne Tyler. Reprinted by permission of Russel & Volkening for the author. *The Rocking-Horse Winner* by D.H. Lawrence. Copyright © 1933 by the estate of D.H. Lawrence, renewed © 1961 by Angelo Ravagli and C.M. Weekley, executors of the estate of Frieda Lawrence. Reprinted by permission of Viking Penguin, a division of Penguin Books, USA. *The Setting Sun and the Rolling World* from THE SETTING SUN AND THE ROLLING WORLD by Charles Mungoshi. Reprinted by permission of the Zimbabwe Publishing House. *On the Right Track* by Dorothy Chisholm. First appeared in "Other Voices," Fall 1990. Reprinted by permission of the author. *Rain* from RAIN AND OTHER STORIES by Maurice Kenny (White Pine Press, 1990). Reprinted by permission of the author. *Miss Brill* from THE SHORT STORIES OF KATHERINE MANSFIELD by Katherine Mansfield. Copyright © 1922 by Alfred A. Knopf, Inc. and renewed 1950 by John Middleton Murray. Reprinted by permission of Alfred A. Knopf, Inc. *Biography of a Story* from COME ALONG WITH ME by Shirley Jackson. Copyright © 1948, 1952, 1960 by Shirley Jackson. Reprinted by permission of Viking Penguin, a division of Penguin Books USA, Inc. *Shirley Jackson's Dramatic Point of View* from WRITING THEMES ABOUT LITERATURE, 4e by Edgar V. Roberts. Copyright © 1977. Reprinted by permission of Prentice-Hall, Englewood Cliffs, N.J. *On "Miss Brill"* from KATHERINE MANSFIELD by Kate Fullbrook. Reprinted by permission of Indiana University Press. *Inside Memory* excerpts from INSIDE MEMORY: PAGES FROM A WRITER'S WORKBOOK by Timothy Findley. Copyright © 1990 by Pebble Productions. Reprinted by permission of HarperCollins Publishers Ltd., Toronto. *The Liar* by Tobias Wolff. First appeared in "The Atlantic Monthly." Copyright © 1980 by Tobias Wolff. Reprinted by permission of the author. *Mules* from MY CAREER WITH THE LEAFS AND OTHER STORIES by Brian Fawcett. Reprinted by permission of Talon Books, Vancouver. *The Harness* from THE REBELLION OF YOUNG DAVID AND OTHER STORIES by Ernest Buckler. Reprinted by permission of the Canadian Publishers, McClelland & Stewart, Toronto. *Diary of a Temp* from HEY, WAITRESS AND OTHER STORIES by Helen Potrebenko (Lazara Press, Vancouver, 1988). Reprinted by permission of the author. *Through the Fields* by Lyudmila Petrushevskaya. From THE NEW SOVIET FICTION compiled by Sergei Zalygin. Compilation copyright © 1989 VAAP, copyright agency of USSR. English translation copyright © 1989 by Abbeville Press, Inc. Reprinted by permision of Abbeville Press, Inc. *The Painted Door* from THE LAMP AT NOON AND OTHER STORIES by Sinclair Ross. Reprinted by permission of the Canadian Publishers, McClelland & Stewart, Toronto. *Totem* by Thomas King. Reprinted by permission of the Bukowski Agency for Thomas King. *Bread* from MURDER IN THE DARK by Margaret Atwood. Copyright © 1983 by Margaret Atwood. Reprinted by permission of the author. *What I Have Been Doing Lately* from AT THE BOTTOM OF THE RIVER by Jamaica Kincaid. Copyright © 1981, 1983 by Jamaica Kincaid. Reprinted by permission of Farrar, Straus & Giroux, Inc. *The Dog That Ran In Circles* by Gangadhar Gadgil. Reprinted by permission of the author.

Photo Credits

Front and back cover, p. 236 Harold Sund/The Image Bank; pp. VI, 270 Ellen Shuster/The Image Bank; pp. 21, 64 Harold M. Lambert/Comstock; p. 32 Mel Digiacomo/The Image Bank; p. 86 Michel Tcherevkoff/The Image Bank; pp. 124, 200, 210, 260 H. Armstrong Roberts/Comstock; pp. 144, 188 Michael DeCamp/The Image Bank; p. 158 Ron Brenne/The Bettmann Archive; pp. 176, 351 Chris McElcheran; pp. 308-9 Max Hilaire/Stockphotos Inc./ The Image Bank.